PLOT OUTLINES OF 101 BEST NOVELS

Everyday Handbooks

PLOT OUTLINES
of 101
BEST NOVELS

CONDENSATIONS BASED ON ORIGINAL WORKS

Including Portions of 100 BEST NOVELS CONDENSED
Edited by Edwin A. Grozier, with New Condensations
Prepared for This Edition by Margaret Gillett

NEW YORK

BARNES & NOBLE, INC.
PUBLISHERS · BOOKSELLERS · SINCE 1873

TABLE OF CONTENTS

Page

Page

Page

LIST OF AUTHORS

PUBLISHER'S NOTE

The following condensations were prepared for this edition by Margaret Gillett, of the faculty of Dalhousie University, Halifax, Nova Scotia: *An American Tragedy, The Bridge of San Luis Rey, Camille, Candide, Dr. Zhivago, The Egoist, Fathers and Sons, The Horse's Mouth, Huckleberry Finn, Lord Jim, The Old Wives' Tale, The Pickwick Papers, Point of No Return, The Portrait of a Lady, Pride and Prejudice, The Red and the Black, The Red Badge of Courage, Tom Jones, U.S.A.,* and *Wuthering Heights.*

The condensations of *Cousin Pons, Crime and Punishment, Madame Bovary, Moby Dick,* and *Of Human Bondage* were prepared by Lawrence Falconer.

The remaining condensations, selected from *One Hundred Best Novels Condensed* (edited by Edwin A. Grozier), were originally published in serial form in *The Boston Post,* where they attracted so much favorable comment that they were later reprinted in nearly one hundred daily newspapers in the United States and Canada and published in book form by Harper & Brothers.

In the Preface to the original volume Edwin A. Grozier wrote: "The object of . . . publication . . . is twofold: first, to enable the busy and casual reader to become acquainted with the masterpieces of fiction with the minimum of time and exertion; second, through an appetizing condensation, to induce readers to seek the great originals."

In preparing the new edition the contributors and the publisher have attempted to follow this standard by reproducing as closely as possible the style and tone, as well as the action and thought, of the original works. These novels, representative of many times and countries, are part of our universal heritage of literature. By reading them we gain an understanding of human experience under varied conditions and an appreciation of good writing.

~◆~

ABBÉ CONSTANTIN

by

LUDOVIC HALÉVY

CONDENSATION BY CHARLES E. L. WINGATE

LUDOVIC HALÉVY, French author, was born in Paris on January the first, 1834. His father was a clever, versatile writer of verse, prose, vaudeville, and drama: his uncle, Fromantal Halévy, was for many years associated with the opera; hence the double and early connection of Ludovic with the Parisian stage. At the age of six he might have been seen playing in that "Foyer de la Danse" with which he was to make his readers so familiar.

At eighteen he joined the ranks of the French administration and occupied various posts, the last being that of secrétaire redacteur to the Corps Législatif. In that capacity he enjoyed the special favor and friendship of the famous Duke of Morny, then the president of the Assembly.

In the spring of 1860, being commissioned to write a play for the manager of the Varieties, Halévy asked the collaboration of Henri Meilhac, and the proposal was immediately accepted, thus beginning a connection which continued for more than twenty years.

The joint work of the two authors had a great vogue, but Halévy is best known to more recent readers by his "L'Abbé Constantin," published soon after the conclusion of the Franco-Prussian War.

It has been claimed that Zola had presented to the public an almost exclusive combination of bad men and women; in "L'Abbé Constantin" all are kind and good, and the change was eagerly welcomed by the reading public.

1

Halévy died in Paris on the 8th of May, 1908. Among the most celebrated works of the joint authors were: "La Belle Hélène," "Barbe Bleue," "La Grande Duchesse de Gérolstein," and "La Périchole."

With a step still valiant and firm the old Abbé Constantin walked along the dusty road of the little village where for more than thirty years he had been the curé. At the entrance of the Castle of Longueval he stopped and mournfully regarded the big blue posters fixed on the pillars.

They announced the sale of the castle, the former home of the curé's dear old friend, the marquise, who had recently died.

And the result of that auction?

The great estate bought by two entire strangers!

"Do you know who they are?" asked Madame de Lavardens.

"Yes. Mrs. Scott is an American possessing a colossal fortune. Ten years ago Mrs. Scott begged in the streets of New York, they say. They are rich parvenus who amuse themselves by throwing handfuls of gold out of the window, and who will turn up their noses at us and care nothing for our traditions or our life."

Such was the story.

But when young Mrs. Scott and her beautiful sister arrived, to take possession of the castle, and called immediately upon the abbé, he learned a different tale. Religious, generous, amiable, and lovable they proved.

And they were certainly beautiful, particularly the younger sister, Bettina Percival. Both had the same large eyes, black, laughing, and gay, and the same hair, not red, but fair, with golden shades which daintily danced in the light of the sun.

At the curé's little home they met Jean Reynaud, the son of that gallant doctor of the village who, while advancing with the soldiers in the war of 1870 to carry on his work of mercy side by side with his dear old friend the abbé, had suddenly been struck by a bullet and killed on the spot. Jean, inheriting the noble traits of his father, was beloved by the whole village.

But he was poor, while the American sisters were immeasurably rich.

As acquaintances and friendships grew, very pleasing it was to the gentle, lovable old curé to learn that his new parishioners were most anxious to extend their benefactions among the poor in the hamlet, asking him, indeed, to be their medium. And it delighted him to learn that those stories about begging in the street and questionable life were mere calumnies.

They had, indeed, been poor until an inherited silver-mine made them fabulously rich. Now they had hosts of admirers—Mrs. Scott because she was frankly flirtatious, and Bettina because, as she realized, the fortune-hunters—thirty-four of them she counted, including a French duke and a Spanish noble—sought her wealth. But through it all they retained their genuine simplicity and sweetness of heart.

And when, one day, they all went over with Jean to visit the little church, and Bettina at the organ played a reverie of Chopin, good gentle Abbé Constantin's heart was filled with such joy that the tears came to his eyes.

But all this left a deep problem in Jean's mind—"Which of the two sisters is the prettier?" At first he was convinced that it was the coquettish Mrs. Scott who charmed him the more; then he would see Bettina, smiling and blushing amid the sunlit clouds of her floating hair, and he would declare to himself, "I was mistaken—the prettier was Miss Percival."

So, in the confusion of his meditations, he would say, "Is it possible that I have fallen madly in love at first sight? No; one might fall in love with a woman, but not with two women at once."

The days went on and Jean and Bettina were often thrown into each other's company. What resulted is best pictured in Miss Percival's own remark to her sister when one day she exclaimed:

"He is the first man, positively the first, in whose eyes I have not read, 'Oh how glad I should be to marry that little body's millions!' "

And then, as Mrs. Scott went up-stairs to kiss her sleeping children, Bettina remained long leaning on the balustrade of her balcony.

"It seems to me," said she, "that I am growing to be very fond of this place!"

One day when Jean was telling of his expectations of promotion and the probability that he should wander from garrison to garrison, finally coming back to the little house that was his father's, as an old colonel on half pay, she exclaimed:

"Always quite alone?"

"Why quite alone? I certainly hope not."

"You intend to marry?"

"Yes, certainly."

"Yet you have refused several good opportunities. Tell me why."

"Because," he replied, "I think it best not to marry rather than to marry without love."

"And I think so, too."

She looked at him; he looked at her; and suddenly, to the great surprise of both, they found nothing more to say—nothing at all.

But now Jean is no longer tranquil; with impatience and at the same time with sorrow he sees the moment of his departure approach. Yet how could he stay and resist the temptation of Bettina's charm?

As an honorable man Jean felt for Bettina's money horror, positive horror.

In Bettina's mind the sensation of love had come at the same time that it had to Jean's. But while he, horrified, had cast it violently from him, she, on the contrary, had yielded in all the simplicity of her perfect innocence to this flood of emotion and of tenderness.

As Bettina grew more tender, Jean became more gloomy. He was not only afraid of loving; he was afraid of being loved. He felt he ought to remain away, but he could not; the temptation was too strong.

He tried to avoid Bettina at receptions and even to leave without saying good-by.

"If I touch her hand," he thought, "my secret will escape me."

His secret! He did not know that Bettina read his heart like an open book.

When Jean descended the stairs these words were upon his lips:

"I love you, I adore you, and that is why I will see you no more!"

But he did not utter them; he actually fled into the darkness.

Bettina, standing in the hall door and taking no notice of the rain driving across her bare shoulders, watched him go.

"I knew very well that he loved me," she thought, "but now I am very sure that I, too—oh yes! I, too—"

Meanwhile Jean hastens to his dear old friend the curé to tell him that he is going away immediately to Paris to seek exchange into another regiment, to leave the little hamlet forever. And then in his emotion he confessed to the abbé that he adored Bettina.

"It is a madness which has seized me," he exclaimed. "Ah! if she were only poor!"

"Do you know what I think, Jean?" exclaimed his good friend, "Jean, I believe that she loves you."

"And I believe it, too; but that is the very reason I must go. Her money is the great obstacle."

At that moment some one knocked gently at the door.

It was Bettina.

Going directly to Jean, she cried, "Oh, how glad I am you are here."

Then she took both his hands in hers and, addressing the curé, she said, "I have come to beg you, Monsieur le Curé, to listen to my confession."

And to herself she was saying, "I wish to be loved! I wish to love! I wish to be happy and to make him happy! And since he cannot have the courage to say it, I must have the courage for both!"

"I am rich, Monsieur le Curé," she continued, aloud, "very rich, but I love money most for the good which it allows me to do. So I have the care of this money, and I have always wished that my husband should be worthy of sharing this great fortune in order that he should help me make good use of it. I thought of another thing, too—'He who will be my husband must be some one I can love!' There is a man who has done all he can to conceal from me that he loves me, but I do not doubt that he loves me. You do love me, Jean?"

"Yes," said Jean, in a low voice, his eyes cast down, looking like a criminal, "I do love you."

"I knew it very well, but I wanted to hear you say it. And now, Jean, I say to you, 'I love you!' Do not come near me, yet. Before I came here I thought I had a good stock of courage, but you see I have no longer my fine composure of a minute ago. And now, Monsieur le Curé, I want you to answer me, not him. Tell me, if he loves me and feels me worthy of my love, should he not agree to be my husband?"

"Jean," said the old priest, gravely, "marry her; it is your duty."

And as Jean took Bettina in his arms the girl continued: "You have often told me, Monsieur le Curé, that Jean was almost like your own son. Now you will have two children, that is all."

A month later Bettina, in the simplest of wedding-dresses, entered the church. The old curé said mass. Jean and Bettina knelt before him. He pronounced the benediction. Then floated from the organ the same reverie of Chopin's which Bettina had played the first time she had entered that village church where was to be consecrated the happiness of her life.

And this time it was Bettina who wept.

ADAM BEDE

by

GEORGE ELIOT

CONDENSATION BY ELLERY SEDGWICK

GEORGE ELIOT was the pen name of the English writer Mary Ann (or Marian) Evans. She was born in 1819 at Arbury Farm in Warwickshire and died at Chelsea, December 2, 1880. Her father, Robert Evans, was the agent of Mr. Francis Newdgate, and the first twenty-one years of the novelist's life were spent on the Arbury estate. At her mother's death, while Miss Evans was still in her teens, she became her father's housekeeper and pursued her studies away from school and classes. All through her youth she was somewhat subdued by a very strict religious training, and she was a great reader of religious and philosophical subjects, and in later years she wrote of them also.

In 1841 the family moved to Coventry, and it was there that Miss Evans made the acquaintance of Mr. and Mrs. Charles Bray and Mr. Charles Hennell, who became her stanch friends. Both Mr. Bray and Mr. Hennell were men of literary tastes; the latter had, just before this time, published "An Enquiry Concerning the Origin of Christianity." Miss Evans's ideas and opinions were much affected by the line of thought this work contained.

In 1851 she became the assistant editor of the "Westminster Review." She made several notable contributions to the "Review," and during the time of her connection with it made the acquaintance of many distinguished authors of that period; among them, Herbert Spencer, Carlyle, Harriet Martineau, Francis Newman, and George Henry Lewes. Her friendship with Mr. Lewes led to a closer relationship, which she regarded as a marriage, but which caused much criticism among her friends.

Miss Evans first attempted the writing of fiction in 1856,

6

and published in "Blackwood's Magazine" the first of the "Scenes of Clerical Life." Although she received much encouragement from private sources, notably Charles Dickens, the critics were rather noncommittal. Then in 1859 Miss Evans wrote and published what in the judgment of many is her masterpiece, "Adam Bede." It has been said that in the character of Adam Bede she drew a portrait of her father; and certainly Dinah Morris, the heroine of the story, was one of her own favorite characters. There followed "The Mill on the Floss," "Silas Marner," "Felix Holt," "Middlemarch," "Daniel Deronda," "The Spanish Gypsy," a drama, and "Romola," which may be called a historical novel.

Some one has said that "Jane Austen despised the greater number of her characters, but George Eliot suffered with each of hers."

She had a great accumulation of book knowledge, but this was opposed in many ways to the practical life led among all sorts and conditions of persons, so that at times some of the spontaneity of joy was lacking in her writings. But there were those full of pathos, as when she wrote of Maggie Tulliver in "The Mill on the Floss."

The death of Mr. Lewes, which occurred in 1878, was also the death-blow to her artistic vitality. She later married Mr. J. W. Cross, but she never really recovered from the shock of the loss of Mr. Lewes.

That last year of the eighteenth century Hayslope was a pleasant neighborhood to live in. It was far enough away from the noise of "Boney's" battles to sleep in peace. Men chatted of crops and rents, and listened to the gossip of women folk regarding Dinah Morris of Snowfield, Mrs. Poyser's own niece, who had turned "Methody" preacher and would stand right before men on the village green, talking to them of the comfort they could find in their friend, Jesus Christ.

And, worse still, Dinah was so attractive and so gravely loving that the men, and women, too, gladly listened to her. Big Adam Bede, the carpenter, would have liked to see more of her, had he eyes for any one except old Poyser's niece, Hetty Sorrel. As for Hetty, she had no thought for Adam; Captain Arthur Donnithorne, heir of the estate, had whispered too many things in her pretty ear.

It was natural enough. There, in her aunt's white dairy, rounding her dimpled arm to lift a pound of butter out of the scale, Hetty had the beauty of a fluffy kitten. Her large, dark eyes had a soft roguishness, and her curly hair, pushed away under her cap, stole back in delicate rings on her forehead. Of course, the dashing captain had no foolish ideas about marriage, but then, as he bent over her shoulder, he was soldier enough to feel his head turn very fast. He had no wish to harm her, you may be sure of that, for he had great pride in the Donnithorne estate, and it is pleasant for a rich young man to be liked and admired.

One August evening Adam walked homeward through a grove of grand beeches, the glory of the estate. As carpenter and woodsman, he delighted in fine trees, and paused to look at a huge beech which stood at the turning before the grove ended in an archway of boughs.

All his life he remembered that moment, for there, not twenty yards away, stood two figures, close, with clasped hands. They started. The girl hurried away, while Arthur Donnithorne walked slowly forward. He was flushed and excited, but reassured himself by remembering that Adam was a sensible person, not likely to babble. That the big, sober carpenter loved Hetty, Arthur had no idea.

"Well, Adam," said Arthur, carelessly, "you've been looking at the fine old beeches, eh? I overtook pretty Hetty Sorrel as I was going to my old lodge in the woods; so I took her to the gate, and asked for a kiss for my pains. Good night."

Adam dared not move lest he spring on Arthur like a tiger.

"Stop a bit," he said in a hard, peremptory voice.

"What do you mean?" Arthur felt his temper rising.

"I mean that, instead of the honorable man we've all believed you, you're a selfish scoundrel!"

Arthur found it hard to control himself.

"Well, Adam, perhaps I have gone too far in taking notice of the pretty little thing and stealing a few kisses. You're such a grave fellow you don't understand temptations. Let's say no more. The whole thing will soon be forgotten."

"No, by God," said Adam, "it'll not be soon forgot, as you've come in between her and me when she might have loved me. It'll not be soon forgot, as you've robbed me of my happiness when I thought you my best friend. You're a coward and a scoundrel, and I despise you."

The color rushed back to Arthur's face. He dealt a lightning blow which sent Adam staggering back, but the delicate-handed gentleman was no match for the workman's great strength. After a fierce struggle Arthur fell motionless, while Adam, in sudden revulsion of feeling, knelt over him like an image of despair gazing on death.

To his intense relief, Arthur gradually revived. Adam got him to his feet, supported him to the little cabin, and laid him on a couch. Then he spoke out.

"I don't forget what's owing to you as a gentleman, but in this thing we are man to man. Either tell me she can never be my wife— tell me you're lying when you say you haven't harmed her—or else write her a letter, telling her the truth that you won't see her again."

Arthur struggled, suffered, promised, and Adam, half comforted, left, not knowing that there, in the waste-basket, hastily stuffed under the papers, lay a woman's silk kerchief.

When Hetty read Arthur's letter she gave way to despair. Then, by one of those convulsive, motiveless actions by which the wretched leap from temporary sorrow to life-long misery, she determined to marry Adam. The big carpenter was in the seventh heaven, Hetty fitful and depressed. For family reasons, the marriage could not be hastened, and as the months passed she determined at any cost to seek out Arthur, whose regiment was at Windsor. Telling her uncle she was going to Snowfield to see Dinah for a little change of scene before her marriage, she started out, ignorant of the country, panic-stricken, and forlorn, eager to shun every familiar face, longing only to feel again the protection of her lover's arms.

On Arthur, meanwhile, life seemed again to smile. After rejoining his regiment, his sharpest regrets for Hetty began to lose their sting. Soon he was transferred to Ireland, and there learned that by his grandfather's death he was lord of the manor. Home he came, fast as chaise and postboy could drive, home to dear old Hayslope sleeping on the hill, where he was to live his life, married to some lovely lady, respected and appreciated by his tenants. A pile of letters awaited him. He opened the first, and, with a violent convulsion shaking his whole frame, read the words, *"Hetty Sorrel is in prison for the crime of child murder."*

Clutching the letter, Arthur rushed from the room like a hunted man, and, springing to the saddle of a waiting horse, set off at a gallop.

That very evening a young woman knocked at the door of the village jail. There was about her a deep, concentrated calmness which induced the jailer to grant her request to visit the condemned cell. As the heavy door closed behind her, she hesitated before the pallet bed.

"Hetty, Dinah is come to you."

Slowly, very slowly, Hetty rose and was clasped in Dinah's arms.

"You won't leave me, Dinah?"

"No, Hetty," whispered Dinah. "I'll stay with you to the last. But, Hetty, there is some one else in this cell."

"Who?" whispered Hetty, frightened.

"Some one who has been with you all your hours of sin and trouble. It makes no difference, Hetty, whether we live or die. We are in the presence of God. Confess the sin you have committed against your Heavenly Father. Let us kneel together. He is here."

There in the silence and darkness Hetty, who through her trial had sat like a stone image, poured forth her pitiful story.

"It was because I was so miserable, Dinah. I didn't know where to go. I tried to kill myself, and I couldn't. I went to Windsor to find him. He was gone, and I didn't know what to do. I daren't go home again. Then the baby was born. . . . I did do it, Dinah. I buried it in the wood—the little baby. It cried. . . . I heard it all night—and I went back. And then I thought I would go home, and all of a sudden I saw a hole under a nut-tree, and it darted over me like lightning I'd lay the baby there and cover it with grass and chips. I couldn't cover it quite up, Dinah. I thought somebody'd come and take care of it. Dinah, do you think God will take away that cry and the place in the wood, now that I've told everything?"

"Let us pray, poor sinner," breathed Dinah. "Let us pray to the God of All Mercy."

Comforter and comforted, their prayer was heard. Two days later, in the very shadow of the scaffold, Arthur Donnithorne brought a hard-won reprieve.

Though spared from death, Hetty was sentenced to transportation. Dinah returned to her works of mercy at Snowfield. In remorse and shame, Arthur Donnithorne went back to the army, while Adam Bede, squaring his shoulders to the world, turned again to his work-bench.

For him all the joy of life seemed over, and never would he have thought of seeking it again had not his mother dropped into his heart one day the name of Dinah. Long and soberly he thought, and then he went to find her.

VIRGIL'S ÆNEID

CONDENSATION BY PROF. WILLIAM FENWICK HARRIS

PUBLIUS VIRGILIUS MARO was born in 70 B.C. and died in 19 B.C. Like so many of the great writers of Rome he was not born at the great city, but near Mantua, in a region that produced many of the great men of the empire. He was of humble stock and constantly shows in his writing his familiarity with farm life, but despite his simple origin he received an extremely liberal education on both the Latin and Greek sides; the farmer's son finally became a friend of the great men of the time and one of the cosmopolitan figures of the empire. Despite misfortunes with his ancestral property, the patronage of Mæcenas and the friendship of Augustus allowed him to travel freely and to devote himself to a life of letters. The Greek literature of Alexandria made a great impression on him and shows itself in the "Eclogues," poems of pastoral life modeled largely after the charming Greek poet Theocritus, which in their turn have had a very great influence on that type of poems so popular in all ages. Somewhat in the same line are the "Georgics," which in charming form display a very profound knowledge of farming on the part of the poet. They were perhaps written with the patriotic motive of starting a movement back to the farm.

The great work of Virgil was the "Æneid," which he left, however, in an unfinished state and wished to have destroyed at his death. It was to be the perfect story of his nation's origin. It has remained one of the possessions of the world's literature.

Virgil was one of the great figures of the Middle Ages.

He was supposed to have foretold the birth of Christ and was regarded as the greatest pagan. It was claimed that he shared with the Bible the power of settling all difficulties; one had only to open the "Æneid"; the first passage on which one chanced gave an omen. The rôle he plays in Dante shows the esteem in which he was held.

Arms and The Man of Destiny are the subject of Virgil's story—in which he portrays the birth of a nation.

The author goes far back into history as Homer told it, to find a national hero for his people. But his story has one great difference from the "Iliad" and the "Odyssey," from which it borrows so much besides a hero. Homer's tales are spontaneous stories of the great chiefs who stand at the beginning of Greek history, while Virgil, a man of letters and a patriot, who would make plausible the divine mission of his race to rule the world, deliberately chooses his hero and then makes for him a history to suit his needs. One wonders sometimes whether Æneas or the Italian nation is the hero of the great national story.

In Homer, Æneas stands alongside Hector as one of the great champions of Troy. When the city falls he is one of the few Trojans to escape destruction. With his venerable father Anchises on his shoulders, his son held by the hand, and his wife following, he makes his way to the shore and takes ship with a large company of his following to seek a new land and found a new kingdom. But he has hanging over him the inveterate hostility of the goddess Juno, the persistent foe of all that was Trojan. It is at this point that Virgil takes up the tale of his Man of Destiny. After the fashion advised by Horace, he plunges into the midst of things.

After some six years of wandering Æneas sets sail for Italy, after he has lost his father in Sicily. His wife had long since perished. At Juno's orders the god of the winds sends forth a tempest which drives the ships to Africa. His mother, the goddess Venus, does her best to make up for the harshness of Juno, foretells to him the greatness that lies in store for him and his race, and directs him to Carthage, the rising city of Queen Dido. Happy chance brings the hero and the queen together, a generous and kindly hospitality follows, the ever-watchful Venus produces in place of Æneas's son Ascanius her own mischievous Cupid. The Queen of Carthage can no more resist.

A regal entertainment is set before the visitors in a scene of vast magnificence. At the end of the banquet the queen demands his story from the royal wanderer, just as King Alcinous had asked the same from Odysseus. With all the magnates of her court gathered around, with Æneas's companions as well, the queen fondling the little Ascanius in her arms—remember that rogue Cupid was playing the part—the prince began the famous tale of the last night of Troy, the stratagem of the wooden horse, the story of Laocoön, and all the rest, to which follow his own escape with his people, and his many years' wanderings, his meeting with Andromache in Epirus, and all the events that had taken the six years of his life.

Then follows the famous fourth book of the "Æneid," the great story of the passionate love of Dido for the Man of Destiny. It is one of the most widely read, the most admired, the most discussed stories in the world's literature. Virgil summoned to it his greatest art; he did not hesitate to borrow from the great writers of the past, particularly from the "Medea" of Apollonius Rhodius, the fine tale of romantic love which has come from Alexandria in the late days of the Greek genius. Virgil is not a supreme artist in the portrayal of character as Homer was, but in the picture of the tender and pathetic passion of the queen he rose to his highest point. The queen's confession of her love to her sister; the great hunting-party for her lover's entertainment; the storm that separates the hunters and drives the royal pair to a cave alone; the queen's tenderness; and then the flight of the pious Æneas; the queen's entreaties; the portrayal of all the passion of a slighted woman; and finally her own self-inflicted death as the hero flees to a higher duty—it is splendidly done. For the hero as an individual there can be nothing but the most perfect contempt. His only excuse is that he is the Man of Destiny; individuals must play a subordinate rôle in the great drama of a race. The Italian who reads the story remembers the bitter enmity between Rome and Carthage, remembers the years of trouble Hannibal was later to lay on the descendants of Æneas, and must have a reason for it all. The modern reader has a different point of view and wishes that the poet had found a more glorious rôle for the national hero, the mighty founder of a race destined to rule the world. For Æneas thoroughly deserved the imprecations heaped upon his head by the dying Dido. Homer would have found a more human way out of the difficulty.

For the modern world the interest in the "Æneid" grows less after the great tale of Dido's passion is told. The Trojans set sail for Italy once more, and once more are driven to Sicily. There the prince celebrates great funeral games on the anniversary of his father's death, after the fashion of those which Homer pictures Achilles celebrating in honor of the dead Patroclus. The Trojan women, weary of the long wanderings, try to burn the ships, but are only partly successful. Æneas leaves them and all who wish to tarry, and at last reaches Italy, where he makes the famous descent to the lower regions to consult his father; he perhaps, after the episode of Dido, feels the need of being told again of the great destiny of himself and his race. The journey is, of course, in imitation of Odysseus's descent to Hades, and was the great model for Dante.

Æneas journeys on to the mouth of the Tiber and forms an alliance with King Latinus, which includes marriage with the king's daughter, Lavinia. If the reader is inclined to murmur: "What, again? Naughty man!" the answer is that good Æneas has been under the burden from the first of being the Man of Destiny, and the union with the daughter of King Latinus is to produce the Latin race. But not without a final struggle on the part of the jealous Juno, who raises up enmity under the leadership of Turnus, one of the suitors for the hand of Lavinia. He can compete with fate no more successfully than could poor Dido, and after glorious battles perishes in single combat at the hand of the Man of Destiny.

ALICE IN WONDERLAND

by

LEWIS CARROLL

CONDENSATION BY NEWTON NEWKIRK

LEWIS CARROLL (Charles Lutwidge Dodgson) was born in the village of Darebury, Cheshire, England, January 27, 1832. He was a mathematician as well as author, and while the literary life of "Lewis Carroll" was familiar to a wide circle of readers, the private life of Charles Lutwidge Dodgson was retired and practically uneventful.

He took a first class in the final mathematical school in 1854, and the following year was appointed mathematical lecturer at Christ Church, a post he continued to fill until 1881. He published books of a purely mathematical nature first; but in 1865 he published, under the pseudonym of "Lewis Carroll," "Alice's Adventures in Wonderland," a work that was the outcome of his keen sympathy with the imagination of children and their sense of fun. This whimsical story was an immediate success, and the name of "Lewis Carroll" has ever since been a household word.

Mr. Dodgson was extremely fond of children, and it was an open secret that the original of Alice was a daughter of Dean Liddel. A dramatic version of the Alice books was produced at Christmas, 1886, and has since enjoyed numerous revivals.

Throughout this dual existence Mr. Dodgson persistently refused to be publicly identified with "Lewis Carroll," although his authorship of "Alice in Wonderland" and "Through the Looking-Glass" was well known.

He died at Guilford on the 14th of January, 1898; his memory is appropriately kept green by a cot in the Children's Hospital, Great Ormond Street, London, which was erected and endowed perpetually by public subscription.

Alice sat nodding sleepily on a mossy bank beside her big sister, who was reading.

Presently a pink-eyed white Rabbit ran by, looking at its watch and crying, "Oh dear—I shall be late!" Alice bounded after the Rabbit, across a field and into a hole under a hedge. After running through the hole a distance she suddenly stepped off into space and began to fall. She fell slowly, and it was a very pleasant sensation. Alice was wondering whether she would stop at the earth's center when, bump!—she landed on a heap of leaves, unhurt.

The Rabbit was scampering down the passage. Springing to her feet, she pursued, but it disappeared around the next corner and Alice found herself in a long hall of many doors, all locked. On a table was a golden key which fitted the smallest door, only fifteen inches high. Unlocking this, she beheld a beautiful flower-garden, but could not squeeze through the door.

On the table she found a bottle labeled "Drink Me." Alice tasted —it was delicious and she drank it all. Soon she shrank to only ten inches in height. "Now I can go into the garden!" cried Alice, running to the door, but, alas! she had relocked it and left the key on the table far beyond her reach.

Beneath the table in a glass dish she found a cookie on which were the words, "Eat Me." She ate this and soon grew nine feet tall. Presently the Rabbit entered and, seeing Alice, fled in dismay, dropping his gloves and fan. Alice picked them up and began to fan herself. Soon she was only two feet high and dropped the fan in a fright. Thereupon she stopped growing smaller and knew it was a magic fan.

Hearing footfalls, she turned to see the Rabbit standing near. It was nearly as tall as she and seemed very angry. "You go to my house and bring me a pair of gloves and a fan!" commanded the Rabbit, sternly. Alice, badly frightened, started to obey. Strangely enough, the hall vanished and she found herself running through a deep wood. Soon she came to a little white house. The doorplate said "W. Rabbit." Entering, she hurried up-stairs to the Rabbit's bedroom and found, not gloves and a fan, but a bottle on the bureau. It was not labeled, but Alice drank the contents. She grew so rapidly that the room was hardly big enough to contain her, although she was lying on the floor with her head drawn up to her chin.

While she was in this predicament some one threw a handful of pebbles through the window into the room. These turned into bits of candy. Alice ate several of them and soon shrank until she could escape from the house. Running into the wood, she sat down beside a mushroom to rest.

"What can I do for you?" asked a voice. Alice looked up, and on top of the mushroom sat a blue Caterpillar, smoking a pipe.

"Oh, please, sir," replied Alice, "make me larger!"

"That's easy," said the Caterpillar; "one side of this mushroom will make you taller, and the other side shorter."

Before Alice could ask more the Caterpillar disappeared.

Alice broke off a piece from each side of the mushroom. After eating a bit of one she grew so short her chin struck her foot. Hastily eating some of the other, she grew so tall her head was among the tree-tops. "Oh, dear, shall I never be my regular size again!" she cried, nibbling from the first piece and shrinking down to only nine inches.

In despair she started to walk through the wood, and soon came to a little house about four feet high. Without knocking, Alice walked into the kitchen. The Duchess sat rocking a little pig in her lap, the Cook was sprinkling quantities of pepper into a kettle of soup, and a Cheshire Cat on the hearth grinned from ear to ear at her. All three sneezed violently from time to time.

"Please go away—I don't like your grin," said Alice to the Cat.

"All right," replied the Cat, and vanished, beginning with the tail and ending with the grin—but the grin remained after the rest had disappeared.

To escape from this horrid grin Alice ran out of the house and into the wood, closely pursued by the grin. Seeing a little door open leading into a big tree, Alice slipped through and slammed the door behind her, shutting out the grin.

Turning about, she at last found herself in the beautiful garden. Standing about a rose-tree near the entrance were three gardeners painting the white roses red. "Why are you doing that?" asked Alice.

"Because," replied one, "the Queen does not fancy white roses."

"Hush!" said another; "here comes the Queen now!"

Alice turned eagerly to behold the royal procession. There were soldiers with clubs, courtiers bedecked with diamonds, and the royal children were ornamented with hearts, while in and out among them hopped the White Rabbit. Last of all came the King and Queen of Hearts.

When the Queen came to Alice she stopped and asked, "My child, do you play croquet?"

"Y-y-y-yes," stammered Alice, much confused.

"Then here is your mallet," replied the Queen, handing Alice a live flamingo. Then the game began, and such a crazy game of croquet Alice had never seen.

The croquet balls were live hedgehogs and the soldiers bent over to make the arches. Besides, the ground was full of hummocks and ridges. All played at once. When Alice would get ready to hit her ball with the flamingo's head, either the hedgehog would walk off, or the soldier making the arch would stand up to rest his back.

"How do you like the game?" asked a voice. Looking up, Alice beheld the grin of the Cheshire Cat. Before she could answer the Cat's head appeared, but no more of it.

"I don't like it at all," replied Alice, dropping her mallet, which at once flew off. The Cat turned to look at the King, who did not like being grinned at, and complained to the Queen, who ordered the Cat beheaded on the spot.

"That is all very well," said the King, "but I should like to know how it is possible to behead a cat which has no body?" While they were arguing the Cheshire Cat vanished, head, grin, and all.

Alice went to look for her flamingo, but could not find it. When she returned, all the players had gone to the Palace. Alice followed and, entering, found a trial in progress. The King and Queen sat on their throne hearing the evidence. The Knave of Hearts was being tried for stealing some tarts the Queen had made. Several witnesses testified, but they talked of everything else except the stolen tarts.

"What a silly trial!" thought Alice, nibbling absent-mindedly at a piece of mushroom she had left. Almost before she knew it she grew so tall her head bumped against the ceiling.

"Call the next witness!" commanded the King.

"ALICE!" cried the White Rabbit.

"But I don't know anything about the stolen tarts," protested Alice.

"That's very important," remarked the King.

"It's against the rules for a witness over a mile high to testify," said the Queen.

"Leave this court at once!" ordered the King, addressing Alice.

"I sha'n't leave until I hear the verdict," retorted Alice.

"In that case," said the King, "let the jury consider the verdict."

"Sentence first and verdict afterward," objected the Queen.

"How absurd to have a sentence before a verdict!" said Alice, scornfully.

"Off with that girl's head!" shouted the Queen pointing at Alice.

"Will you please stoop down so I can carry out the Queen's orders?" asked the Royal Executioner, politely.

"No, I won't!" cried Alice; "you are all nothing but a naughty pack of cards, anyhow, and I am not afraid of you!"

Thereupon the whole pack rose up into the air and flew straight into Alice's face.

"Come, Alice dear, wake up," said her big sister, shaking her gently; "you've been sleeping nearly an hour and it's time to go home."

Then little Alice knew that her wonderful journey had been only a wonderful dream.

∽◊∾

AN AMERICAN TRAGEDY*

by

THEODORE DREISER

CONDENSATION BY MARGARET GILLETT

THEODORE DREISER (1871–1945) was the twelfth of thirteen children reared in poverty by pious German Catholic parents in Terre Haute, Indiana. He went to public schools in Warsaw, Indiana, and worked at odd jobs until he entered Indiana University, where he remained only one year. In 1892 he became a newspaperman, starting as a reporter on the old Chicago "Globe." Later he moved to the St. Louis "Globe-Democrat" and finally worked as drama critic and correspondent for the St. Louis "Republic." His experience as a journalist undoubtedly contributed to his later realism as a novelist.

Dreiser was married in 1898, after which he settled down to writing seriously. For the next decade he was connected with various periodicals, as contributor and editor, while he was working on his novels, as well. "Sister Carrie" (1900), his first novel, was suppressed as sordid. "Jennie Gerhardt" (1911) fared better, although it was not widely acclaimed at the time it appeared, but "The Financier" (1912), "The Titan" (1914), and "The Genius" (1915) established Dreiser as a novelist.

However, his fame rests mainly on "An American Trag-

* By permission of The World Publishing Company, publisher of *An American Tragedy,* copyright, 1925, 1926, 1953.

edy" (1925), *his novel based on actual court records of a crime. It was dramatized and had a long and successful stage production in New York City. In 1931 it was made into a movie which did not satisfy the author, and he sued the producer. The social-biological struggle of the story is a more or less recurrent theme in Dreiser's work, and the "tragedy" is a social one as well as an individual debacle for the hero.*

Between 1918 and 1929 Dreiser published four collections of short stories, and between 1926 and 1935, two volumes of poems. These were followed by numerous essays of social criticism. In 1927 he visited Russia and the following year put out "Dreiser Looks at Russia." His last novels were "The Bulwark" (1946) and "The Stoic" (1947).

Dusk—of a summer night.

And the tall walls of the commercial heart of an American city of perhaps 400,000 inhabitants. And up the broad street, now comparatively hushed, a little band of six—a man of about fifty, short, stout, a most unimportant-looking person, who carried a small portable organ such as is customarily used by street preachers. And with him a woman perhaps five years his junior, taller, not so broad, but solid of frame and vigorous, very plain in face and dress, and yet not homely, leading with one hand a small boy of seven and in the other carrying a Bible and several hymn books. With these three, but walking independently behind, was a girl of fifteen, a boy of twelve, and another girl of nine, all following obediently, but not too enthusiastically, in the wake of the others.

The principal thing that troubled Clyde Griffiths up to his fifteenth year, and indeed long after, was the shabby calling of his parents, the mission they conducted that was attended mostly by the idle, the odd, and the mentally disturbed. It was the compulsory duty of the Griffiths children to take part, but to Clyde, the elder boy, hymn-singing in the street brought shame, not salvation. He constantly thought of how he might better himself if he had a chance.

Because Mr. and Mrs. Griffiths were so wrapped up in evangelizing the world, they had neglected to keep their children in school for long in any one place. As soon as he was old enough, Clyde left school and secured a place as assistant to a soda water clerk in one of the cheaper drug stores in Kansas City.

He was not bad-looking, with a straight, well-cut nose, high white forehead, wavy hair, and black eyes that were melancholy at times. If only he had a better collar, a nicer shirt, finer shoes, a good suit, like some boys had! His first position did not enable him to satisfy these ambitions and consequently he sought a place as a bell-boy in the city's most luxurious hotel.

Now for the first time in his life he had money to spend on himself and friends of his own age. The other bell-hops introduced him to a new world of pleasures and vices that set him agape with wonder and, at first, with a timorous distaste—the sophistication of dining out, the tingle of cocktails, the acquaintance of girls, the thrill of dancing, the erotic pleasures of a brothel. As soon as he met Hortense Briggs he was beside himself with admiration and desire and, although he soon discovered she was a heartless flirt, a gold-digger, and not really sincere with anyone, the witchery of her smile was too much for him. He foolishly ran after her, but she, knowing he was ardent and inexperienced, compelled him to content himself with the crumbs of her company while allowing him to buy her little things— a bag, a scarf, a purse, a pair of gloves—anything she could reasonably ask without obligating herself too much.

However, she did consent to go with him and several of his hotel friends and their girls on an automobile ride. It was a disastrous excursion. Clyde made little progress with Hortense, who lavished her attentions on the driver of the car, but much worse was to follow. On their way back, stimulated by their drinking and dancing at a country inn, and driving at break-neck speed to be at the hotel in time, they struck and killed a child. In the ensuing chase the car, which had been "borrowed" without the owner's knowledge, was wrecked. As soon as they could extricate themselves and before the police arrived, Clyde and his friends fled.

For three years Clyde wandered about the Middle West taking numerous menial jobs and an assumed name. At twenty, he was a little taller, more firmly built, and considerably more experienced. He had come in contact with rough usage but had developed a kind of self-reliance, together with a conscious gentility of manner and pleasing smoothness of address. When he thought it safe, he began to use his own name again and luckily obtained a position as a bell-boy at the exclusive Union League Club in Chicago.

By chance, his uncle, Mr. Samuel Griffiths, owner of the prosperous Griffiths Collar and Shirt Company in Lycurgus, New York, happened to visit the club. The youth made himself known, and his uncle, taken by Clyde's gentle demeanor and striking likeness to his own son, Gilbert, offered him a job in the factory.

At first, because he had no special training of any kind, Clyde was put in the shrinking department. It was not pleasant work, and he began to wish he had not come. He was lonely. His rich relatives ignored him, and his cousin Gilbert, who was jealous of the youth who looked so much like himself, was openly hostile. On the other hand, the town and factory people, knowing Clyde was a Griffiths, thought it unnecessary and even presumptuous to suggest ways of entertaining him. True, a young man at his boarding-house was more than willing to be friendly and introduced him to an attractive girl, but since they were of no social consequence and Clyde *was* a Griffiths, he felt obliged to snub them.

In due course, however, Samuel Griffiths realized that some little courtesy was appropriate and Clyde was invited to dinner. At the Griffiths' mansion he met Sondra Finchley, the most adorable and feminine girl he had ever laid eyes on—so different from any he had ever known, so superior. Her effect upon him was electric and it roused a stinging sense of what it was to want and not to have.

This invitation to the world of high society was not followed by another, and Clyde's hopes of raising his station seemed in vain. Yet they revived when he was promoted with a salary increase from fifteen dollars to twenty-five dollars a week to the supervision of a small department employing some twenty-five girls. On making this appointment, Gilbert looked at Clyde coldly and emphatically admonished him to keep aloof from the employees, both inside and outside the factory.

Despite this warning Clyde, lonely as he was, and with a disposition easily inflamed by the chemistry of sex, was inclined to think of the girls with thoughts that bordered on the sensual. One, Roberta Alden, possessed a charm that no one else in the room had, a certain wistfulness and wonder combined with a more intelligent and spiritual quality. By degrees he proceeded to crave her even though she was not of that high world to which he aspired.

Yet, he was a Griffiths and still kept to himself, spending his spare time acquiring as many social accomplishments as possible. He learned to swim and dive. But canoeing fascinated him really. Then imagine his delight when, one Sunday, his rented canoe rounded a point on Crum Lake and there was Roberta standing on the bank!

She was charmed by his personality and by the glamour of the superior world in which she thought he moved. She too knew the difficulties that social contact would bring, but still the contact was made and soon they were meeting secretly and often.

They were deliciously happy. Then came the wonder and delight of a more intimate form of contact, of protests gainsaid, of scruples overcome, and yielding to the wild, convulsive pleasure motivating both. Yet, not without, before all this, an exaction on the part of Roberta to the effect that never—come what might (the natural consequences of so wild an intimacy strong in her thoughts)—would he desert her.

One evening as Clyde walked along an avenue between his boarding-house and Roberta's, a closed car of great size driven by a chauffeur, stopped directly in front of him. He recognized the young lady inside as Sondra Finchley, whom he had met at the Griffiths. She mistook him for his cousin Gilbert and offered him a ride.

Sondra was soon glad she had made the mistake, because Clyde turned out to be so much more pleasing than Gilbert, whom she did not like. She hit upon the idea of having him taken up by some of the best families and invited to dances, dinners, and parties, just to irritate Gilbert. To her relief, he proved socially acceptable. He was so charming and so devoted to her that soon she found herself in love with him.

Clyde was now faced with the problem of freeing himself from Roberta. What had she, a poor farmer's daughter, to offer to offset the imaginative pull of such a girl as Sondra and all the wealth, beauty, and social position she represented? He made excuses for seeing Roberta less often, his tone lost its tenderness, his embraces became apathetic. Roberta was just beginning to realize their romance was finished and she should leave Lycurgus when she found herself pregnant.

Clyde could not bear the thought of marrying Roberta, but to deny his responsibility entirely was to risk exposure and the death of all his hopes. Fearful and embarrassed, he procured some pills from a druggist in Schenectady, and delivered them to Roberta with a great sense of satisfaction. But the remedy did not work. And a doctor in a nearby town who he hoped would perform an abortion refused to help. There seemed to be no way out and he drifted aimlessly. But Roberta finally announced to Clyde that if he could not get her out of her predicament he would have to marry her.

Time was running short when Clyde happened to notice a newspaper headline, "Accidental Double Tragedy at Pass Lake—Upturned Canoe and Floating Hats Reveal Loss of Two Lives.". . . Supposing he and Roberta were in a boat and it should capsize—an accidental, unpremeditated drowning then a glorious future with Sondra? What was he thinking? He, Clyde Griffiths, nephew of Samuel Griffiths, commit a horrible crime, murder?!!! Yet his mind kept dwelling on the idea.

He pretended to give in to Roberta's demands and, with assumed tenderness, suggested they take a trip before their wedding. He took her to an isolated lake, rented a boat, rowed to a secluded spot. But a sudden palsy of the will overtook him. Roberta, sensing something eerie in his mood, moved toward him and, suddenly revolted by her presence and his own failure, he flung out at her. His camera, unconsciously held in his hand, struck her face. Even as he began to apologize for this unintended blow, she lurched backward, capsizing the boat. The accident had happened! She could not swim. He waited until her struggles ceased and then swam to safety.

Roberta's body was found almost immediately and a letter to her mother in her pocket led to her identification. Circumstantial evidence pointed to murder and, inevitably, to Clyde. Samuel Griffiths, utterly shocked by the scandal, nevertheless provided the best local lawyers for his nephew. For months they drilled Clyde in the most sympathetic version of his story they could concoct. However, their flimsy defense could scarcely compete with the pathetic appeal of Roberta's letters, the stricken weary pain of her parents, the damning testimony of numerous witnesses, and the vigorous prosecution of the District Attorney. The twelve gaunt, religious members of the jury, who were convinced of Clyde's guilt before they sat down, returned the expected verdict: "Guilty of murder in the first degree."

Clyde was incarcerated in the death house with thirty other murderers, slowly consumed by fear and watching his neighbors one by one go to that Chair. His mother, stubbornly believing in his innocence, raised money for an appeal. But in vain. Without new evidence or extenuating circumstances her pleas to the Governor for mercy were also fruitless. For Clyde, the dread news that he must die was as fascinating as it was terrible; he did not feel as distrait as he expected—but did he really deserve death?

In the dark of a midwinter morning he was taken from his cell toward the room with the Chair that he had seen so often in his dreams. He was pushed toward that—on through the door which was now open to receive him—but which quickly closed again on all the earthly life he had ever known.

ANNA KARENINA
by
LEO N. TOLSTOI

CONDENSATION BY MARY FRANCES RUSS

COUNT LEO TOLSTOI was born in 1828 at Yasnaya Polyana, near Toula, the family estate that has become famous throughout the world as the residence of the great novelist, reformer, and dreamer. He died in 1910 at a little railroad station which he had reached on a journey the object of which was to let him end his days in solitude. But a whole world was looking on.

At first he studied Oriental languages, then law, and finally became a soldier, taking part in the Crimean campaign. His long series of writings began with "Childhood," "Boyhood," "The Morning of a Landed Proprietor," and articles on his experiences as a soldier. His realism was already a dominant note, as well as his power to see through shams and conventions. He soon retired from the army and began his life of service to the peasants about him at his own estate. "War and Peace" appeared in 1864–69, and the great novel "Anna Karenina," 1875–76. Already he was dealing with the mighty problems of life and humanity and trying to solve them in whatever way seemed to him right, no matter what answer the world had given to them. "My Religion," "The Kreutzer Sonata," "Resurrection," are perhaps the best-known books, which have been translated into many languages. A whole library of books has been written about him in many languages.

*Tolstoi is one of the unique figures in the history of the
world. Seer, prophet, fearless seeker after truth no matter
where the quest might lead, he drew to himself the respectful
attention of all thinking people, no matter how divergent
their thoughts from his. His belief that Christianity is a
faith to be actually lived by and his championship of the
doctrine of non-resistance are the outstanding points of a
thought which covered all humanity.*

"And . . . Anna had friendly relations with the society . . .
which with one hand lays fast hold of the court lest it fall absolutely
into the demi-monde which its members affect to despise, but whose
tastes are precisely similar."

Anna Karenina's intimates were of this circle in St. Petersburg
society. Practically forced into a loveless marriage with Aleksei
Karenin, twenty years her senior, Anna had been a faithful wife for
eight years. Karenin held a high official position and everything in
his life was subordinated to his career. He was a tireless worker, and
such social hours as he enjoyed were spent in circles best suited to his
advancement, but his charming and adaptable wife made friends
in all quarters. While a man of admirable character, Karenin had
an utterly unlovable personality. He was very calm, cool, absolutely
just, but love—warm, human love—was a stranger in his household.
All the affection of Anna Karenina's heart was lavished on her seven-
year-old son, Serozha, who adored his mother.

Into this setting, so cunningly fashioned for it, stepped Trouble,
in the most attractive person of Aleksei Vronsky.

In the city of Moscow lived Anna's brother, Stepan Oblonsky.
Stepan, lovable and popular, had a wife, children, a salaried official
position and some money, but, being always in debt, this fact and his
little *affaires du cœur* kept him just sufficiently worried to enable him
to really enjoy life.

While on a visit to Moscow, Anna Karenina met Vronsky.

Count Vronsky was rich, handsome, loved his regiment and his
horses, and was voted a "capital good fellow." He had appeared in
Moscow that winter and had been attracted slightly to Stepan's sister-
in-law, Kitty. Kitty was a pretty and popular débutante, daughter
of Prince Scherbatsky of the old nobility. Among many admirers,
she was sure of two serious suitors. One was Vronsky, the other
Levin.

Konstantin Levin was also of the old Muscovite nobility and had known Kitty all her life. As his mother had died in his babyhood, the family life of the Scherbatskys had appealed to him strongly. He was now thirty-two, and, although feeling unworthy of Kitty, was determined to offer himself to her. He was really a splendid match. He had a magnificent country estate of eighty-one hundred acres, plenty of money, and his share of masculine attractions. He was a thinker, always immersed in the deepest problems concerning the world, everything in it, on it, and beyond it. He had been brought up in the orthodox faith, but, since attaining manhood, had been assailed with all kinds of doubts, until now he was practically an unbeliever. "He could not believe; he was also equally unable to disbelieve." After completing his university course he spent most of his time on his great estate, wrestling with his problems of agriculture and peasant labor. He came into Moscow on occasions and dipped into its social life, but his own life was so clean and simple that he had little patience with the dissipations of his town friends.

Kitty's parents had many quarrels over her prospects. Her mother favored the brilliant Vronsky; her father said "Levin was worth a thousand men." Kitty herself had set her heart on Vronsky although fond of Levin. In due time she experienced the pleasing pain of refusing Levin, but, to her chagrin and deep humiliation, the proposal from Vronsky did not materialize. The latter did not dream that his attentions to her were regarded seriously. Poor Kitty met her crushing disappointment at a large ball, when, instead of choosing her as his mazurka partner, Vronsky led out—Madame Karenina!

In spite of their endeavors to hide the magic glow which enveloped them, it was obvious to Kitty, as to others, that Anna and Vronsky had both been touched with the same flaming torch.

Anna Karenina had met her man. She knew it. She was afraid. Her customary serenity deserted her so completely that she left for Petersburg the next day, cutting short her visit. The calm routine of her daily life took on a new and attractive aspect; she longed to see her son—even her husband. But—Vronsky took the same train to Petersburg.

They met constantly in society. Anna called all the forces of reason, prudence, pride, to her aid, but she could not conceal the rapture she felt in Vronsky's presence. Her intimates became extremely interested. This was, indeed, an affair after their own hearts. According to their code, anything was proper so long as outward conventions were observed. Karenin coolly pointed out the danger of her course. He assured her he looked upon jealousy "as a humiliating and wounding sentiment." (Anna would have respected some truculent conversation.) His spineless attitude enraged her, and by the end of a year she and Vronsky had become all in all to each other. They had but one object in life—to be together.

Karenin waited for the blow to fall. It was finally accomplished by Anna's public exhibition of emotion when Vronsky met with a racing accident. Upon being upbraided by her husband, she confessed her love for Vronsky. Mingled with the pain Karenin felt a sense of relief. He immediately began to plan on getting out of the mud without being splashed. He considered dueling, divorce, separation. Being afraid of a pistol, he concluded that his services to the government were too valuable for him to risk his life. The scandal of a divorce might react against himself and a separation would throw Anna into Vronsky's arms. The latter was the last thing he wanted. It would not punish Anna. His decision was to allow her to remain in his home—perhaps resume their old relations. He knew this would make her most unhappy. His justification for this attitude was its religious significance.

In the meantime Levin was trying to forget Kitty by devoting himself to work. He became much interested in uplifting his peasants, who did not appreciate his efforts. He reached the conclusion that he had found the way to happiness, but one glimpse of Kitty showed him his error and stirred up his old feeling for her. Kitty's health had so failed after her disappointment in Vronsky, that she had been sent abroad to take a cure. Now, having been restored to health and having a new outlook on life, she realized that it was Levin whom she really loved, and when he again asked her for her hand she gladly consented.

According to Karenin's decision, Anna still had her place as mistress of his household. Karenin was aware that she and Vronsky still maintained their relations, but could do nothing about it. In time, Anna gave birth to a daughter and was thought to be dying. Karenin's conduct was magnanimous, even toward Vronsky's baby. Vronsky attempted suicide through sheer humiliation. But Anna recovered, which Karenin had not counted on, and with her returning health came the conviction that Vronsky was the light of life to her. She became so unhappy that, in a moment of weakness, Karenin was prevailed upon to consent to a divorce, even to take the blame and give her the boy. This generosity she could not accept, and with Vronsky and her baby left her husband's home and her son, on that inevitably fatal journey of love without the law.

They went abroad and at first were radiantly happy. Then Vronsky tired of the aimless life. They returned to Russia and settled in the country. Anna's position became so unbearable to Vronsky, who adored her, that he finally urged her to appeal to Karenin for a divorce. When Karenin refused, owing to various circumstances, matters grew worse than ever. Anna could not go into society, so became introspective. Without cause, she grew very jealous of Vronsky. She took to morphine as a sleeping-potion.

Suicide—under the rushing wheels of a railroad train—was Anna Karenina's way out.

Vronsky's grief was overwhelming. After many weeks of illness he organized a squadron of cavalry and entered the Serbian war.

Konstantin Levin found his happiness with his wife and small son, and found that his old faith had lived in his heart, although hidden, when an old peasant explained why a certain man was good in the words "he lives for his soul, he remembers God."

THE ARABIAN NIGHTS
by
THE PRINCESS SHEHERAZADE

CONDENSATION BY ALFRED S. CLARK

The marvelous tales that SHEHERAZADE told to King Shahriar, stories of love and adventure and mad magic, cannot be attributed to any one author, for the very good reason that there never was an author. They are popular stories that, perhaps about the year 1450, were put into the present form by a professional story-teller, presumably a Persian.

In primitive communities, where few of the people can

*read and where books are difficult to get, these professional
readers are in great demand. They pick up here and there
tales that appeal to all and bind them into a long narrative.
Some people have thought that Homer's long poems origi-
nated in this way.*

*Everywhere in the near East the traveler finds these story-
tellers to-day. An eager audience collects to hear them, each
paying a small fee for the privilege of listening. The enter-
tainer declaims as he walks to and fro and always stops his
narrative just before an exciting climax, so that he will be
assured of listeners on the morrow. His audience follows his
recital with breathless interest, especially when he illustrates
thrilling episodes with lively pantomime.*

*Year after year these groups of listeners gathered cen-
turies ago. The story-teller discarded the tales that did not
hold the attention of his listeners. Gradually the process of
elimination went on until only the best were handed down
by word of mouth from generation to generation. Then some
unknown benefactor of mankind had them written down and
connected them with the framework of Sheherazade and
Shahriar. And these are the "Arabian Nights" that have
delighted children and grown men and women for decades.*

Sheherazade was a vizier's daughter and when she besought her
father to wed her to King Shahriar it was cause for grief to the
vizier. For each day was it Shahriar's wont to put to death his bride
of the day before. It befell, however, that Sheherazade had her will.
As she had hoped, the king was wakeful and to beguile him she
began a story of magic. Dawn broke before she had finished, and so
eager was Shahriar to hear it all that he gave no order for her
execution.

For a thousand and one nights did this befall while Sheherazade
told tales of love, war, and sorcery, of kings, beggars, and rogues,
of lands where diamonds were more plentiful than pebbles and bigger
than eggs, of intrigues in the lanes and bazaars of Oriental cities.
In towns and deserts and far islands did necromancers work their
wills. Horses flew; dogs talked; mermaidens and creatures greater
than whales peopled the deeps; ogres and enormous apes crept out
of forests; birds so great that their wings darkened the day swooped
from the skies. Here too were lovers in palaces and hovels, bold and

cowardly, yet all so enamoured that they swooned at the very thought of the beloved. Underlying all was the colorful Orient with barbers and porters jostling caliphs and princesses in the thronged and picturesque lanes of three cities whose very names conjure up romance —Bagdad, Cairo, and Damascus.

Now these are the best liked of Sheherazade's tales:

THE STORY OF ALADDIN'S LAMP

Of Aladdin, son of a poor tailor in China, a prankish scamp. An African magician guided him to a subterranean cave where he found the lamp that summoned the genie. Out of nothingness did this genie spread banquets for Aladdin and robe him in rich raiment. He provided him retinues of slaves, bearing basins heaped high with precious stones, who carried to the king Aladdin's suppliance for the hand of the beautiful Princess Badroulboudour. In a night did the genie raise a palace of glowing wonders, of shining marble and gold and silver, with windows incrusted with diamonds, emeralds, and rubies, with fragrant gardens and open courts. So Aladdin married the princess and they knew great joy. But the magician returned, stole the lamp, and in a trice transported the palace and the princess to Africa. Then was Aladdin woeful, but by magic he found his beloved, poisoned the magician, seized the lamp, and came to China, where he and Badroulboudour lived happily ever afterward.

THE STORY OF SINBAD

Of Sinbad the sailor and his marvelous voyages. Wherein it is related that Sinbad landed upon what seemed an island, but which was a great fish that sank into the sea. And of other voyages and greater wonders, of which one marvels most at the adventure with the roc, the bird so huge that it feeds its young with elephants. Sinbad had fastened himself to the roc's leg and it bore him to an impenetrable valley strewn with precious stones, from which he escaped by binding himself to a sheep's carcass and was borne away by a vulture. And of the giant who roasted men and whom Sinbad blinded with a red-hot iron. And of the terrible Old Man of the Sea who sat upon Sinbad's shoulders and could not be shaken off until he was intoxicated with wine and Sinbad slew him.

THE STORY OF THE FORTY THIEVES

Of Ali Baba and his discovery of the stone that swung wide when a voice cried "Open, Sesame!" In the cave was the booty of forty thieves and Ali Baba took home sacks bulging with gold and silver. The robbers traced him, and in the guise of a merchant the captain lodged with him. In the yard were stored great jars, one filled with oil and the others concealing the thieves. Ill would it have fared with Ali Baba had not Morgiana, a cunning slave, detected the trick and with boiling oil scalded to death the wicked miscreants. The captain escaped, but returned in a new disguise, and again did Morgiana save her master by stabbing his enemy. So Ali Baba married her to his son and he lived joyously upon treasures from the cave.

MANY OTHER FASCINATING STORIES

Of the Magic Horse of ebony and ivory, so fashioned that its rider, by pressing divers buttons, could fly whither he willed. It bore a Persian prince to a great palace in a metropolis girt about with greenery. There he looked into the eyes of a princess and they were enraptured. It befell that they rode away on the Magic Horse, but before they were wed an evil man abducted the princess. The disconsolate prince wandered far and at last he found her whom he loved, and again they journeyed through the air to his home, where they were married with exceeding pomp and lived happily.

Of a poor fisherman who drew his net from the sea and found therein but a brass bottle. He cut open the top and there streamed forth a cloud of smoke. It collected, and, behold! it was a genie, so huge that his head was in the clouds. He would have killed his rescuer had not the wily fisherman insisted that never could he have come from the bottle. The silly genie squeezed himself inside, whereupon the fisherman clapped on the top, nor would he remove it until the genie swore to serve him faithfully. This oath it was that led to the finding of the ensorcelled prince with legs turned to stone and the lake wherein swam fish of four colors that had once been men. After marvelous happenings, the prince was made as other men and the fish were men and women. And the fisherman was so rewarded that he was the wealthiest man of his time.

Of Prince Camaralzaman and the Princess Badoura, beautiful beyond compare, and of how each saw the other in sleep and was smitten with great love. But when they awakened they saw not each other, for they had been brought together by genii who had carried Badoura out of China to the confines of Persia. Grief so afflicted both that they sickened and were insane from sorrow. Then a messenger from Badoura journeyed far over land and sea until he found Camaralzaman and returned with him to China, where the lovers were wedded. But while they were traveling to Camaralzaman's land he wandered away. Badoura dressed herself in his raiment and passed herself for a man. It befell that she found favor in the eyes of a king and was married to a princess. And Camaralzaman too came to this land and knew not his wife, who heaped honors upon him. At last she revealed herself and was known as a woman and Camaralzaman took also to wife the princess whom Badoura had married and they were happy together.

Of a merchant who, awaiting death at the hands of a cruel genie, was joined by three old men, one leading a gazelle, another two black hounds, and the third a mule. Now it is related that the gazelle and the mule had been wicked wives transformed by magic, and likewise had the hounds been evil brothers. When the genie was told these stories of enchantment, he was so diverted that he spared the merchant's life.

ABOUT HARUN-AL-RASHID

And of many tales concerning the Caliph Harun-al-Rashid and his going disguised into the lanes and bazaars of Bagdad, where he chanced upon strange people who told him strange stories of magic. Once he supped with three ladies of dazzling beauty, and with him were a porter dazed with the magnificence he saw, and three mendicants, sons of kings, all blind in the left eye. Not knowing the caliph, they told of their fantastic adventures and sufferings and he rewarded them. And again he encountered a beggar who implored him to strike him, a youth who spurred cruelly a mare upon which he rode, and a rope-maker who had risen suddenly from poverty to affluence. Their tales, too, did he hear and them, too, did he reward. Nor should Abou-Hassan the Wag be forgotten, whose trickery in pretending that he and his wife were dead won so much gold and so many laughs from the caliph. And of like import is the mad tale of the humpback who seemed dead and of the talkative barber who restored him to life, of all those who had believed themselves murderers of the humpback and of the amazing tales that they related.

So it came to pass that by the end of the thousand and one nights Shahriar so delighted in the cleverness of Sheherazade that he wedded her again with regal pomp and they lived happily ever after.

BEN-HUR
A TALE OF THE CHRIST*
by
LEW WALLACE

CONDENSATION BY PROF. WILLIAM FENWICK HARRIS

LEWIS WALLACE, generally known by the nickname Lew, was born in 1827 at Brookville, Indiana, and perhaps was, quite unconsciously, potent in spreading the idea, dear to some, that in that state is located the literary center of this country. He died in 1905.

Like the students of to-day in the great struggle, he left his books for the Mexican War. He served again in the Civil War and rose to be Major-General in the Volunteer army. As after the Mexican episode, he returned again to the law; he was Governor of the Territory of New Mexico from 1878 to 1881, and minister to Turkey from 1881 to 1885, when as a good diplomat he won the esteem of the late unlamented Abdul Hamid and could really put through business with that scientifically dilatory tyrant.

He is known by his three books "The Fair God" (1873), "Ben-Hur" (1880), and "The Prince of India" (1893). The first is a very clever reconstruction of the story of the conquest of Mexico by the Spaniards. The reader feels a great sympathy with the highly developed natives who fell helpless before the superior arms of the invaders. The story, however, is by no means to be put in the same class with "Ben-Hur." The skill, the knowledge, the reverence with which the story of Christ is told (largely through the lives of others) have made "Ben-Hur" one of the books to take a secure hold on the public, both as book and on the stage, where the famous chariot-race has won a classic place.

* Printed by permission of, and arrangement with, Harper & Bros., authorized publishers.

"The workmen put their hands to the cross and carried it, burden and all, to the place of planting. At a word they dropped the tree into the hole; and the body of the Nazarene also dropped heavily and hung by the bleeding hands. Still no cry of pain—only the exclamation divinest of all recorded exclamations, 'Father, forgive them, for they know not what they do.' The cross, reared now above all other objects, and standing singly out against the sky, was greeted with a burst of delight; and all who could see and read the writing upon the board over the Nazarene's head made haste to decipher it. Soon as read, the legend was adopted by them and communicated, and presently the whole mighty concourse was ringing the salutation from side to side, and repeating it with laughter and groans:

" 'King of the Jews! Hail, King of the Jews!'

"The sun was rising rapidly to noon; the hills bared their brown breasts lovingly to it; the more distant mountains rejoiced in the purple with which it so regally dressed them. In the city the temples, palaces, towers, pinnacles, and all points of beauty and prominence seemed to lift themselves into the unrivaled brilliance, as if they knew the pride they were giving the many who from time to time turned to look at them. Suddenly a dimness began to fill the sky and cover the earth—at first no more than a scarce-perceptible fading of the day; a twilight out of time; an evening gliding in upon the splendors of noon. But it deepened, and directly drew attention, whereat the noise of the shouting and laughter fell off, and men, doubting their senses, gazed at one another curiously; then they looked at the sun again; then at the mountains, getting farther away; at the sky and the near landscape, sinking in shadow; at the hill upon which the tragedy was enacting; and from all these they gazed at one another again, and turned pale, and held their peace.

" 'It is only a mist or passing cloud,' Simonides said, soothingly, to Esther, who was alarmed. 'It will brighten presently.'

"Ben-Hur did not think so.

" 'It is not a mist or a cloud,' he said. 'The spirits who live in the air—the prophets and saints—are at work in mercy to themselves and nature. I say to you, O Simonides, truly as God lives, He who hangs yonder is the Son of God.'

"And leaving Simonides lost in wonder at such a speech from him, he went where Balthazar was kneeling near by, and laid his hand upon the good man's shoulder.

" 'O wise Egyptian, hearken! Thou alone wert right—the Nazarene is indeed the Son of God.'

"Balthazar drew him down to him and replied, feebly, 'I saw Him a child in the manger where He was first laid; it is not strange that I knew Him sooner than thou: but, oh, that I should live to see this day! Would that I had died with my brethren! Happy Melchior! Happy Gaspar!"

" 'Comfort thee!' said Ben-Hur. 'Doubtless they too are here.' "

Within the frame of the story of Christ is told the tale of Ben-Hur, beginning with the appearance of the three Wise Men, Balthazar, Melchior, and Gaspar, and ending with the sublime tragedy on Golgotha. From the days of the scenes at the manger until the culmination of the great story, the figure of Christ appears but once, and that for a moment, but over all that happens in the intervening years hovers the gentle spirit; thrilling as the episodes are in themselves, strongly as the characters are portrayed, they are but a preparation for what is to follow, a mere worldly setting for Him who was too great for all save a few to understand at that time.

Some twenty-one years after the scenes at the manger, a young Jew, Ben-Hur, a prince in Jerusalem, rich, happy, ambitious, was standing by a parapet of his palace, watching the progress of Valerius Gratus, imperial governor of Judea. As the Roman passed beneath the wall amid the jeers and insults of the Jews, the young prince leaned far out to see the new governor, a loose tile was displaced, and, as bitter fate would have it, fell full upon the governor. The accident was not fatal, but it was an opportunity for exemplary justice, especially as the estates of the Jews were very desirable to the governor and his friend Messala, hitherto almost brother to Ben-Hur though the latter had been. The unhappy Jew was sent as a rower to the galleys, where the limit of life was at most but a year. His mother and sister were immured in a secret cell in the Tower of Antonia, where they were doomed to the fate of lepers. The only act of kindness Ben-Hur could remember during the years that followed was on the day he was dragged to the galleys. "The hand laid kindly upon his shoulder awoke the unfortunate man, and, looking up, he saw a face he never forgot—the face of a boy about his own age, shaded by locks of yellowish bright chestnut hair; a face lighted by dark-blue eyes, at the time so soft, so appealing, so full of love and holy purpose, that they had all the power of command and will." That was in Nazareth.

How Ben-Hur in time became a rower on the flagship of Arrius, duumvir and admiral; how the flagship was destroyed in a great sea-fight; how Ben-Hur rescued the admiral, became his adopted son and his heir, learned at Rome the manner of Roman war and Roman sports, returned to the East a Roman officer in the train of a consul setting forth on a great campaign against the Parthians; how he discovered that his father's old steward, Simonides, had succeeded in saving from confiscation the vast intangible wealth of the Hurs and had multiplied it many times, till the young Roman-Jew was the richest private citizen in the world; the discovery that Messala was entered for the highest stake in the great sporting event of the Orient; how Ben-Hur won the affection of Ilderim, the Arab shiek, who had entered his steeds of the desert for the great event—all this leads up to the dramatic encounter of the famous chariot-race. The author drew his description of the race from one written over twenty-three hundred years ago by the tragic poet Sophocles. It is one of the curiosities of literature that the great scene, through the pages of Lew Wallace's novel, has become as famous on our stage as it was so long ago on that of Greece.

By his victory in the arena Ben-Hur exacted ancient Jewish justice on his hated adversary, who was crushed in body and impoverished in fortune—he had wagered on his success all the wealth he had stolen from his former friend. The victor almost fell prey, however, to the vampire daughter of Egypt who was rival for his love with the gentle Jewish Esther. But henceforth his thoughts were concentrated on Him who was attracting all eyes. Was he Messiah or king? Ben-Hur, in his hatred of Rome, in his pride of race, dreamed only of a king of this world, who should right ancient wrongs and exalt his chosen people. And so he threw himself with all his force, with all his wealth, with all the knowledge gained at Rome, into making secure and strong the way of the king whom he would follow. But it was for one supreme in things spiritual rather than material that the way was being made ready. And Ben-Hur's mother, rescued with her daughter from her long imprisonment by a chance change of jailers, but hopeless lepers both, saw the truth sooner than her son.

" 'O Master, Master!' she cried as He passed upon the road, 'Thou seest our need; Thou canst make us clean. Have mercy upon us—mercy!'

" 'Believest thou I am able to do this?' He asked.

" 'Thou art He of whom the prophets spake—Thou art the

Messiah!' she replied. His eyes grew radiant, His manner confident.
" 'Woman,' He said, 'great is thy faith; be it unto thee even as
thou wilt.' "

And so, in the end, Ben-Hur recognized what Balthazar had
known from the beginning. "O wise Egyptian, hearken! Thou alone
were right—the Nazarene is indeed the Son of God!"

THE BRIDGE
OF
SAN LUIS REY*

by

THORNTON WILDER

CONDENSATION BY MARGARET GILLETT

*THORNTON WILDER (1897–   ), better known as
a playwright than as a novelist, was born in Madison,
Wisconsin, where his father was editor of the "Wisconsin
State Journal." Thornton was taken to China at the age of
nine when his father became American Consul-General at
Hong-Kong and Shanghai. Educated through high school in
Chefoo, and later in Berkeley and Ojai, California, he also
attended Oberlin College, took his B.A. at Yale in 1920,
and did graduate work at the American Academy in Rome.
His studies were interrupted for a year during World War I
while he was a corporal in the Coast Artillery. From 1921
to 1928, he was housemaster and taught French at Lawrence-
ville School in New Jersey, while he continued his studies
at Princeton, where he received his M.A. in 1925.*

"The Cabala," his first novel, was published that year,

* By permission of Grossett & Dunlap, Inc., publishers of *The Bridge of
San Luis Rey,* copyright, 1955, by Thornton Wilder.

along with a play, "The Trumpet Shall Sound." However,
it was "The Bridge of San Luis Rey" (1927), later made
into a movie, that brought him fame and the Pulitzer prize
for fiction. The following year he gave up teaching, pub-
lished a collection of short plays, "The Angel That Troubled
the Waters," and left for Europe to write "The Woman of
Andros" (1930). This novel added considerably to his rep-
utation as a writer of great sensitivity and taste.

From 1930 to 1936, he lectured on literature at the Uni-
versity of Chicago. During this period appeared "The Long
Christmas Dinner and Other Plays in One Act" (1931) and
"Heaven's My Destination" (1935), a novel. After he left
Chicago, he went to France for a year before settling in
New Haven, Connecticut. His plays, "Our Town" and "The
Skin of Our Teeth" won the Pulitzer prize for drama in
1938 and 1943, respectively. "The Merchant of Yonkers"
(1939), another play, was revised into "The Matchmaker"
and produced in England in 1954.

In 1941 the United States State Department sent Wilder
to South America on an educational mission, and in 1942
he became a major in the Army Air Corps Intelligence in
Italy. "The Ides of March," a novel on the life of Julius
Caesar, appeared in 1948. He lectured at Harvard in 1950–
51 and in 1953 went to Europe again, this time on a lecture
tour.

In 1961 he announced the completion of the first segment
of a double cycle of fourteen one-act plays on "The Seven
Ages of Man" and "The Seven Deadly Sins," which would
sum up his philosophy of life and art.

On Friday noon, July 20, 1714, the finest bridge in all Peru broke
and precipitated five travelers into the gulf below. This bridge was
on the high-road between Lima and Cuzco and had been woven of
osier by the Incas more than a century before. It had been thought
indestructible and its collapse was an incredibly ominous event. The
Peruvians were appalled by the catastrophe and crossed themselves
in apprehension when they heard the news.

Brother Juniper, a little red-haired Franciscan, who happened to
witness the five gesticulating figures tumbled from the span, asked
himself: "Why did it happen to those five?" He felt he must justify

this Act of God, and his determination was so strong that he spent six years collecting all the facts of the victims' biographies which he later compiled in a volume, a copy of which finally found its way into the library of the University of San Marco. But poor Brother Juniper himself was misunderstood, considered a heretic and burned in the public square.

*   *   *   *   *

One of those fated to be on the bridge at that moment on that day of destiny was Dona Maria, the Marquesa de Montemayor. She was the daughter of a merchant who had for years acquired the money and the hatred of the Limeans. Her childhood was unhappy: she was ugly; she stuttered; she lived alone and she thought alone. At twenty-six she was forced into marriage with a ruined nobleman who, in spite of her enormous dowry, treated her with contempt. When she gave birth to a daughter, she fastened on her such an idolatrous love that Doña Clara, as the child was called, escaped her mother's stifling affection as soon as she could by marrying a suitor from Spain.

Left alone in Lima, the Marquesa became an eccentric, spending her time in writing endless letters to her daughter which, as a result of their literary merit, have since become the textbook of schoolboys. At the end of four years she made a trip to Spain to visit her daughter, but they quarreled constantly and there was no reconciliation between them. The Marquesa returned to Peru a sad and disillusioned woman who found her principal consolation in *chicha,* an intoxicating drink, and occasional attendance at the theater where the great Perichole was playing.

In her extremity she borrowed Pepita, a twelve-year-old girl from the orphanage, to be her companion. This little girl's assignment to the crazy duties in Doña Maria's household had been made by Madre Maria de Pilar, the Abbess in charge of the orphanage, who loved Pepita dearly and planned it as part of the girl's training to be her successor. It was this simple girl who finally taught the Marquesa courage and selflessness. Then, returning from a pilgrimage to the Shrine of Cluxambuqua, where the Marquesa had gone to pray for her pregnant daughter, they were both tossed into the deep as the cords parted on the Bridge of San Luis Rey.

*   *   *   *   *

One morning, long before Pepita had come to the convent, identical twin boys had been discovered in the foundlings' basket before the door. The good Abbess became very fond of Manuel and Esteban, as she named them, and they grew rapidly into straight and sombre young men. Although they had a thoroughly religious upbringing, they showed no desire for the clerical life but became scribes instead. Since they were always together, the oddity of their resemblance was the source of many jokes and laid upon them a curious shame. As a result, they evolved a private language which they often used in public to conceal their thoughts from all but each other.

The Archbishop of Lima, being something of a philologist and hearing of their secret tongue, sent for the twins so that he could make a study of the phenomenon. But he could learn little from them because they could tell him little of the telepathy that existed between them. Manuel and Esteban did not understand themselves how their love for each other made them one. But at last the first shadow fell across their unity and it was cast by a woman, an actress, called the Perichole, with whom Manuel had fallen in love from a distance. This same actress happened to summon Manuel, the scribe, to write some letters for her and, because they were missives of a clandestine nature, she extracted a promise from him that their contents would be kept secret—even from his brother. However, Esteban knew how Manuel felt about the woman and offered to leave him so that he would be free to give himself wholly to the actress. In loyalty to his brother, Manuel vowed that he had no love for her and that he would refuse to serve her as a scribe any longer.

Then one evening he accidentally tore the flesh of his knee on a piece of metal. It became infected and on the third night he died. Esteban fled from the room in wild sorrow and would not enter the building where his brother's body lay. The Abbess was sent for to take charge but she could not persuade Esteban to return.

"Well, if you will not come," she said, "will you tell me which you are?"

"Manuel," said Esteban.

A period of wandering ensued for the youth until the Abbess spoke to a wise man, Captain Alvarado, about the distracted boy. The Captain offered him a place on his ship, which was ready to sail on a long voyage to distant lands. At first Esteban refused to leave Peru, but later he said he would go if he could have his wages first so he could buy a gift for the Abbess before he left. The Captain agreed and they started for Lima. When they reached the Bridge of San Luis Rey the Captain descended below to supervise the passage of some merchandise, but Esteban crossed by the bridge and fell with it.

* * * * *

Uncle Pio was not only the Perichole's maid, he was her singing master, her coiffeur, her masseur, her reader, her errand boy, her banker, and rumor added: her father. Uncle Pio came of a good Castilian house, illegitimately, and he ran away at ten to live by his wits. He spread slanders at so much per slander, and he sold rumors about crops and the value of land. Finally, the value of his services came to be recognized in high circles. His discretion was so profound that one government party used him even when it was known that he also worked for the enemy party.

He never did one thing for more than two weeks at a time, even when large gains seemed to be likely to follow. He had three aims in life: independence, to be near beautiful women, and to be near the theater. But for all his activity and association with the mighty, nothing made Uncle Pio rich. And he was lonely—until he discovered the child, later called Camila, singing ballads in cafés. He bought her, gave her a cot in his lodging, fed her, and wrote songs for her. He taught her singing and acting, and to his amazement she turned into a beautiful woman. They loved each other deeply but without passion, for Camila, the Perichole, spent her passion on the elderly Viceroy who adored her, and for whom she bore three children. But she never really loved the Viceroy and Uncle Pio knew it. In due course she developed a passion for respectability, too, and became very religious to support it. Camila was about thirty when she left the stage, and five years later she had a secure place in society. She was a great lady now, and more beautiful than ever, though growing stout. Then she caught the small-pox and was dreadfully scarred. After that she retired to her country house where she went about heavily veiled and would see no one, not even Uncle Pio. But he devised a stratagem to keep in touch with her. He persuaded her to let him tutor Don Jaime, her son, for a year, so that the boy might become a gentleman instead of a rustic. He was taking him back to Lima when the bridge toppled them both into the abyss.

* * * * *

The Abbess, who had lost two of her adoptive children, Pepita and Esteban, in the fatal crash, sat at the memorial service pale and firm. She had accepted the fact that there would be no Pepita to carry on her work. Camila, the Perichole, had intended to attend the service for her son and Uncle Pio but her heart was too heavy, she could not go. Later she visited the Abbess, knowing she would understand, and the heavily veiled woman poured out her loneliness and despair in the nun's friendly lap. "All of us have failed," said the Abbess. Then Doña Clara came from Spain to pay tribute at her mother's grave. She also spoke to the Abbess, for her heart was full. But even while she was talking other thoughts were running through the Abbess' mind. "Even now," she thought, "almost no one remembers Esteban and Pepita, but myself. Camila alone remembers her Uncle Pio and her son; this woman, her mother. But soon we shall die and all memory of those five will have left the earth, and we ourselves shall be loved for a while and forgotten. But the love will have been enough; all those impulses of love return to the love that made them. Even memory is not necessary for love. There is a land of the living and a land of the dead and the bridge is love, the only survival, the only meaning."

CAMILLE
by
ALEXANDRE DUMAS, FILS

CONDENSATION BY MARGARET GILLETT

ALEXANDRE DUMAS (1824–1895), dubbed "fils" to distinguish him from his famous father, was the natural child of an alliance between Dumas "père" and a Paris dressmaker, a fact which plagued the son all his life. Young Dumas joined his father's world of letters when he was only sixteen. In spite of their great devotion, the two frequently quarreled over the elder Dumas' spendthrift habits.

Although Dumas "fils" began his literary career with a volume of verse in 1847, he succeeded first in fiction, branching out later into drama and criticism. Altogether he produced sixteen plays with good construction, witty dialogue, and theatrical flair, of which, strangely enough, only one, "Camille" (1852), survives. This was an adaptation of his earlier short novel.

When the playwright was in his thirties, George Sand became his confidante, and he poured out to her all his personal troubles, including his chagrin at the public scandal caused by his father's dissolute living. At the same time his own love affairs were distracting him from his writing until he finally settled down and married a Russian princess who bore him two daughters.

By 1859 both father and son were celebrities and "père," renowned for his genius was enormously proud of his celebrated and talented son. After his father's death in 1870, Dumas "fils" rose to his greatest heights as a dramatist and was elected to the French Academy (1874).

According to the narrator, this is a true story, observed from life and faithfully recorded after the death of its main character, the most beautiful and devastating courtesan of mid-nineteenth-century Paris, Mlle. Marguerite Gautier.

Excessively tall and thin, she wore clothes arranged in cunning array that flattered her figure and gave it such exquisite proportion that she moved with an elegance and dignity in complete contradiction to her accepted social status. Her costume was on all occasions adorned with a bouquet of camellias. For twenty-five days of the month these were white, and for five they were red; no one ever knew why. And camellias were the only flower she ever wore, so that she came to be called the Lady of the Camellias.

In 1842, when she was but twenty and already ravished by the malady which in five short years was to overtake her completely, Marguerite went on her doctor's orders to a fashionable spa for rest and recuperation. There she met an old and fabulously rich duke who had just lost his daughter to the same dread disease, consumption. Finding in Marguerite the living image of his own child, he begged her to let him love her and provide for her as his own. In return for her promise to lead a moral life, he offered her all that money could buy and exacted nothing from her for himself save her filial devotion.

Intrigued by this unusual proposition, Marguerite accepted the duke's love as well as his lavish gifts of horses, diamonds, and furs, together with an enormous stipend for luxurious living and entertainment. However, when she returned to Paris with all its gay associations and with her health and vitality partially restored, she found the restrictions on her customary manner of living too confining and she rebelled. Ultimately, of course, the duke was forced to accept her on her own terms, and Marguerite had all the freedom she enjoyed in addition to the duke's bounty.

My own acquaintance with Mlle. Gautier was only at a distance. I had seen her often, either in her carriage in the Champs-Élysées or at the theatre. I knew her best, of course, by reputation. Indeed, it was simply the announcement of the auction sale of her belongings that had caught my eye and brought me to her apartment at all, even after her death. There, amidst all the finery of a kept woman, I bought one article which I could scarcely afford, a book, and I bought it more out of obstinacy in bidding than anything else. It was a copy of *Manon Lescaut* and it contained on the first page an inscription in these words:

Manon to Marguerite
Humility

It was signed "Armand Duval." Naturally, I imagined this to be a token from one of her lovers.

Two days after the sale was ended, M. Duval, a dishevelled young man, called upon me and seemed so agitated over the book, desiring it so greatly, that I gave it to him. He was deeply grateful and promised to call upon me later, when he would be in better control of himself, to explain its importance for him. I thought I understood his feelings, and we parted good friends.

When, after a time, he didn't return, I sent him a note asking him to come to see me. I was still curious about his connection with Mlle. Gautier, since he did not seem to have even a fraction of the fortune necessary to be included on her roster of lovers. The next day I received his reply, saying that he had been away from Paris, had just returned but was ill and would I please call on him.

As I had imagined, he was one of Marguerite's lovers, undoubtedly the most distinguished of them all, for she loved him in return. From his own lips I heard the tragic tale of their devotion through many difficulties, of her sacrifices for him and, finally, her renunciation of him at the request of his father.

The first time he saw her, he told me, was in the Place de la Bourse, where she had come in her carriage to do some shopping. She was dressed all in white and he was captivated at once by her delicacy and extravagant beauty. A few days later at the Opéra Comique, a friend introduced him to her and he was so ill at ease that he made a fool of himself—or so he thought.

Again, later, he saw her at the theatre, and, through another acquaintance, Prudence Duvernoy, who had been a kept woman in her youth but was now a milliner and a neighbor of Mlle. Gautier, arrangements were made for him to visit the latter in her apartments. This meeting turned out to be far more auspicious than the previous one.

At this time Marguerite's favors were being sought by the young Comte de N., whose wealth rivaled that of the old duke, but Marguerite found him an insufferable bore and was glad of every opportunity to evade his attentions without discouraging his support.

This first visit, at which M. Duval was able to see Marguerite for a few minutes alone, was followed by many more, and he fell madly in love with this bewitching woman who seemed to return his passion with a sincerity that surprised even herself.

Since he had comparatively little financial resources, Armand took to gaming and was rather successful at it for a beginner, so that he was able to supplement his income sufficiently to buy small gifts for his mistress. These she cherished far beyond the enormously more valuable gifts of the duke and the count.

But even with all this evidence of her love, Armand was jealous and often treated her very cruelly in the frenzy of his passion. Prudence counseled him to be realistic. She reminded him that he could not hope to shoulder all of Marguerite's debts and therefore he must be patient while she entertained the noblemen who could.

"Then, besides that," continued Prudence, "admit that Marguerite loves you enough to give up the count or the duke, in case one of them were to discover your liaison. . . . What equal sacrifice could you make for her?"

To this Armand had no answer but to agree.

An idyll of several months together in the country, paid for by the unsuspecting duke, gave Marguerite a chance to recover at least the appearance of health at the same time that it convinced Armand of her complete devotion and dependence on him for love and affection. However, the duke, finally warned of the lovers' deceit, withdrew his support, and the creditors began to close in.

As if the curtain had fallen on the only happy scene of an inevitable tragedy, Armand's father began to be alarmed by the rumors of his son's attachment to such a notorious woman, and he brought great pressure to bear to separate the lovers.

The terrible denouement followed swiftly as Marguerite was persuaded to leave Armand—for his own good, as the father insisted—and return to her former life as the mistress of the Comte. On the other hand, Armand, misunderstanding her motives and in a state of shock from her desertion, allowed himself to be packed off by his father, first to his family home and later on a tour of the East.

It was soon after he left for Marseilles to board ship there that Marguerite began to fail. Armand had reached Alexandria when he heard the news of her serious illness, and he started back immediately, but he was by then already too late.

M. Duval related each detail of the love story, sparing himself no heart-rending detail, a revelation which seemed somehow to relieve his awful grief over her loss and his punishing regret for the pain he had caused her by his overpowering jealousy.

In his description Marguerite Gautier was, indeed, revealed as a woman of great character as well as beauty—"character" in a rather special sense, perhaps, which I hesitate to delineate further for fear of being considered an apostle of vice.

CANDIDE*

by

VOLTAIRE

CONDENSATION BY MARGARET GILLETT

FRANÇOIS MARIE AROUET DE VOLTAIRE (1694–1778) was the son of a minor government official in Paris. When he was nine years old he went to a Jesuit seminary for his preparatory education. At seventeen he began to study law, which he came to despise. As a result, he turned to writing and was finally banished from Paris for several months on suspicion of lampooning the Duc d'Orleans. When he was in his early twenties he was accused of a worse offense—a more serious lampoon—and was thrown in the Bastille.

After his release, Voltaire continued to be involved in political intrigues, and soon after "Oedipe," his tragedy, was successfully performed in 1718, he was again threatened with imprisonment. He finally escaped to England in 1726. There his exile was somewhat relieved by his association with Pope, Chesterfield, Swift, and other literary figures, and he succeeded in getting permission to return to France a few years later.

Back in Paris Voltaire became wealthy by buying shares in the government lottery and by speculating in the corn trade. Always an opportunist, he came under the patronage of Mme. de Pompadour, who helped him to be appointed royal historiographer and arranged his election to the French Academy.

In 1750 he went to Berlin as Frederick the Great's chamberlain but quarreled with the monarch and moved to Geneva in 1755. "Candide" (1759), usually classified as a philosophical tale, is an outstanding example of his caustic

48

wit and independent spirit. Although his writings cover the fields of drama, philosophy, romance, history, literary criticism, and poetry, he is best known for his satire against religious intolerance. Voltaire was critical of traditional institutions and beliefs, which to him seemed absurd, and in being so made many enemies. In his later years his efforts toward reform began to be appreciated and he was showered with distinctions.

In the castle of Baron Thunder-ten-tronckh in Westphalia, there lived a gentle and naïve youth named Candide. It was not certain who his father was, but it was thought that his mother was the Baron's sister. Also in the castle lived the Baroness, her son, her pretty, seventeen-year-old daughter, Cunegonde, and their tutor, Dr. Pangloss, whose instruction all centered around the idea that this is the best of all possible worlds.

One day while walking in the Park, Cunegonde observed the tutor giving a lesson in experimental physics to one of the waiting maids. She blushed but continued to watch, fascinated and unseen. Next day the Baron caught her and Candide in fond embrace, imitating their tutor and the waiting maid. Forthwith he expelled Candide from the castle. After wandering distraught and penniless as far as the neighboring town, the poor boy was rescued by two men dressed in blue who promptly impressed him into the army of the King of the Bulgarians. However, when a war began, he was terrified by the slaughter, hid himself, and fled to Holland, where he was again succoured on the brink of starvation by an Anabaptist named Jacques. All this time he was becoming something of a philosopher himself and beginning to understand causes and effects.

With two coins that the good Jacques had given him, he aided a beggar covered with sores who turned out to be Dr. Pangloss, himself a refugee from the castle in Westphalia, which he said had been entirely destroyed in an enemy raid and all besides himself put to the sword. According to his report, Cunegonde had been raped and disemboweled. Even he was dying, he said, from the pox that he caught from the waiting maid, and he had no money for doctor's fees. Candide begged his patron, the Anabaptist, to help his old tutor, and the generous Jacques not only gave Pangloss money for medical treatment but also hired him as a bookkeeper in his business.

At the end of two months, when he had to go to Lisbon on business, Jacques took the two philosophers with him. But misfortune followed, and in a terrible gale at sea the ship sank with all hands, excepting only Candide, Pangloss, and a brutal sailor who had killed the good Jacques during the storm. Then when the survivors arrived at Lisbon there was a frightful earthquake in which thirty thousand lives were lost. Candide was injured but rescued from death by Pangloss. After these experiences Candide began to have some doubts about this being the best of all possible worlds, but out of deference to his tutor he quickly suppressed them.

When the earthquake had subsided, it was decided by the wise men at the university of Coimbre that certain precautions must be taken to prevent further disasters of the same kind. Since they were strangers and Pangloss had been so indiscreet as to discuss philosophy with "a familiar of the Inquisition," he and Candide were seized, among others, for sacrificial victims and the doctor was hanged. At this point Candide asked himself again, "Is this really the best of all possible worlds?" Just as he was released and about to expire from the severe flogging he had received, an old woman accosted him and said: "Courage, my son, follow me." She took him to a hovel and nursed him back to health. After three or four days, when he had recovered somewhat, she led him about a quarter of a mile into the country. When they came to an isolated house they went inside and upstairs to a gilded apartment where the old woman brought Cunegonde to him. He thought he was dreaming. Cunegonde was supposed to be dead.

Then the girl told him her story. It was true that everyone else had been butchered in their castle in Westphalia, but one of the enemy captains had saved her for himself. After he had tired of her she had been sold into slavery and finally had been brought to Lisbon where she now belonged to the Lord High Inquisitor. At the *auto-da-fé* at which Pangloss and Candide were to have been sacrificed, she had recognized Candide and asked that he be spared. As she was relating this, the Lord High Inquisitor walked in and Candide had the presence of mind to run him through before he could recover from his surprise.

At the old woman's suggestion all three took Andalusian horses from the stable and rode hastily off to Avacena and safety. But en route a monk stole Cunegonde's jewels, which were intended to pay for their lodging, so that the old woman—who could only ride on one buttock anyway—said they should sell her horse and she would ride postillion behind Cunegonde. In this way they arrived at Cadiz, where Candide disported himself so well in military exercises that he was made an officer and sent on a mission to the new world. The three set out by ship with two servants and the two remaining horses to what was to be really the best of all possible worlds.

On shipboard the old woman told the harrowing tale of her own misfortunes—how, even though she was the daughter of Pope Urban X and the Princess of Palestrina, she had been sold into slavery and held in a siege which lasted so long that the soldiers who were starving had cut off one buttock of each of the imprisoned ladies for food. From then on Cunegonde treated her as an equal and with extra respect.

Finally, when they arrived in Buenos Ayres they went to call on the governor, who had a splendid mustache and fell precipately in love with Cunegonde. Since the old woman had learned that a vessel had arrived to arrest Candide for the murder of the Lord High Inquisitor, she advised Cunegonde to accept the proposal of the governor. On the other hand, Candide, urged by his faithful valet, Cacambo, whom he had brought with him from Cadiz, decided to flee. Cacambo saddled the Andalusian horses and the two made haste to the Paraguayan border, where they unexpectedly found Cunegonde's brother, now a Jesuit Commandant in that country. It seems he had not been slain in Westphalia, as reported, but had been saved by a German Jesuit who enlisted his services for the foreign missions. He was as surprised to learn that his sister was in the neighboring country as he was infuriated to hear that Candide wished to marry her. To save himself from the Jesuit's wrath, Candide had to dispatch him on the spot. Then, dressed in the dead man's clothes, he escaped from Paraguay with Cacambo.

After a great deal of further wandering and a terrifying adventure among cannibals, they came to the country of El Dorado, the ancient land of the Incas where children played with pieces of gold and precious gems and everything was in such good order that no law courts or prisons were necessary and there were no priests or monks. For a month the two travelers enjoyed the hospitality of this place which seemed to warrant, above all, the title of the best of all possible worlds. The people were so gracious that Candide asked the king if he might take some of their yellow mud and diamond pebbles with him when he left. The king laughed. "I cannot understand," said he, "the taste you people of Europe have for our yellow mud; but take as much as you wish, and much good may it do you." Candide had in mind to ransom Cunegonde with this treasure, but he decided he had better not go to Buenos Ayres himself. Instead he sent Cacambo with the gold and arranged to meet him and Cunegonde in Venice later.

On his way back, Candide was tricked out of many of his precious stones until he had only a few left when he arrived in Italy. At last Cacambo appeared and related a tale of great woe. Cunegonde was in Constantinople, he said, and enslaved. On hearing this, Candide vowed to go immediately to her rescue. To his amazement two of the galley slaves on the boat that was taking him to Constantinople turned out to be Dr. Pangloss, who had been miraculously revived after his hanging, and Cunegonde's brother, who had magically recovered from his wound. When Candide offered to buy the latter's freedom, he forgave him his insolence in wanting to marry his sister.

After paying for the release of the two prisoners, Candide and the others continued on to Constantinople where they found Cunegonde grown old and ugly. But Candide gallantly kept his word, married her, bought a small farm, and all lived happily ever after in what they helped make for themselves the best of all possible worlds.

CAPTAINS COURAGEOUS*
by
RUDYARD KIPLING

CONDENSATION BY JAMES B. CONNOLLY

RUDYARD KIPLING was born December 30, 1865, in Bombay, where his father, John Lockwood Kipling, artist and author, was professor in the British School of Art. He was educated at the United Services College, Westward Ho, North Devon, scene of the lurid Stalky novel.

* Printed by permission of, and arrangement with, Century Company, authorized publishers.

*At seventeen he was in India once more, a journalist.
Before he was twenty-four he had completed "Plain Tales
from the Hills" and six more of his best stories, which established his fame throughout the world. In the tales of
native life and adventure "beyond the pale" India was revealed anew with a brilliance, color, and passion unsurpassed; Mulvaney and his pals, the exuberant "Soldiers
Three," captivated men from sea to sea.*

*Within the next ten years Kipling traveled round the
world, married, lived in America, England, and South
Africa, and finally became so imbued with imperialism as
almost to destroy his art.*

*His "Barrack Room Ballads" and "Seven Seas" revealed
him as an inspiriting poet who "splashed at a ten-league
canvas with brushes of comet's hair."*

*Of his three novels, "The Light that Failed" is a tale of
Suez; "Captains Courageous," of Gloucester fishermen; and
"Kim" breathes again the subtle and mysterious fascination
of India.*

*With the "Jungle Books" Kipling enthralled a new au-
dience. These, and the incomparable "Just So Stories," written to his son, who was killed in the war, enshrined him in
the hearts of children the world over.*

He was awarded the Nobel prize for literature in 1907.

Harvey Cheyne's father was immersed in amassing more money,
his mother was busy with her nerves, and so we have Harvey, at
fifteen years, the insufferable type that most grown males want to
heave a brick at on sight.

He was a passenger on this ocean liner, and she was crossing the
Grand Banks in a fog. He came into the smoking-room saying: "You
can hear the fish-boats squawking all around us. Wouldn't it be
great if we ran one down!"

He asked for a cigarette. Somebody with a diabolical sense of
humor passed him a thick, oily cigar. Harvey lit it up and went
on deck. He began to feel queer, but he had bragged of never being seasick; so now he went aft to the turtle-deck, and he was
still there, wrestling with the cigar and not caring much what happened, when a long gray sea swung out of the fog and took him overboard.

Harvey was next aware of being on a pile of fish with a broad-backed man in a blue jersey, who said: "You in dory with me. Manuel my name."

Later he was hoisted aboard of a schooner and lowered into her heaving fo'c's'le, where men in oilskins gave him a hot drink and put him to sleep in a bunk. When he awoke, a boy whose name was Dan asked him smilingly if he was feeling better. The schooner was the *We're Here* of Gloucester, and the boy's father, Disko Troop, was her skipper.

Harvey went up on deck to see Disko, and demanded that he be taken back to New York, where as he told Disko condescendingly, his father would pay them very well for their trouble; he added many other items to what his father could and would do. Disko, as it happened, was an old-fashioned type of Bank fisherman, wise in the ways of fish, but knowing little of the great world. He decided that this boy with his talk of his father's immense wealth must be crazy; with an idea of restoring the poor boy to sanity, he offered him the berth of second boy on the *We're Here* at ten dollars and fifty cents per month.

Harvey had a fit of sullenness, but his sullenness worried nobody; he went to work. The dories were returning to the vessel with their catches of fish; so for the first work of his life Harvey was set to helping Dan hoist in the dories, to swabbing the gurry from their insides, and then to nesting them on the deck. By the time he had finished doing that and eating his supper it was nighttime, and Manuel, Penn, Long Jack, Old Salters, Tom Platt—all hands were standing by to dress fish.

Manuel and Penn stood deep among the fish, flourishing sharp knives. "Hi!" shouted Manuel, with one finger under the gill of a cod, the other in an eye. The blade glimmered, there was a sound of tearing, the fish, slit from throat to tail, dropped at Long Jack's feet. "Hi!" cried Jack, and, with a scoop of a mittened hand, dropped the cod's liver into a basket; another wrench and a scoop sent head and offal flying. The gutted fish slid across to Old Salters, who snorted fiercely, ripped out the backbone, and splashed the headless, gutless fish into a tub of water.

Harvey pitched the washed fish down into the hold, whence came tramplings and rumblings as Tom Platt and Disko moved among the salt-bins. The rasping sound of rough salt rubbed on rough flesh from below made a heavy undertone to the click-nick of the knives in the pens, the wrench and schloop of torn heads, the flap of ripped-open fish falling into the tub on deck.

At the end of an hour Harvey wanted terribly to rest, but also for the first time in his life he was one of a working gang of men; and so, beginning to take pride in the thought, he held on grimly. Not till the last fish was stowed below did a man rest. But when that moment came! Disko and Old Salters rolled toward their cabin bunks, Manuel and Long Jack went forward. Tom Platt waited only long enough to slide home the hatch, Penn to empty a basket of fish livers into a big cask.

All hands were below and asleep, except the two boys; they had to stand watch; so by and by the moon looked down on one slim boy in knickerbockers, which was Harvey, staggering around the cluttered deck; while behind him, waving a knotted rope, walked another boy, which was Dan, yawning and nodding between taps he dealt the first boy to keep him awake.

The *We're Here* was on a salt-fishing trip, which meant four months away from home; so there was time for Harvey to learn many strange new things if he cared to. After a time, as the pride in honest work well done began to grip him, he cared. He learned to fish from a dory; to make his way in safety around a heaving vessel's deck; to know what each rope and sail aboard a vessel was for. Disko allowed him, when the wind was light, to steer the vessel from one berth to another, and wonderful was Harvey's sense of power when he first felt the vessel answer to his touch of the wheel. Almost did he come to understand, as a fisherman understands, the never-absent dangers of the Banks—the eternal fogs, the tides, the gales, the wicked seas; and learned, too, fishermen's opinion of the officers of the great steamers who, after cutting a vessel down, raise high hands to heaven and swear with unanimity that the careless fisherman had never—absolutely never—shown so much as a single light.

He saw one day a foul, draggled, unkempt vessel heaving up past the *We're Here*, for all the world like a blowsy, frowsy, bad old woman sneering at a decent girl—saw her sail off into a patch of watery sunshine and—go under—taking all hands with her! He saw, while his hair stood on end, a whiteness moving in the whiteness of the fog with a breath like the breath of a grave; and then he heard a roaring, plunging, and spouting; that was his first iceberg. He saw the surf break over Virgin Rocks; and the fish strike in so thick on a shoal that scores of dories stood riding gunwale to gunwale while their crews battled for the catch. He saw a gale break so sudden and fierce that everywhere on the sea were men in dories cutting riding-lines and racing for their vessels, but some never making their vessels.

So he passed four busy, wonderful months, growing in body, mind, and soul with every hour that passed; and then came the great day when they left the Banks for home. Toil, hardship, and danger were now mostly behind them; there was left little to do but stand watch and study the folding and packing away of the morning mists, the hurry of winds across the open spaces, the glare and blaze of the high sun; to harken to the grinding of the booms against the masts, the creaking of the sheets against the bitts, the sail filling to the roaring winds.

Now about the time the *We're Here,* a hundred quintals of fish in her hold, was laying her course for Gloucester, Harvey's father was beginning to wonder in his mahogany offices in Los Angeles if it wasn't a better game to drop the ceaseless struggle for more power and wealth. What was the use of it all—with no son to hand it to? He was still wondering when one day an excited secretary brought him a telegram.

It was from Harvey, safe in Gloucester. Mr. Cheyne laid his face down on his desk, breathed heavily for a while; and then, heaving orders right and left, started that run of which railroad men talked for many a day. Three days and a half it was from coast to coast, with railroad specialists along the way dividing huge bonuses; for it was the great Harvey Cheyne who was racing east to see his rescued boy, and the boy's mother was with him.

Not without fear did he meet that boy. He had a memory of a pasty-faced, bad-mannered lad. What he met was a boy with tough-ened figure and a keen, clear eye, a boy who was inordinately proud that a Gloucester skipper said he had well earned his ten dollars and fifty cents and his keep a month. On the end of an ancient wharf Harvey Cheyne and his boy had such a talk as they never could have had four months before. When it was over they knew each other better.

Railroads, lumber, mines—such things did not interest young Harvey. What his heart yearned for was to some day manage his father's newly purchased sailing-ships on the Pacific coast. The ships he got when he was ripe for them; and for Dan, son of Disko Troop

—seeing that he could not offer money—he got a berth as mate of one of them, with the promise that some day he would go master of the best he could build.

"Great ships these of my father's? Oh yes," says Harvey. "But back in Gloucester are the able little vessels. The *We're Here,* she's one. I owe a heap to her—to her and her crew."

THE COUNT OF
MONTE CRISTO

by
ALEXANDRE DUMAS

CONDENSATION BY ALFRED S. CLARK

ALEXANDRE DUMAS was of mixed blood, the grandson of a French marquis and a native of the West Indies. His father was a private in the French army when the Revolution broke out. He was swiftly promoted until he held the rank of general-in-chief in Spain, but he quarreled with Napoleon, and when he died he left but thirty acres of land to his widow and two children.

Alexandre was born on July 24, 1802, in a town not far from Soissons. As a boy he had few advantages, for his mother was poor. He was, however, carefully instructed by a kindly priest. He then studied law, but his desire to write drove him to Paris, where he began his career by penning vaudeville sketches and melodramas.

He wrote plays for several years and his "Henri III" scored the first great success of the romantic drama. Short stories appeared at intervals, and then his novels. "The Three Musketeers" came out in 1844, and thereafter romance after romance came in such rapid succession that his collected works in French fill two hundred and twenty-seven

*volumes. He told Napoleon III that he had written twelve
hundred books.*

*Dumas did employ a host of collaborators and his par-
tiality for jokes made his practice seem worse than it really
was. On one occasion an ardent admirer ventured to remark that he had found a mistake in geography in one of
his novels. "Which one?" asked Dumas. The worshiper
gave the title. "Oh, the devil!" cried the novelist. "I have
not read it. Let me see, who did that for me? It was the
rascal Auguste. I'll fix him for that."*

*His principal collaborator was Auguste Maquet. He was
an able writer, but, as many critics have pointed out,
Maquet without Dumas would hardly be remembered to-
day, while Dumas without Maquet would still be Dumas.
Almost always when he worked with Maquet, Dumas would
suggest the subject for a story. Then he would draw up an
outline and put down chapter headings and divisions.
Maquet would then fill in the outline and afterward Dumas
would rewrite the whole story, usually adding and altering
a tremendous amount and infusing it with the genius that
was lacking.*

*Prodigiously as Dumas worked, he wasted just as prodi-
giously. He entertained a whole army of parasites, and in
his last years was constantly harassed by creditors. He had
married, in 1840, Ida Ferrier, an actress, but they did not
long live together. His daughter came to his aid in 1868
when he was debt-ridden and ill, and two years later, on
December 5, 1870, he died in the home of his son, the author
of the popular "Camille."*

On February 28, 1815, Edmond Dantes sailed into Marseilles. He
was but nineteen years of age and ardently in love. His conscience
was clear; he had violated no law. Yet the next night he was in a
cell in the gloomy Château d'If, a fortress on a bare rock off Marseilles. And fourteen years were to pass before he strode again in
the sunlight.

Three men had wrought his ruin. Danglars envied Edmond's
rapid promotion. Fernand was crazed with love for Mercedes, Edmond's beloved. Danglars wrote and Fernand despatched a letter
warning the authorities to intercept the missive Edmund was bear-

ing to Paris. Chance decreed that this warning, addressed to Villefort's father, fell into the hands of the unscrupulous Villefort himself.

Of this dark intrigue Edmond knew nothing. At his captain's dying request, he had called at Elba, where he had seen the captive Napoleon and been intrusted with a sealed letter. Villefort, a turncoat devoted to the aristocracy, had changed his name to make men forget that his father was a Bonapartist. He destroyed the incriminating letter before Edmond's eyes and promised that the lad should soon be free. Even as he spoke the words he knew that in the disappearance of this youth lay his own security.

Thus it happened that while the Corsican came out of Elba by stealth and rode to Paris amid tumultuous cheers, Edmond lay in a dungeon. The thunder of the guns at Waterloo did not penetrate the walls of the Château d'If. Napoleon was borne away to St. Helena; the Hundred Days were over. And Dantes knew naught of these things. He ate out his heart in thoughts of Mercedes and wondered what mad freak of fortune had thrust him away from the world of men.

Days dragged into years. He lost track of time. Confined in a black and slimy dungeon, he saw only his jailer. There were moments when he hoped, hours when he despaired, weeks when he raved in impotent anger. Four years rolled past. He was starving himself to death. Then he heard a rasping, scratching noise. The spark of human hope burned anew. He swallowed his broth; he must win back his strength. Somewhere near him was a human mole, burrowing stealthily, worming toward freedom.

Four days later a section of flooring fell in and out of a dark tunnel sprang an old man. He was the Abbé Faria, a prisoner for eight years. His tunnel, dug with arduous toil, had failed to reach the sunlight, but it led to fellowship. Unsuspected by their jailers, the two men met daily and studied unweariedly. Out of his ripe wisdom and his prodigious memory, the abbé taught Edmond mathmatics, history, and languages.

Less guileless than Edmond, he was able to prove, from the youth's own story, that Danglars, Fernand, and Villefort were responsible for his living death. So Edmond had a new incentive for freedom. He sought revenge. The abbé revealed, too, the secret of the great treasure of gold and jewels that lay in a cave on Monte Cristo, an uninhabited island off Italy.

The years rolled on. Another attempt to escape was frustrated by the paralysis of the abbé's right side. Edmond refused to leave him. He was a very different man from the carefree sailor who had been so suddenly jerked from the gaiety of a marriage feast to the gloom of a dungeon. He was a man of the world—educated, cynical.

One night he heard a cry of anguish. Hurriedly he rolled aside the great stone that concealed the tunnel opening, crawled swiftly to his neighbor's cell. He found him writhing in agony. At dawn he was dead.

That night Edmond carried the corpse to his own cell and laid it down on his own bed, face to the wall, so that the jailer would think it Edmond asleep. Secreting a crude knife with which to effect an escape, he then sewed himself into a coarse sack in which the jailers had put the body. Two men later bore out the supposed corpse, weighted the legs with a great iron ball, and swung the sack powerfully. Edmond suddenly realized that he was falling from a great height. He had been flung from the château roof into the sea.

He screamed aloud as he struck the water, and then the weight dragged him into the ice-cold depths. He ripped open the sack, convulsively cut the rope that was knotted to the shot, and rose to the surface. He had not forgotten how to swim. He struck out in the blackness for an islet. Just as he was losing hope, his knee struck rock. He staggered to his feet and above him rose a gloomy mass, his goal.

At daybreak he flung himself into the sea and was pulled aboard an outward-bound bark. Each moment Marseilles receded farther into the distance. He learned from his shipmates that it was February 28, 1829. He had been shut away from the world for fourteen years. He wondered what had become of Mercedes. Then he thought of Danglars, Fernand, and Villefort. A baleful light flickered in his hard eyes.

Edmond had fallen in with a band of smugglers. On one of their voyages he gazed eagerly at a granite mass rose-hued in the dawn. It was Monte Cristo. A few weeks later chance brought him to the island. None of his comrades suspected the leaping thoughts that thronged in Edmond's mind. They were simple folk, easily deceived. Edmond fell from a rock and complained that he could not move. He was confident, he insisted, that he could cure himself if he were left here. At last they sailed away. When the boat was out of sight he leaped to his feet, seized his pickax, and cried, "Open Sesame!" He was alone on Monte Cristo.

Following the clues of the abbé's ancient manuscript, he located the great slab of rock overgrown with vegetation. He slashed at the edges with his pickax and made a hole. With his horn of powder he easily blasted the rock away. Before him was an iron ring embedded in a flagstone. He raised it and saw a flight of stairs. With hope mingled with a strange misgiving he descended, broke open a passage into an inner cave, and dug away the earth over an oak coffer bound with iron. He burst it open and there blazed gold coins, bars of gold, diamonds, rubies, and pearls that glittered in glorious profusion.

When Edmond came back to France it was as the Count of Monte Cristo—fabulously wealthy, romantic in appearance, a performer of miracles. His betrayers had risen to heights of fame and affluence. Danglars was a wealthy banker; Fernand an honored warrior; Villefort high in office. Mercedes, believing Edmond dead, had yielded to Fernand's importunate pleadings and had married him.

Zealously did the Count of Monte Cristo devote his days and nights to ruin these three. Usually it was in his own unrecognized personality that he dazzled Paris with his feasts, his extravagances, his prodigal outlays. Everyone paid court to this mysterious stranger who rained gold about him. Sometimes he disguised himself—now as the Abbé Busoni, now as the Italian Zazzone, now as the English Lord Wilmore, now as Sinbad the Sailor.

He tortured Danglars, Fernand, Villefort methodically and yet so skilfully that they did not know the hand that directed the blows that fell upon them. Piece by piece Danglars' fortune was lopped away. At last he was beggared, the bitterest blow that could have befallen him. Fernand, enmeshed slowly in revelations of his guilty past, finally blew out his brains; Villefort, his crimes dragged into the light of day, went raving mad. Mercedes, made poor but happy in the love of her devoted son, lived on, penitent.

Yet there were those whom Monte Cristo rewarded. The noble Morrel, his former employer, was saved from bankruptcy by a mysterious Englishman who presented him with notes he could not meet. And on the uninhabited island of Monte Cristo Morrel's son, true and tried as his father, learned that Villefort's daughter, the girl who had remained fine through all vicissitudes, still lived. She stood beside him on the pinnacle of the island and they looked with blurred eyes into the distance, where each moment a ship grew fainter and fainter. It was bearing from their sight the man who had once been Edmond Dantes. With him was the radiant Haydee, the mysterious princess whose beauty had outshone all the beauties of Paris. In her love Edmond had at last forgotten all that he did not now want to remember.

COUSIN PONS

by

HONORÉ DE BALZAC

TRANSLATED FROM THE FRENCH BY ELLEN MARRIAGE
CONDENSATION BY LAWRENCE FALCONER

HONORÉ DE BALZAC (1799–1850), though trained in law and licensed in 1820, became one of the most prolific writers who ever lived. Within the next three years (1820–1822) he ground out sixty pages a day in his Paris garret to complete thirty-one volumes of adventure. This phenomenal production brought him so little income that he left writing temporarily to try his hand at publishing (1825–1828) until he failed financially at that as well. Still determined to remain in the literary field, he turned to the stage but also without success. As a result, he was constantly harassed by poverty until his "Scenes from Private Life" brought him recognition as a writer in 1830.

His own private life, however, continued to be frustrating, and he spent a great deal of time traveling about Europe in pursuit of aristocratic ladies who seemed impervious to his advances. One Russian countess whom he met in 1833, he courted for eighteen years until she finally married him just a few months before his death.

Meanwhile he had decided to write a "Human Comedy" to rival Dante's "Divine Comedy," and with this colossal project set for himself, he worked steadily for twenty years and finished about three-quarters of the ninety-six novels of his gigantic plan. The grand scale of Balzac's ambition may be estimated from the magnitude of his accomplishments: 350 titles with as many as one hundred characters in a single novel.

Although his characters sometimes lack proportion, he reveals a wide and discerning understanding of human nature. Two of the best of his long list of novels are "Cousin Bette" and "Cousin Pons" (1847). Balzac is considered the founder of the realist school of French novelists.

Towards three o'clock in the afternoon of one October day in the year 1844, a man of sixty or thereabouts was walking along the Boulevard des Italiens. There was a smug expression about his mouth although his grey eyes looked forlornly out of his broad and flat countenance, surmounted by a mountainous nose. This elderly person adhered so faithfully to the fashions of the year 1806 that all who saw him approaching smiled—an "Empire man" in 1844! He was M. Sylvain Pons, the composer of a number of well-known sentimental songs, a couple of operas, and a cantata that had won for him the *grand prix* of the Institut.

The Government sent Pons to Rome to make a great musician of himself; in Rome he acquired a taste for the antique and works of art. He became an admirable judge of "bric-à-brac," and returned to Paris about 1810 a rabid collector but penniless. In his years of travel Pons was as happy as was possible to a man with a great soul, a sensitive nature, and a face so ugly that "success with the fair" was out of the question. He won a reputation with his delicate, graceful, and ingenious music. But before long his notes were drowned in floods of German and Italian music. The worthy man was now ending his days as the conductor of an orchestra in a boulevard theatre and a music master in several young ladies' boarding-schools.

In spite of his limited resources, Pons—a tireless bargain-hunter—had amassed through the years a collection of almost two thousand exquisite objects of art, many of them masterpieces. You might think Pons the happiest man on earth, but he was a slave to one of the Seven Deadly Sins: he was a glutton. A narrow income, combined with a passion for bric-à-brac, forced him to solve the problem of gratifying his stomach by dining out.

While he was a celebrity, always willing to "oblige" at the pianoforte, Pons was a welcome guest in many fine houses. With his decline and fall as an artist came his transformation from invited guest to parasite and hanger-on. He made himself necessary by undertaking a host of small commissions, running errands, making purchases. He became a harmless, well-meaning spy set by one family on another. Now Pons, old and ugly and poor, received few invitations. But he dined regularly with four interrelated familes; his "cousins" he called them, though his only relative was the daughter of the first Mme. Camusot de Marville, now dead. These people accounted him less than nothing. Though he suffered from their contempt and insults, he hid his feelings for his stomach's sake.

In the year 1835 chance avenged Pons for the indifference of womankind by finding him a prop for his declining years. Pons took to himself a life-partner, an old man and a fellow musician. So congenial were their ways of thinking and living that a week after their first meeting they could not live without each other. Pons' friend was Schmucke, a man also old and hideous, a composer doomed, like Pons, to remain a music master. The noble-hearted German had kept his child's simplicity much as Pons had clung to his costume of the Empire. The two old men lodged together, and idlers of the quarter dubbed them "the pair of nutcrackers."

There was only one source of disagreement between the two companions. Schmucke did not approve of Pons' insatiable craving to dine out, which led him to endure humiliations and insults. One day Pons was so brutally affronted by Mme. Camusot de Marville, a tigress of a woman, her stepdaughter Cécile (Pons' cousin), and the servants that he left the house without staying for dinner. "I am growing too old," he told himself. "The world has a horror of old age and poverty—two ugly things. After this I will not go anywhere unless I am asked." Heroic resolve!

Schmucke was overjoyed. Mme. Cibot, the portress, who already served as their housekeeper, was prevailed upon to provide the two lodgers with breakfast and dinner, and she was an excellent cook. After three months of dining with Schmucke, however, Pons fell to regretting the delicate dishes, the liqueurs, the good coffee, and the table talk and gossip of the fine houses where he used to dine. He grew melancholy. His condition was noted at the theatre. "The old gentleman is failing," said the flute, Wilhelm Schwab.

M. Camusot de Marville was satisfied for a while with his wife's explanations of the absence of Pons, who had been a weekly dinner guest for twenty years. But after a while he went to Pons and discovered why he had absented himself. He was outraged and demanded that Pons be reinstated as an honored guest. Others who had become uneasy about Pons' absence from their homes invited him to dine with them as before. It was unspeakably pleasant to Pons to have all his old enjoyments restored to him without any loss of self-respect. But Schmucke mourned his loss as a dinner companion.

About that time Schwab invited Pons and Schmucke to his wedding. He was marrying a wealthy young lady. His dear friend, Fritz Brunner, had just inherited a great fortune, and the two of them were setting up a banking house. Schwab was anxious for Brunner, a bachelor inclined to reckless living and melancholy, to marry. And Pons, newly reconciled with his "cousins," was immediately smitten with a desire to make a match between Brunner and Cécile, who at three-and-twenty was still unwed. A meeting was arranged between Brunner and the de Marvilles. All went well; Fritz and Cécile seemed well pleased with each other. The de Marvilles were in ecstasies at the prospect of the marriage, and both mother and daughter were now sincerely devoted to Pons and spoke of settling an annuity upon him.

But when Fritz Brunner learned that Cécile was an only child, he withdrew on the grounds that a girl whose will is law to her indulgent parents, who has never been contradicted, will not make a good wife or mother. When this decision was made known to them, Cécile fainted and her stepmother turned savagely upon Pons: "It is a plot of your weaving; I see it all now. . . . I hope, M. Pons, that in the future you will spare us the annoyance of seeing you in the house where you have tried to bring shame and dishonor." She convinced her husband and all her acquaintances who were friends of Pons that the old man had arranged the whole thing from a desire for revenge. He was an outcast.

Pons became ill of a nervous fever, and then of an attack of jaundice. "You will soon get over it," the doctor told him. But he told Mme. Cibot that Pons would die unless he was well nursed.

Now Mme. Cibot had recently learned that Pons' "rubbish" was worth a great deal, perhaps a million francs. This information had come to her from M. Rémonencq, who had a small curiosity shop next door. He had begun as a dealer in old iron and hoped to end as an art dealer, with a fine shop on the boulevard.

Mme. Cibot hoped to inherit part of Pons' fortune in return for her services over a period of ten years or so. She was the kind of woman who, once she sees the end in view, will pass from scrupulous honesty to the last degree of scoundrelism in the twinkling of an eye. She told Dr. Poulain—who after learning of Pons' wealth said he would visit him twice a day—that she would nurse Pons "like a king." She set herself to irritate Pons, to lead the poor man to consider himself on his death bed, and to drop hints about his will—all the time proclaiming that she loved him like a mother.

Rémonencq had long had his eye on Mme. Cibot, still handsome at fifty, and the prospect of her inheriting money from Pons added greatly to her charms. He persuaded Mme. Cibot to allow the Jew Magus, the greatest connoisseur in Paris, to appraise Pons' collection without Pons' knowledge, for he would never allow a dealer to look at his collection. After a quick inspection Magus pointed out to Mme. Cibot four paintings; he offered her two thousand francs commission on each if she could get them for him for forty thousand apiece—she forced him to double the commission—and he offered Rémonencq a commission on ten other pictures.

The portress pretended that she had seriously strained her back in lifting Pons into bed when he had fallen. The clever and needy Dr. Poulain divined that for some reason she was feigning injury. He diagnosed her case as rupture and plied her with various remedies. Finally she underwent a sham operation, which was successful and enhanced the doctor's fame. The doctor, having taken a fee for a sham illness, was now at the mercy of Mme. Cibot and felt that the devil had him by the hair. Mme. Cibot offered to go shares with him if he could persuade Pons to make his will in her favor. Dr. Poulain suggested that Mme. Cibot discuss the matter with an impecunious lawyer friend of his, M. Fraisier.

The man of law interrogated Mme. Cibot regarding Pons' wealth and his next of kin. He informed the portress that the father of Pons' nearest relative, Cécile, was a powerful man, president of the Chamber of Indictments at the Court of Appeal in Paris, a man who could, if he wished, send her to guillotine. Furthermore, the wife of de Marville was a woman so vindictive that she would spend ten years, if necessary, setting a trap to destroy an enemy. Such a woman would not allow Pons' property to go out of the family. Mme. Cibot could hope for no more than a legacy of thirty to forty thousand francs; he would guarantee her the former sum if she would put the business in his hands. The urgent thing to be done was to get Pons to make his will.

La Cibot persuaded Schmucke to give up all his outside activities in order to nurse Pons at night and sleep by day. She called upon the owner of the theatre and represented Pons as delirious and dying. Gaudissart gave her a thousand-franc note for Pons (which she kept for herself) and decided to replace him. Thus Mme. Cibot deprived both men of their positions and made them financially dependent upon her.

Fraisier called upon Mme. Camusot de Marville and in return for her promise that he should be a justice of the peace and his friend Poulain head of a government hospital he informed her of Mme. Cibot's designs on Pons' fortune and undertook to thwart the portress's ambitions to get it all.

To help Pons along his way to the grave, Mme. Cibot let him know that he was being replaced as orchestra conductor. She said that Schmucke had requested her to report that Pons was unable to resume his work. Before Pons had an opportunity to question Schmucke, she informed the German that his friend's mind was wandering.

Mme. Cibot now informed Schmucke that he and Pons owed her and her husband three thousand francs for lodging, food, services, and medical expenses, that she had paid for many things out of her own money (because she loved them), and that M. Cibot demanded immediate payment. When Schmucke refused to sell some of Pons' pictures without his knowledge, she forced him to do so by obtaining a judgment. Four pictures were sold to Magus and four to Rémonencq for a total of five thousand francs, which seemed to the naïve German like a good sum of money for "chim-cracks." Each buyer then paid off Mme. Cibot with thirty thousand francs. Unframed canvases were placed, by Rémonencq, in the empty frames, in case Pons should be able to stick his head in the door of the salon.

"On the average," said the grimy old Jew, "everything is worth a thousand francs."

"Seventeen hundred thousand francs!" exclaimed Fraisier in bewilderment.

Confident that Pons was in a deep sleep because she had given him a double dose of a sleeping draught, Mme. Cibot led the three men into his bedroom to examine the articles there. Suddenly Pons awoke, recognized Magus, and began to shout: "Thieves! . . . Help! Murder! Help! . . . Get out, all of you!" The three men left the room quietly. Mme. Cibot prevented Pons from getting out of bed and tried to persuade him that he had just had a raving fit.

When Mme. Cibot left him, Pons summoned his strength and managed to reach the salon. He discovered the substituted paintings in the frames that had held his masterpieces and fell in a faint upon the floor, where Schmucke discovered him two hours later. Schmucke admitted that he had permitted the sale, because of the judgment. Pons tried to convince Schmucke of the woman's villainy and offered to prove it to him.

At this time Mme. Cibot's husband was dying, for Rémonencq had been introducing poison, each time he visited the Cibots, into the herb tea that Cibot took for his ailing health.

Pons requested Schmucke to get him a notary. When the man arrived, Mme. Cibot left her dying husband to accompany him to Pons' room. She listened outside the door, as Pons knew she would, while he wrote a will as the notary dictated it. The will provided that Pons' collection should go to the King, for the Louvre, provided that annuities of 2,400 francs for Schmucke and 200 francs for Mme. Cibot be granted. Pons directed that the will be put in a drawer and the key be placed under his pillow.

Next, Pons requested Schmucke to have Mlle. Heloïse Brisetout, a ballet-girl of the theatre, visit him. When she arrived, he asked her to send him an honest notary and Schwab and Brunner as witnesses the following morning.

At four o'clock in the morning Mme. Cibot came to take Schmucke's place by Pons' bedside, and the German concealed himself in a closet to observe, as Pons had directed him. Mme. Cibot secured the key, unlocked the drawer, and hurried with the will to Fraisier, who was waiting nearby. The lawyer opened the sealed envelope with a fine wire and read the will. It was the ruin of all his hopes, for a legacy to the King could not be contested. He substituted a sheet of blank paper for the will before resealing the envelope. He informed Mme. Cibot of the paltry annuity left her. "Why, he is a finished scoundrel!" she exclaimed. She returned to Pons' room and was thinking of burning the will in the fireplace when her arms were grasped by Pons and Schmucke. She fell face downwards in a fit, either real or feigned.

The next morning Cibot was receiving the Sacrament and there was such a commotion in the house that the arrival of Pons' notary and witnesses was not noticed. Pons revoked the previous will and constituted Schmucke his universal legatee. Pons then became so weak that a priest was summoned to give him also the Sacrament. He died with his hand clasped in his friend's.

Fraisier persuaded the de Marvilles to contest Pons' will on the grounds that Schmucke had exerted "undue influence" and used "unlawful means" to have the will made in his favor, that he had sequestered the testator and prevented the family from approaching the deceased during his last illness. Schmucke would be confronted with a summons; the de Marvilles would offer to settle an annuity upon him if he abandoned his claims; Schmucke would be advised to accept this settlement, and because of his character he would do so.

But when Schmucke learned of the charges against him, the good man suffered a stroke; he never regained consciousness and died ten days later.

Fraisier, now a justice of the peace, is very intimate with the de Marville family. Pons' collection was inherited by Cécile. She and her mother speak affectionately of the man whom they, in effect, murdered.

Rémonencq married Cibot's widow and got his fine shop on the boulevard. But she is the sole owner of the shop now. For Rémonencq, by the terms of the marriage contract, settled the property upon the survivor and left a little glass of vitriol about for his wife to drink by mistake; but she put the glass elsewhere and he swallowed the draught himself. The rascal's appropriate end vindicates Providence, who is sometimes accused of neglect.

CRIME AND PUNISHMENT

by

FËDOR DOSTOEVSKI

TRANSLATED FROM THE RUSSIAN BY CONSTANCE GARNETT

CONDENSATION BY LAWRENCE FALCONER

FËDOR MIKHAILOVICH DOSTOEVSKI (1821–1881) was born in Moscow of a Catholic family originally from Lithuania but with some Norse ancestry. His father, a member of the property-less nobility, was a staff doctor at the Moscow hospital for the poor, and when Fëdor was a child, the family lived adjacent to the hospital, so that he knew suffering and poverty at first hand. The household was run under very strict paternal discipline, and young Dostoevski seems to have been very restrained until he went to boarding school at sixteen. Later he attended military school and studied engineering in St. Petersburg. In 1839, while he was away, his father was murdered by rebellious serfs whom he had abused on his country property. Four years later Fëdor was graduated and entered civil service for one year.

But his father's fate had made a great impression on him, and as he matured, his interest in the lot of the peasants increased. In 1844 he joined a socialist study circle and two years later his first novel, "Poorfolk," championing the serfs against the landlords, appeared. It met with success and he wrote a second novel "The Double" (1846) immediately. In 1850, after a deeper involvement in the socialist movement, Dostoevski was exiled for four years to Siberia for political defection, an experience described in "Memoirs of a Dead House" (1862), after which he was required to serve in the army for four more years.

Meanwhile, although he had discovered he was afflicted with epilepsy, he married, but his wife, ill herself with tuberculosis, lived only a few years. In 1859 he was allowed to return to St. Petersburg, where he became a magazine editor.

70

At this time, he experienced a religious conversion. His great period as a writer began with the publication of "Notes from Underground" in 1864, followed by "The Gambler" and "Crime and Punishment" in 1866. The next year the author married the secretary to whom he had dictated his great novel (his first wife had died in 1864). In 1868 when "The Idiot" appeared, Dostoevski was so burdened with gambling debts that he fled to Europe to escape his creditors.

He spent four years in Germany, Italy, and Switzerland and became antagonistic to the European way of life. He returned to Russia in 1871 when "The Possessed" was published, and he resumed his career as a journalist. But Dostoevski was a changed man. No longer a socialist, he was almost reactionary with extreme racial prejudice and pronounced chauvinistic attitudes.

As a writer, Dostoevski used material which was often almost pathological, for example "The Brothers Karamazov" (1879–80) with its theme of parricide. He raised difficult psychological questions. However, he was also able to portray balanced characters. He has been considered by many critics to have exerted the strongest single influence on the twentieth-century novel.

One hot evening in July a young man stole out of his garret room, hoping to avoid his landlady, to whom he was heavily in debt. He was crushed by poverty; he had left the university and given up tutoring because of his shabby clothes.

"I want to attempt a thing like *that* and am frightened by these trifles," he thought.

He walked but a short distance to the place where he was going to rehearse his project. He rang the bell of the old woman's flat, and soon the door opened a crack and her sharp, malignant eyes peered out.

"Raskolnikov, a student. I've brought you something to pawn." He drew out of his pocket an old-fashioned silver watch, for which he sullenly accepted the old woman's offer of a rouble and a half, minus interest he owed her.

When he was in the street he felt giddy and thirsty and entered a tavern. At a nearby table sat a man who introduced himself as Marmeladov. He was very drunk and spoke with pompous dignity.

His wife, he said, was a lady of education and refinement, though irritable. A poor widow with three children, she had married him out of need. But he had lost his position as a government official because of drunkenness. His own daughter Sonia had gone out on the streets to support the family; she had been given a yellow ticket and the landlady had made her leave the house.

Raskolnikov took the drunkard home to his miserable family and left in the wretched flat the coppers he had received as change at the tavern.

The next day Raskolnikov received from his mother a letter saying that his sister Dounia had agreed to marry a certain Luzhin, a well-to-do counsellor of middle age. The mother and sister hoped that this man would pay for Raskolnikov's studies and, later, take him into his office. Raskolnikov understood clearly; Dounia was sacrificing herself for his sake.

What seemed like fate intervened. He learned by chance that the pawnbroker would be alone the next evening. "A stupid, worthless, horrid old woman," he had heard a student say of her. "What value has her life? No more than the life of a louse."

The next day the thing was done. The old woman lay in her blood. Raskolnikov removed a fat purse from around her neck and found a box containing various articles made of gold, which he stuffed into his pockets. Unexpectedly, the woman's simpleton sister returned to the apartment. She did not try to defend herself as he struck her, too, with the axe.

The next morning as he lay shivering with horror and fever, the porter pounded on his door and handed him a police summons. "I must get it over with," he decided. At the police station he was informed that his landlady had made a complaint against him for recovery of the money due her. He signed a paper with shaking fingers. He heard two officers discussing the murder. As he walked toward the door he fainted. When he recovered consciousness he was questioned about his illness. He was not detained, but he felt that he had incurred suspicion.

He removed the stolen articles from his room, where he had hidden them, to a hole under a huge stone in a deserted courtyard; he had never thought to look inside the purse.

Regaining his room, he lapsed into delirium. His student friend Razumihin brought in a doctor, Zossimov, who inferred that something was preying on Raskolnikov's mind. One day as the young man was convalescing, the talk of these two men, who had come to visit him, turned to the pawnbroker's murder, which the police were investigating on the theory that it had been committed by one of her customers.

The conversation was interrupted by the entrance of a portly, elegantly dressed gentleman, who announced himself as Raskolnikov's sister's fiancé, Pyotr Petrovitch Luzhin, and informed Raskolnikov that his mother and sister would arrive in St. Petersburg shortly.

The discussion of the murder was resumed and led to an argument about the economic causes of crime. Raskolnikov seized the opportunity to fling it in Luzhin's face that he had told Dounia that what he liked best about her was that she was poor and would have to regard him as a benefactor. Luzhin left in a rage.

Raskolnikov dressed and went out to a tavern, where he avidly read newspaper accounts of the murder. Zametov, a police clerk, sat down beside him and listened attentively as he discussed the crime.

Afterwards, Raskolnikov was almost on the point of going to the police, when he came upon a crowd gathered about a man who had been run over by a coach. It was Marmeladov, his head crushed. "I know him!" Raskolnikov shouted to a policeman. "Make haste for a doctor! I will pay."

Marmeladov was carried to his house, where a few minutes later he died, in the arms of his daughter Sonia. Raskolnikov pressed twenty roubles upon Katerina, the distracted widow, and promised to come again. The eldest child, Polenka, kissed him and wept on his shoulder. He departed feeling that his illness was now over, that he could live again.

He went to Razumihin's and his friend, worried about his excited state, accompanied him home, where he found his mother and sister waiting. They embraced him joyfully, but he stood like one dead and then fell into a faint. When he recovered he told of his quarrel with Luzhin and said to Dounia: "You want to marry Luzhin for *my* sake. But I won't accept the sacrifice! This marriage is an infamy!"

The mother was dismayed, and Dounia angry. Razumihin drew them outside and explained that Raskolnikov was unwell and must not be irritated. He had become immediately infatuated with Dounia, a tall, beautiful girl, intelligent, kind, and of strong character.

The next day Raskolnikov decided to consult Razumihin about the pledges he had left with the murdered pawnbroker. A relative of Razumihin's, Porfiry Petrovitch, was in charge of the investigation and was interviewing those who had had dealings with the old woman. Razumihin took his friend to see Porfiry, who was a youngish man, stout and jolly except for his cold and penetrating eyes. Raskolnikov stated his business clearly and exactly, feigning embarrassment at not having the money to redeem his articles. Porfiry looked at him ironically. "I have been expecting you," he said. "You are the only one who has not come forward."

Porfiry mentioned that he had been much interested in Raskolnikov's article "On Crime" in the *Periodical Review;* Raskolnikov was amazed; he didn't know that the article had been published. Porfiry referred to Raskolnikov's interesting statement that the commission of a crime is always accompanied by illness. But he was even more interested in his statement that certain "extraordinary" persons have a moral right to do some things that "ordinary" people may not do.

Raskolnikov objected that the "extraordinary" man has this right only if it is necessary for him to overcome legal obstacles in order to fulfill an idea, for the benefit of humanity. He went on to say that great men, like Napoleon, do not hesitate to shed blood, and still people worship them.

"And when you wrote the article, did you . . . he-he-he . . . perhaps . . . fancy yourself an extraordinary man?"

"Quite possibly," answered Raskolnikov contemptuously. When he left, Porfiry requested him to call at his office the following day.

That evening Raskolnikov had a new visitor—Arkady Ivanovitch Svidrigaïlov. (He was a man who had persecuted Dounia with his attentions while she was a governess in his home. There had been a scandal, and she had left her position. The man's wife had died shortly thereafter, of apoplexy it was said.)

Svidrigaïlov asked Raskolnikov to arrange a meeting between him and Dounia, so that he might present her with ten thousand roubles —with no obligations involved—and try to persuade her to break the engagement. Raskolnikov, suspicious, refused to arrange the meeting. Svidrigaïlov departed, still friendly, saying that his wife had left Dounia three thousand roubles.

Later that night Dounia dismissed Luzhin after an angry scene. Her brother and mother were overjoyed at her deliverance, as was Razumihin, who henceforth became part of the family.

Raskolnikov left them to go to Sonia. Brutally, he placed before her the probable future of her family—that Katerina would soon die of her consumption, the children would be reduced to beggary, and Sonia would sooner or later become ill. Sonia broke into bitter sobs. All at once Raskolnikov bent down to the floor and kissed her foot. "I do not bow to you, I bow down to all the suffering of humanity," he said wildly.

He noticed the New Testament on the chest of drawers and asked her to read the story of Lazarus to him. Sonia began to read, falteringly at first but at last triumphantly, her voice like a bell.

"We are both accursed," Raskolnikov told her. "Let us go our way together." He left, promising to return the next day, while Svidrigaïlov, who had taken lodgings in the same house, stood on the other side of the door, listening.

The next morning Raskolnikov went to Porfiry's office with a statement concerning the watch and ring he had pawned. During the interview Porfiry confided that it was better not to formally interrogate a suspect and not to arrest him. "If I don't touch him but let him suspect that I know all about it and am watching him, he will keep circling round me like a moth round a candle."

That afternoon Raskolnikov confessed his crime, not to the police but to Sonia. She promised never to leave him. When he tried to explain that he had wanted to be one of those who could overstep barriers, like Napoleon, she was completely bewildered. Finally he asked her, "What am I to do now?"

"Go at once, stand at the cross-roads, bow down to all the world and say, 'I am a murderer.' You must suffer and expiate your sin. Then God will send you life again." She gave him a wooden cross to wear, but he refused it saying, "Not now, Sonia."

Several days later he had another interview with Porfiry, who described the kind of man who had committed the crime, a mind unhinged by theories. "You, Rodion Romanovitch, you are the murderer." By confessing, said Porfiry, he would shorten his sentence. But Raskolnikov was not yet ready to confess.

He hurried to see Svidrigaïlov, who had hinted what he had learned from his eavesdropping. It had occurred to him that Svidrigaïlov might use his secret against Dounia, and he threatened to kill him if he did. But Svidrigaïlov declared that he was betrothed to a beautiful girl of fifteen, "worth paying for." It amused him that the young murderer should disapprove of him. He did, however, go to Dounia and in a locked room convinced her of her brother's guilt, offering to keep the secret if she would yield herself to him. But he did not resist when she tried—and failed—to shoot him, and at last he gave her the key.

That evening Svidrigaïlov went to see Sonia and told her he was going to America. He gave her receipts for money that he had deposited for the children. (Katerina had meanwhile died.) He also gave her three thousand roubles' worth of bonds so that she might leave off her life of shame, and he left her wondering. Next he called on the parents of his betrothed. He told them he had to make a journey. He kissed the little girl and presented her with a betrothal gift of fifteen thousand roubles and then departed. At dawn he shot himself.

On this same day Raskolnikov went to say good-by to his mother and sister and to assure them that he had always loved them. Then he went to Sonia, who was waiting for him. "I have come for your cross," he said, smiling, and she put the wooden cross about his neck. In the Hay Market he bowed down and kissed the earth. Because of the laughter and jeers of the spectators, the words "I am a murderer" died on his lips. He strode to the police station and made his confession.

Epilogue. Raskolnikov received a light sentence—eight years of penal servitude—because it seemed that he had committed the crime in a state of temporary insanity and because various persons testified to his benevolent and self-sacrificing character.

Soon after Raskolnikov and Sonia set off for Siberia, Dounia and Razumihin were married. Raskolnikov's mother died of a brain fever.

For a long time Raskolnikov was very depressed and sullen, even with Sonia. He felt no repentance, only disgust for his weakness and clumsiness. He became ill and was in the hospital for weeks.

When he first saw Sonia after his release from the hospital, something seemed to seize him and fling him at her feet. He wept and threw his arms about her knees. A light of infinite happiness came into her eyes. She knew that he loved her and that for both of them a new life had begun.

THE CRISIS*

by
WINSTON CHURCHILL
CONDENSATION BY WILLIAM HOWARD TAFT
FORMER PRESIDENT OF THE UNITED STATES

WINSTON CHURCHILL, whom we perhaps should call Americanus, to distinguish him from the lively son of Lord Randolph Churchill, who bears the same first name, was born in St. Louis, November 10, 1871, though his father was of Portland, Maine. He was educated at Smith Academy, St. Louis, and graduated from the United States Naval Academy in 1894. The same year found him an editor of the "Army and Navy Journal"; the next year he was managing editor of the "Cosmopolitan Magazine"; in 1903 and 1905 he was a member of the New Hampshire Legislature, and in 1906 he was running for Governor of that state as the candidate of the Lincoln Republican Club on a reform platform, fighting a valiant battle to down the political practices which had grown to be time-honored, if nothing else, in that state. Some of the leaders of the Democratic party fully recognized the good he was attempting to accomplish in this early progressive movement, but the fact that he was not a native of of the state, was a newcomer in politics, and was striving for ideas which were novel and thoroughly distressing to politicians of long experience, prevented his success with the Republicans. Politics, however, have not been entirely the same in the state since; and as an education for a writer on political subjects his experiences could be called laboratory courses. His books appealed to the public in increasing numbers. Beginning with "The Celebrity" in 1898, and "Richard Carvel" in 1899, he later laid a firm foundation for the favor he enjoyed in "The Crisis" (1901), "The Crossing" (1904), "Coniston" (1906), "Mr. Crewe's Career" (1908),

---

"A Modern Chronicle" (1910), *"The Inside of the Cup"* (1913), *"A Far Country"* (1915), and *"The Dwelling Place of Light"* (1917).

The scene is laid chiefly in St. Louis between 1857 and 1865.

Stephen Brice, of the Brahmin class of Boston, after his father's business failure and death, came with his mother to St. Louis, there to study and practice law in the office of his father's friend, Judge Silas Whipple.

Virginia Carvel, the only child of Col. Comyn Carvel, was beautiful and distinguished. The colonel was of an old Maryland family. He was the leading dry-goods merchant of St. Louis and a veteran of the Mexican War.

Judge Whipple was taciturn and abrupt. He concealed a generous heart under a forbidding exterior. He slept in his office. He was a "black" Republican. He secured clients because they needed his professional ability. He took Sunday dinner at Colonel Carvel's, where the discussion over slavery in Virginia's hearing went on with a plainness of speech that only the lifelong friendship of the two men could have made possible. Colonel Carvel was the highest type of a Southern gentleman.

Mrs. Brice, Stephen's mother, bore her reduced fortune with dignity and with high hope in her son's future and a spirit of sacrifice in his interest.

Eliphalet Hopper was a New-Englander in Colonel Carvel's employ. Industrious and saving, he was unscrupulous and mean, valuing only financial success and cherishing jealousy of others' good fortune.

Clarence Colfax, the son of a rich widow, was Virginia's cousin. He ran race-horses, he fought game-cocks. He had "a commanding indolence." He believed society based on slavery was divinely appointed. Masterful, courageous, adventurous, athletic, and handsome, he was a true cavalier, useless except for war.

The events of the story sport with the natural antagonism, in tradition and convictions, of the Puritan Stephen Brice and the lady of the Cavaliers, Virginia Carvel. They met first at a slave-market. A beautiful quadroon is put up for sale. With all his savings of nine hundred dollars Brice determines to buy the girl from a life of shame with an intending bidder and then free her. Virginia, through Colfax, also bids for the girl to use her as a maid. Brice, in sympathy for the pleading mother of the slave, persists in his purpose and, to

Virginia's great disgust, outbids the other two and manumits the girl.

Soon after, on her father's insistence, Virginia protestingly invites Brice to her first party. She snubs him, but finally dances with him. They meet again at a fancy-dress party in which she appears in the costume of her Colonial great-grandmother, and he in that of his grandfather, a Revolutionary colonel. She had only gone on the assurance he would not be there. His appearance prevents her giving way to the wooing of Clarence Colfax.

They meet again at the country-place of the Carvels, where Judge Whipple is convalescent, and there measure each other in discussion. Through Judge Whipple and her girl friends news of Brice is constantly thrust on her.

Silas Whipple knew and felt Lincoln's greatness and leadership. Whipple noted Brice's ability and high qualities, but regretted his Boston narrowness. He sought to broaden him by subjecting him to Lincoln's personality. Under pretense of a business errand, he asked Lincoln to let the young man hear his debate at Freeport with Douglas. Brice was with Lincoln the night before in a tavern, where, hatless, coatless, vestless, he discussed the wisdom of asking Douglas the great question, the answer to which made Douglas Senator and Lincoln President. Lincoln's limpid intellectual honesty, his pure logic, his lucidity of soul and purpose, impress themselves on young Brice and profoundly affect his point of view.

Missouri was saved for the Union by Frank Blair and Nathaniel Lyon. Under their leadership the Germans of St. Louis captured a camp of the golden youth of St. Louis mobilizing as Confederates. Colfax was among those taken, but refused a parole and escaped to the Southern army. These disturbing events brought Brice and Virginia together again. He sought to render the Carvels service, which Virginia resented. Mrs. Brice and Virginia, however, soon became interested in the nursing of wounded soldiers and of Judge Whipple, whom a fatal illness had overtaken. Brice as a lieutenant was in the battle about Vicksburg and found Colfax badly wounded in the captured city. He sent him north to St. Louis, where he was nursed by Virginia. Colfax had distinguished himself by daredevil exploits of great usefulness to his cause. Virginia was enthused by his patriotic devotion to the cause she loved and their engagement was the result. Brice was wounded in the campaigns after Vicksburg and also returned to St. Louis.

The climax of the story comes at the deathbed of Judge Whipple.

Colonel Carvel, though in the rebel army, returns to see his daughter. Hearing of Whipple's illness, he visits Whipple's office, where he finds Virginia and Colfax. In the latter's hurried withdrawal to chase a spy who proves to be Eliphalet Hopper, Virginia and Brice, unexpectedly to each, are thrown together. She is surprised into a betrayal and full realization of her interest in him. Hopper eludes Colfax and creeps into Whipple's outer office. By corrupt transactions with Federal quartermasters he has become a rich man and the real owner of the Carvel business. He finds Virginia alone and threatens, unless she marries him, to betray her father to the Union authorities as a spy. Brice appears, strikes Hopper down, defies him with a counter-threat of prosecution for corruption. This rids the story of Hopper.

Colfax goes South after Virginia has broken their engagement. He is subsequently captured as a spy. Brice identifies him and then intervenes with Sherman to save his life. Meantime, Brice is sent by Sherman to City Point with despatches. There he meets Lincoln again. Lincoln remembers him and invites him to become his aide.

The story closes with the visit of Virginia to Lincoln at the White House, for the pardon of Colfax. Lincoln had heard of the circumstances, sees Virginia, and brings in Brice. After a conversation in which there is revealed to Virginia the constant sorrow of Lincoln's soul and his deep sympathy for the Southern people, he pardons Colfax and leaves Brice and Virginia to that mutual confession of love of which each had long been conscious. They were married at once, but their honeymoon was darkened with the sudden taking off of the Great American.

The story is well told. The plot is not forced and maintains one's interest to the end. Stephen Brice is almost too perfect. The author speaks feelingly of the anxiety of novelists to avoid this danger. Virginia's character is perhaps better done, because easier to endow with attractive failings. Judge Whipple and Colonel Carvel are admirably drawn.

The story weaves in an accurate and valuable description of the causes of the war and of the kind of people that fought the war. St. Louis, the confluence of the two streams of western immigration from the North and the South, was the place to study the mixing but conflicting elements of our people before the Civil War. It was the author's home. He reveals their faults and their virtues with impartial pen. He maintains the just balance. He avowedly and really takes the Lincoln view of the contest, which, as he truly says, has now become the American view both North and South.

The picture of Lincoln is inspiring. The glimpses of Sherman, Grant, and Lyon are vivid and true to life.

The book is written in a most entertaining style. It is charming and sustained in its interest as a love story. It is a great historical novel.

~◊~

DAVID COPPERFIELD

by

CHARLES DICKENS

CONDENSATION BY CHARLES F. D. BELDEN

CHARLES JOHN HUFFAM DICKENS was born February 7, 1812, at Portsea, England, where his father was a clerk in the Navy Pay office. He died at Gadshill Place, in Kent, on June 9, 1870.

His dreams of writing came to him when as a boy he read breathlessly the battered novels in his father's library. He became a reporter on the London newspapers, and wrote (1836) "Sketches by Boz," wherein are, in miniature, all the abounding virtues of his novels.

The "Pickwick Papers" (1837) were a great success. Their inimitable rollicking humor captivated the English reading world. His first extended novel was "Oliver Twist" (1838), followed by "Nicholas Nickleby" (1838–39), "Old Curiosity Shop" and "Barnaby Rudge" (1840–41). He produced some sixteen major novels, the last, "The Mystery of Edwin Drood" (1870), being left unfinished. "David Copperfield" (1849–50), held by many to be his masterpiece, and by not a few to be the greatest story ever written, is supposed to be semi-autobiographical. Many of his novels were published in instalments, and never before or since has any literary publication excited such a furore.

After his initial successes, Dickens' life was a triumphal procession, saddened only by domestic unhappiness. He visited America, where his works were even more popular than in England, in 1842 and 1867–68.

He wrote in his will his own best epitaph, "I rest my claims to the remembrance of my country on my published works." He might well have substituted "the world" for "my country."

It was the writer's imagination that has made his characters seem giants when they are placed beside the characters of later men. It is this imagination, "now humorous, now terrible, now simply grotesque," that Professor Saintsbury terms "of a quality which stands entirely by itself, or is approached at a distance, and with a difference, only by that of his great French contemporary, Balzac."

"Of all my books," writes Dickens, "I like this the best. It will be easily believed that I am a fond parent to every child of my fancy, and that no one can ever love that family as dearly as I love them; but, like many fond parents, I have in my heart of hearts a favorite child, and his name is *David Copperfield.*"

The world, in the main, agrees with the opinion of the great, kindly delineator of humanity, for *David Copperfield* and *Pickwick Papers* hold first and second choice with most lovers of this English author of the middle of the nineteenth century. The reason is not hard to discover. The memory of the sad childhood of the writer forms the basis of the novel and provides the personal flavor. It is in many respects his ablest and clearest book. The narrative, moreover, moves from beginning to end in full swing with mingled pathos and humor. The spirit throughout is kindly, sympathetic, and, above all, human. Mr. G. K. Chesterton, writing of *David Copperfield* and its author, says: "He has created creatures who cling to us and tyrannize over us, creatures whom we would not forget if we could, creatures whom we could not forget if we would, creatures who are more actual than the man who made them."

The novel begins with the birth of its hero, David Copperfield, six months after the death of his father. An eccentric great-aunt, Miss Betsey Trotwood, is present in the house, but departs quite as suddenly as she arrived when she learns that the child is a boy and cannot bear her name. David's mother is quite alone in the world with the exception of plain Peggotty, her devoted serving-woman; Peggotty, with no shape at all, and so very plump that when any little exertion is made after she is dressed, some of the buttons on the back of her gown fly off.

Being, however, youthful and pretty, Clara Copperfield soon marries the stern Mr. Murdstone, who proves to be not only stern, but hard and cruel. On the occasion of his mother's marriage David is sent with Peggotty to visit her brother at Yarmouth, where he, with his niece, little Emily, and nephew Ham, occupy a superannuated old boat now converted into a most delightfully cozy home. Little Emily, with her winning ways, grows very dear to David, as do the honest fisherfolk with whom she lives.

Returning home, David at once becomes an object of detestation to his stepfather, and in consequence is packed off to school. Here his misery continues under a master, or rather bully, Creakle, whose chief zest in life consists in the infliction of pain on some hapless victim. The one bit of brightness in school life is his attachment for James Steerforth, a handsome, debonair, dashing lad, with the faculty of making every one his friend. But school-days are brought to a sudden halt by the death of David's mother, crushed by her husband's ceaseless tyranny. Peggotty is dismissed and Barkis, the stage-driver whose courtship has consisted in the singular message, sent through David, of "Barkis is willin'," finally succeeds in making Peggotty willing also.

After months of utter neglect David is sent to London, where he becomes, at ten years of age, a little laboring hind in a dilapidated old warehouse, in the service of Murdstone & Grimby, wine merchants. Half starved, wearied by long hours of labor amid repulsive companions, including Mick Walker and Mealy Potatoes, David's life is a continued torture. He lodges with a Mr. and Mrs. Wilkins Micawber and their numerous progeny. Mr. Micawber, always in pecuniary difficulties and always expecting something to "turn up" and always in possession of a fine flow of oratory, is alternately buoyed up by a conviction that Fortune is at last about to smile upon him, and reduced to the depths of despair by her sudden and unaccountable withdrawal. David comes to have a genuine liking for the couple, so much so that when the Micawbers, having failed to meet certain financial obligations, are obliged to move to prison, and

David to seek new quarters, he feels such a sense of loneliness that he determines to run away to his aunt, Betsey Trotwood at Dover, an aunt whom he has never seen, but of whom he remembers to have heard.

The aunt adopts him and sends him to school at Canterbury, where he boards with his aunt's lawyer and man of affairs, a Mr. Wickfield, and his daughter Agnes, whose serene goodness becomes a constant inspiration to David. Here also he comes in contact with Mr. Wickfield's clerk, Uriah Heep, "a very 'umble person," an individual with a cadaverous face and a head covered with carroty stubble, red eyes which have a curiously unshaded appearance and which seem to David to be ceaselessly watchful. His groveling humility and clammy handgrasp fill David with uncontrollable loathing and distrust.

Having graduated with honors, David decides to become a proctor and enters the office of Spenlow & Jorkins. He at once falls head over heels in love with Mr. Spenlow's distractingly pretty daughter, Dora, who returns his affection. On hearing that Peggotty's husband is dying, David makes a hurried visit to Yarmouth to comfort his old nurse. While there, Emily, within a few days of becoming Ham's bride, little Emily, the precious treasure of her old uncle's heart, disappears and with her Steerforth. Carried away by his gallantry and persuaded that he will make her "a lady," Emily is none the less distracted by a sense of terrible humiliation and of degradation, for which she implores her uncle's forgiveness. David, overcome by the thought that it was he who first brought Steerforth to Yarmouth, returns to London, to find that his aunt has lost the greater part of her fortune. This makes it necessary for David to add to their income by using all his spare time in clerical and literary work.

Dora continues uppermost in his thoughts, although Mr. Spenlow opposes the match. His sudden death leaves the timid, trustful, artless Dora, to the surprise of all, nearly penniless. David's income, though slender, permits of their marriage.

With all his love for his child wife, as she calls herself, he finds that her gay irresponsibility results in anything but a comfortable home. After vainly trying to develop her childish nature he uncomplainingly makes the best of it and continues to admire her bewitching ways. Meanwhile Uriah Heep has managed by deceit to worm his way into partnership with Mr. Wickfield, after which he proceeds to gain full control of the business. Considering Mr. Micawber likely to be a useful tool, Uriah hires him in the capacity of clerk, at such a a meager salary that Mr. Micawber is obliged to borrow small sums of money from Heep, who takes advantage of this indebtedness to force Mr. Micawber to assist him in his dishonest practices.

At the end of a year Mr. Micawber requests an interview with David and his aunt at Canterbury. They find him filled with righteous contempt for Uriah Heep, the hypocritical plotter, and prepared to make a sweeping exposure, which he forthwith proceeds to do in his loftiest style, which results in the recovery of Betsey Trotwood's money, full restitution to Mr. Wickfield, and, in Mr. Micawber's own words, the final pulverization of Heep. "Blossom," as David delights to call Dora, proves as frail as the name, and in spite of his tenderest care she droops and at length is gone.

As at other times of trial, it is the quick sympathy of Agnes Wickfield that softens the pain, and through her influence David plans to go abroad for a time. Meanwhile out of gratitude to Mr. Micawber for his service in the recovery of her money, Betsey Trotwood offers to help the Micawbers to make a new start in Australia. The family joyfully accept the proposition and prepare to sail on the same ship with Emily and her devoted uncle, to whom she has at last returned and who is accompanying her to the distant colony to begin life anew. Before bidding these good friends farewell, David visits Yarmouth once more and witnesses the last scene of Emily's tragedy. A raging tempest beats a ship to pieces just off the coast. One living person is seen still clinging to the mast, and the irony of fate sends Ham to his death in his efforts to rescue that creature, whose body when washed ashore proves to be that of Steerforth.

After three years' absence abroad, David returns to England, and gradually comes to realize that Agnes Wickfield has always been his guiding-star and held sway in his heart. Betsey Trotwood, fearing that David may still be blind with regard to the feeling of Agnes toward him, guilelessly mentions that she has reason to believe that Agnes is to be married. Whereupon David is determined, at whatever cost to his own feelings, to tell Agnes of his joy in any happiness that may come to her. He soon discovers that she has never cared for any other than himself and that her future happiness will be his as well.

As the years pass and a group of children is added to their home David continues to find Agnes his inspiration as of old.

THE DEERSLAYER

by

JAMES FENIMORE COOPER

CONDENSATION BY ALFRED S. CLARK

To JAMES FENIMORE COOPER's boyhood may be traced his genius for picturing primeval forests and adventures alive with thrill. Son of a hardy and vigorous pioneer, he lived by a rushing stream at the very edge of a deep, mysterious wilderness, in which lurked wild men and wild beasts. About the great roaring fire in his father's hospitable hall sat men of indomitable will and daring. They had grappled with nature and with men in their most primitive ferocity. They told true but lurid tales of doings that profoundly stirred the child's imagination. These men risked death and torture to carry on the life of their new country; so the boy James was saturated with that patriotism which vividly rings through his life and characterizes so clearly his writings.

Small wonder is it that this child later set himself the task of describing the frontier scenes of his native land, and achieved the famous "Leatherstocking Tales" which have kindled the hearts of so many adventure-loving boys. Of these "The Pathfinder" and "Deerslayer" seemed to Cooper himself his best novels. They were both violently assailed when they first appeared, because their author had created so much personal hostility. Nevertheless, they had large sales, and of "The Pathfinder" no less a personage than Balzac writes: "It is beautiful, it is grand. Its interest is tremendous. I know no one in the world save Walter Scott who has risen to that grandeur and serenity of colors. Never did the art of writing tread closer upon the art of the pencil."

The early influences of Cooper's life probably led also to the activities of his last years, when he devoted himself to vast agricultural experiments. His father had helped to conquer the forest; he set himself to conquer the soil.

86

When the young white hunters, Deerslayer and Hurry Harry, reached the Lake Glimmerglass, the Hurons were on the warpath. Floating Tom Hutter, the only settler on the lake, knew the red men's ways and had built his house on piles, a quarter of a mile from shore. With him lived his daughters, Judith, handsome and flirtatious, and Hetty, a young woman with a mind of a child. Hurry Harry, a handsome giant of the woods, had been one of Judith's many wooers.

Floating Tom had another home, the *Ark,* a crude houseboat propelled by sweeps and a sail. Here the hunters found him. As the *Ark* passed an overhanging sapling, warriors, bedaubed by warpaint, leaped for the roof. They fell into the lake, but yells and pattering bullets from shore told that they were out in force.

Hutter was a hardy fighter, Hurry had the strength of ten ordinary men, and Natty Bumppo had won his name of Deerslayer because of his unerring aim with the rifle. They might have withstood a siege of weeks. But Hutter and Hurry, tempted by the bounty for scalps, determined to raid the Indian encampment, where they expected to find only squaws and children. Deerslayer refused to join this cowardly warfare. But warriors were in the tents and the raiders were captured. Deerslayer, now the sole reliance of the girls in Hutter's lake-girdled house, could not attempt their rescue.

His simple honesty and his modesty made a profound impression upon Judith, who had hitherto listened too willingly to the honeyed words of English officers. Her arts were forgotten in the presence of this naïve woodsman who was blind to feminine wiles.

Although the Indians had no canoes, Deerslayer knew that they could quickly make rafts, and he was glad enough that he had agreed to meet at the lake that night his dearest friend, the young Delaware warrior, Big Serpent. At sunset he maneuvered the *Ark* near the rendezvous and Big Serpent leaped aboard. The bank resounded with exultant yells, and a score of savages splashed into the water. Deerslayer and Big Serpent bent to the sweeps and foiled them. Big Serpent's hatred of the Hurons was white hot, for they were carrying into captivity his betrothed, the lissome Hist-oh-Hist.

It was simple-minded Hetty who first went to the rescue of Hutter and Hurry. She believed that reading her Bible to these savages would soften their hearts. She was allowed to converse freely with the captives, for the Indians had a superstitious belief that the gods spoke through those whose wits were weak. Her pleading words, however, fell upon deaf ears. Deerslayer, with keener knowledge of Indian character, ransomed Hutter and Hurry with some ivory chessmen that the red men deemed idols.

While the released captives slept and the girls watched, Deerslayer and Big Serpent paddled away to rescue Hist-oh-Hist, who had sent word by Hetty that she would be on a conspicuous point of land when a bright star came out over a hilltop. The star came out, but Hist did not appear. The Delaware and his paleface comrade crept noiselessly to a ridge where they could overlook the encampment. Big Serpent chirruped like a squirrel, and Hist, guarded by an old hag, was so suddenly silent that they knew she understood.

At last the two women passed them. Big Serpent dragged his beloved toward the canoe; Deerslayer clutched the old woman, but her screams alarmed the camp. He ran for the canoe, but as he pushed it off an Indian landed squarely upon his back. Deerslayer thought not of himself, but gave the canoe so powerful a shove that it glided a hundred feet away. He tumbled into the lake, arose with his assailant, and they floundered in breast-high water. He was quickly surrounded, so he surrendered quietly.

Morning came and the *Ark* was swept toward the house. The keen eyes of Hist detected a moccasin floating against a pile and Big Serpent was sure the Hurons were within. Hurry and Hutter laughed at him and clambered inside through a trap-door. Hardly were they within before there was a heavy fall. To the sharp ears of Big Serpent, the whole house seemed alive. Now and then an Indian yell sounded or a deep bellow from Hurry.

Big Serpent dared not desert the three girls. Suddenly the door burst open and Hurry came raging forth upon the small platform. He stood panting, eyeing his enemies. Then he seized one brave by the waist and flung him far into the lake; two others quickly followed. Four were left. They were without arms and had little desire to close with this demon. He kicked one into the water, he doubled up another by a prodigious blow. The bigger of the two remaining closed with his white foe. They wrestled fiercely upon the narrow platform. Then Hurry raised the red man high above his head, hurled him down, and fell heavily upon him. But at that moment of conquest his arms were bound from behind. The Indians whom he had flung into the lake had scrambled out in time to pinion him.

As the *Ark* drifted past, Hist cried out to Hurry to roll off. He obeyed and fell with a great splash into the water. Hist threw him a rope, which he clutched with hands and teeth, the bullets of the outwitted Indians fell short, and Big Serpent pulled the exhausted giant on board. The Hurons left the house, and when Judith reached it her father was dying. He had been scalped while still alive.

The two men were soon rejoined by Deerslayer, who had accepted a furlough, promising to return at noon the next day if Hist and Judith refused to become Huron squaws. To Hurry's disgust, Deerslayer announced that he intended to keep his pledge. It meant death by torture, and Hurry could not understand how honor could drive a man insane. The giant left the lake stealthily that night, but promised to guide back a company of soldiers.

Judith, having dismissed Hurry forever, tried to tell Deerslayer that she loved him. But the hunter was so humble and Judith so beautiful, that he would not understand. He knew, moreover, that Judith had not always resisted the caresses of an English officer.

The sun was directly overhead when Deerslayer strode back into the Huron encampment. He haughtily refused to save his life by wedding the widow of a warrior he had shot, whereupon her brother hurled a tomahawk at the captive. Deerslayer's hand shot up and caught the weapon as it flew. An instant later it drove back and struck his foe between the eyes.

It gave him his opportunity to escape. As the Indians ran to the dead man's side he burst away with the speed of a deer. Behind him he heard the savage yells of his pursuers. Bullets whistled past, but he ran on untouched. At the edge of a gully, he leaped upon a fallen tree, shouted as if gloating over a free trail ahead, and then crept beneath the tree. His foes jumped upon it as they bounded along, but one after one they raced into the gully. Deerslayer doubled back, reached the lake, and threw himself into the canoe. The paddles were gone and he had to drift, lying flat in the bottom. Bullets cut the sides, making peep-holes. Just as he thought himself safely away, the fickle wind changed and he was driven back, again a prisoner.

The Hurons were now enraged. They bound him, and the young warriors flung tomahawks at him, trying to see how close they could come. This was but preparatory to the tortures. Then Judith, desperate in her love, stalked out of the trees to save him. Her impassioned words had no effect and the fires were kindled at his feet. Hetty leaped forward and stamped out the flames. Then Big Serpent bounded forth and with a rapid thrust cut Deerslayer loose. In his hands were two rifles, and for a moment the Hurons were dismayed. The warrior who had hoped to wed Hist hurled his knife at his rival, but Hist struck up his hand and he fell, Big Serpent's knife quivering in his breast. The red men scattered for their guns, but now a tramping was heard. Redcoats appeared among the trees, led by Hurry. Deerslayer's rifle crackled and two Hurons fell. The rest, cut off from escape, were butchered or made prisoners.

Hetty was mortally wounded, but none of the others were hurt. Judith flung away her reserve as they were leaving this scene of bloodshed and implored Deerslayer to marry her. But he remembered her past, and her beauty could not move him. She turned away and walked on with the soldiers. The captain had been her ardent wooer of the past, and rumors came later to America that on his great English estate lived a lady of rare beauty who did not bear his name. Whether or not it was Judith, Deerslayer never knew.

He trod another trail, with Big Serpent and Hist, back to the Delawares. The Hurons long knew his wrath, but fifteen years passed before he saw Glimmerglass again. His heart beat faster as he looked upon the ruined house and *Ark*, upon that silent sheet of lovely water fringed by deep woods and green hills.

DR. JEKYLL AND MR. HYDE

by

ROBERT LOUIS STEVENSON

CONDENSATION BY IRVING BACHELLER

ROBERT LOUIS STEVENSON was born of cultured parents, November 13, 1850, in Edinburgh. Because his health was delicate from infancy his schooling was desultory, but he early adored the tales and poems read to him by his devoted nurse, Alison Cunningham, and so began the passion for literature which dominated his life. His father, Thomas Stevenson, an able civil engineer, desired Louis to follow his profession, but after more than three years' study he abandoned it. He next read law to please his father, but he genuinely cared only for writing.

Perhaps no figure in literature is more loved for sheer valiance of spirit than Robert Louis Stevenson. He contended all his life against disease with high courage and dauntless gaiety. From 1880 to his death in 1894 his wife was a source of strength and inspiration; yet, exiled from friends, he suffered physical pain and weary disappointment. Nevertheless, in seventeen years he produced four volumes of essays, seven romances, five collections of fantastic tales, two of South Sea yarns, three of poetry, five volumes of travel and topography, one of political history, and left material for several posthumous works.

Stevenson writes in 1883: "I am now a person with an established ill-health—a wife—a dog possessed with an evil spirit—a certain reputation—and very obscure finances."

At this time he and his wife spent one of their happiest periods in their first real home, "La Solitude," in Hyères. At the end of sixteen months he was again flung back into acute suffering. They went to Bournemouth, where they lived in "Skerryvore" until after his father's death. Confined to the house—a condition most irksome to his active temperament—his gallant and buoyant spirit nevertheless flamed into expression at the slightest respite from pain and weakness. He wrote "Kidnapped," one of his most brilliant successes, and the "wild, symbolic" tale of "Dr. Jekyll and Mr. Hyde," the most popular of all his writings.

"Treasure Island" is perhaps the best loved of his romances. Stevenson said: "If this don't fetch the kids, why, they have gone rotten since my time." And again, as he wrote it: "It's awful fun, boys' stories; you just indulge the pleasure of your heart, that's all."

In 1887 Stevenson left the trying climate of the British Isles, never to return. With his family he went to the United States, where he was acclaimed, but his weak condition necessitated an immediate rest at Saranac, New York. Here he wrote for "Scribner's Magazine" the essays including "The Lantern Bearers," "Dreams," and "Pulvis et Umbra," the charm of which is ageless.

Mr. Utterson was a lawyer who believed in letting people go to the devil in their own way. He and Richard Enfield, a man about town, who was at once his distant kinsman and his friend, often walked about the London streets together. One day they came upon a sinister, windowless, two-story building in a byway.

Enfield told of seeing a man in this street run into a little girl, knock her down, and walk over her body. "It sounds nothing to hear, but it was hellish to see," he said. "I collared the man and held him, and, though he made no resistance, he gave me a look so ugly that it set me in a sweat. He offered to pay damages and came to this house to get the money. He gave me ten pounds in gold and a check signed by a man I knew. A forgery? Not a bit of it—perfectly good!"

Mr. Utterson asked the name of the man. Enfield with some hesitation said, "His name is Hyde."

"You see I don't ask you the name of the man who signed the check, for I know it already," said Utterson.

That night the latter opened his safe and took from it a will which he re-examined with care. It provided that in case of the death of Henry Jekyll all his possessions were to pass to Edward Hyde, and in case of the disappearance, or unexplained absence for three months, of said Jekyll, Edward Hyde should step into Jekyll's shoes without delay. As he studied it the lawyer said, "I thought it madness; now I begin to fear it is disgrace."

He decided to talk with Doctor Lanyon, a great physician and an old friend of Jekyll.

"I see very little of Henry now," said Lanyon. "He began to go wrong some ten years ago. He became too fanciful for me."

Lanyon had never heard of Hyde.

From that time forward Utterson began to haunt that sinister doorway into which Hyde had disappeared. He determined to discover its owner. At last one night a small, plainly dressed man approached and drew a key from his pocket. His look suggested deformity, but did not show it. Utterson accosted him and said: "Now I shall know you again. It may be useful."

Hyde gave his address in Soho, admitted knowing Jekyll and disappeared within. Utterson turned away convinced that this loathsome little man had some dark hold upon Doctor Jekyll. In sorrow and in pity he went to call upon Jekyll, who lived just around the corner. He was away.

To the butler Utterson said: "I saw Mr. Hyde go in by the old dissecting-room door, Poole. Is that right when Doctor Jekyll is away?"

"Quite right, sir. Mr. Hyde has a key."

Utterson went home with a feeling that some danger menaced his friend Jekyll.

A year later London was startled by a singularly inhuman murder case. A house-maid, looking from a window, saw a man who resembled Mr. Hyde strike down her master, a venerable, white-haired man, and trample his body underfoot in a hellish fury. The old man was Sir Danvers Carew.

The case came to Utterson, who alone recognized the weapon which the assassin had dropped. It was a cane which he had himself presented to Henry Jekyll. It was another link in the chain. Utterson took an officer to the address which Hyde had given. The latter was not at home.

The house was empty, and nothing suspicious was to be seen except a pile of ashes on the hearth as if many papers had been burned. Among these the detective discovered a partially burnt check-book. Following this clue, they located several thousand pounds at a certain bank.

Hyde did not claim the money. He had gone away, swiftly and safely.

The next step was to visit the sinister house, which was in truth a part of Jekyll's property and known as "The Laboratory." Light fell through a foggy cupola. At the farther end a flight of stairs led to a large room lighted by three iron-barred windows which looked on the court. A fire burned in the grate, and there, cowering close to it, sat Doctor Jekyll, looking deathly sick. He held out a cold hand.

Utterson asked if he had heard the news. Jekyll replied that he had heard it cried in the street. Utterson said: "Carew is my client, but so are you, and I want to know what I am doing. Are you hiding this murderer?"

Jekyll swore that he was not, but added: "He is safe—quite safe. He will never more be heard of."

He showed Utterson a letter from Hyde in a queer, upright handwriting.

As he went out Utterson asked Poole about the man who had brought the letter to his master. Poole was sure no letter had been handed in. The letter must have come in by the way of the laboratory. Utterson's clerk, an expert in handwriting, put the two letters side by side. After careful study he said: "The two hands are in many points identical; they are differently sloped, that is all."

Utterson's blood ran cold in his veins. "Henry Jekyll has forged in defense of a ferocious murderer," he said.

One day Lanyon called on Utterson, looking like a man who had been death-doomed. He refused to discuss Jekyll. He would not have his name mentioned. "I regard him as dead," he said, but would say no more.

In less than a week Lanyon took to his bed and died. A day or two after the funeral, a letter from the dead man came by messenger to the lawyer, a missive marked "Private. Not to be opened till the death or disappearance of Henry Jekyll."

Utterson did not open the letter, but went at once to call upon Jekyll. He saw only Poole, who said his master was hardly ever seen outside the room in the laboratory, and that he had grown very silent and morose. It seemed that something heavy rested on his mind.

One evening as Utterson and Enfield went across the court in the rear of the Jekyll house they saw the doctor sitting at one of the windows, taking the air, with an infinite sadness of mien, like some disconsolate prisoner.

Utterson, shocked at his looks, urged him to come down and walk with him. Jekyll refused sadly. Suddenly as they both stood looking at him his smile vanished and an expression of abject terror and despair came upon his face. He turned away. The window was thrust down. Utterson turned and looked at his companion, Enfield. Both were pale; there was an answering horror in their eyes.

One night Poole suddenly appeared at Utterson's house. He came to say that for a week his master had been shut up in his cabinet and that he was alarmed. "I can't bear it any longer," he said.

He could not explain his fears, but begged the lawyer to go back with him. His face was white and his voice broken.

Utterson found the entire household in Jekyll's house in a state of panic. All the maids were huddled together like scared sheep.

"They're all afraid," said Poole. "Follow me," he added. "I want you to hear, and I want you to be heard—but don't go in, sir."

They knocked on Jekyll's door, but a voice said, "I cannot see any one."

When they returned to the kitchen Poole asked, "Was that my master's voice?" Utterson admitted it was changed. Poole then opened his heart. "I believe my master has been made away with," he said.

Poole thought it strange that the murderer stayed. He said that the man in the cabinet room had been crying out night and day for help, and had thrown out papers on which were written orders for certain drugs.

Utterson examined some of these papers, which were agonized pleas for a special kind of salt which he had used and wanted again. They were all in Jekyll's hand, as Poole admitted. He also explained that once he had caught sight of the man inside. "The hair stood up at the sight of him. If that was my master, why had he a mask on his face?"

Poole said, "That thing was not my master. My master was a tall fine man—this is a kind of dwarf."

They decided to break down the door.

Poole said, "Once I heard it weeping." This added to the terror and mystery.

They stood before the door and Utterson demanded entrance. A voice from within cried, "For God's sake have mercy."

"That is not Jekyll's voice—it is Hyde's," shouted Utterson, and swung his ax against the door.

Shattering the lock, they rushed in. On the floor lay the form of a man contorted and twitching. They drew near and turned the body on its back. It was Edward Hyde, and by his side was an empty vial. He was dead.

Jekyll was not to be found, but the dead Hyde was dressed in what seemed to be a suit of Jekyll's clothes much too large for him.

On the table was a confession addressed to Utterson, and a will drawn in his favor. Lanyon's letter explained the mystery. Hyde had come one night to his office very ill and asked for some powders which Jekyll had left with Lanyon to be given to Hyde when he should call for them. Hyde, a small man, with clothes grotesquely large, eagerly seized the powder and mixed a liquid which had quickly turned from purple to green.

The man drank. He reeled. He staggered. He clutched the table. He seemed to swell. His features changed, and there before Lanyon's eyes, pale and fainting, groping before him with his hands, like a man restored to life stood Henry Jekyll.

Hyde and Jekyll were inhabitants of the same body! By the use of a drug he had been able to change from one personality to the other. Hyde was wholly evil. Jekyll, the amiable, respected professor, had but to drink that powerful drug to become the revolting Hyde.

DR. ZHIVAGO*

by

BORIS PASTERNAK

TRANSLATED FROM THE RUSSIAN BY
MAX HAYWARD AND MANYA HARARI
CONDENSATION BY MARGARET GILLETT

BORIS PASTERNAK (1890–1960), Russian writer who declined the Nobel prize for literature in 1958, was little known outside literary circles before he became involved in the political furore stirred up by his novel, "Dr. Zhivago," which won him that prize. However, his autobiography, short stories, and poems had appeared in English translation as much as a decade before. He was perhaps best known among scholars in his own country for his translation into Russian of Shakespeare and other great European writers.

Of Jewish descent, his father a painter of considerable repute and his mother a concert pianist, Boris was brought up in Moscow in a home where art was recognized and scholarship appreciated. He studied at the University of Moscow and the University of Marburg, Germany, and as a young man traveled in Italy. During World War I he was disqualified from military service by a leg injury but worked in a chemical factory in the Urals. After the Revolution, he was employed in the library of the Soviet Commissariat of

*Education. During this period he began writing poetry with
serious intent. In the late thirties he got into trouble with
the Stalinists because of his failure to give whole-hearted
support to the purge trials but was spared arrest by the
intervention of his colleagues.*

*"Dr. Zhivago" was accepted after Stalin's death by the
Soviet State Publishing House but was later barred. Meanwhile, Pasternak had sold the foreign rights to the book to
an Italian publisher who brought it out in Italian in 1957.
It was promptly hailed as a work of great significance in
the Russian epic tradition. However, Pasternak's quarrel
with his time in "Dr. Zhivago" was interpreted as political
when, in reality, it was philosophical, and he was expelled
from the Soviet Writers' Union.*

*In recent years and until his death, Pasternak lived in
Peredelkino, a writers' colony near Moscow. He is survived
by his second wife and three sons. English translations of
his poems have appeared in many American literary maga-
zines since 1957.*

A small boy, Yurii Zhivago, stood sobbing on his mother's grave.
He was an orphan now, for his father, a wealthy industrialist whom
he hardly knew, had committed suicide not long before. His uncle,
Nikolai, a free-thinker who had left the priesthood, would be his
guardian.

When Yurii was older and his uncle moved to Petersburg, he was
left in Moscow with some relatives, the Gromekos. They had a
daughter, Tonia, of Yurii's age and Yurii's friend and classmate,
Misha Gordon, lived with them. The three youngsters were a happy
though strange triumvirate of adolescents, dedicated to purity and
considering everything physical to be "vulgar."

*   *   *   *   *

Waves of revolution were beginning to sweep across Russia at the
time Mme. Guishar arrived in Moscow from Belgium. Her lover,
the lawyer Komarovsky, a friend of her late husband and a lecher
by avocation, had secured quarters and a small dressmaking business
for her. After Mme. Guishar had become his mistress, he exacted
further payment for his favors by corrupting her daughter Lara.

This man was the same evil genius who had encouraged Yurii's father to the dissipation that finally resulted in suicide.

* * * * *

As Yurii matured he took up the study of medicine. Inevitably he became engaged to Tonia at her dying mother's wish.

Lara matured, too, but far more drastically and her life under Komarovsky's domination became a nightmare. She tried to shoot him but failed. After the affair blew over, she married Pasha Antipova, her childhood sweetheart and they became school teachers in Yuriatin, a country town in the Urals. But in a few years Pasha found the narrowness of the provincial community stifling and enlisted in military service.

* * * * *

It was the second autumn of the war. Yurii had married Tonia and she had given him a child. He was at the front with his medical unit when Lara, who had taken up nursing in order to follow Pasha, was assigned to the same hospital.

Dr. Zhivago and Nurse Lara Antipova were often brought together by their work, but their contact was only in line of duty and both were anxious about their children. After she had been convinced that her husband had been killed, Lara took a chance she had to return to her daughter and to their home in Yuriatin. Later, when the doctor was relieved and able to go back to Moscow, he also left but he found everything in the city changed. There was nothing for sale in the shops and people huddled on corners and in doorways secretly exchanging bits of food or selling half a package of tobacco as if it were gold.

* * * * *

In the third year of the war, Yurii's uncle, Nikolai, returned from Switzerland. Their meeting was an unforgettable event. Nikolai was bubbling over with radical, Bolshevik convictions. They spoke of the titanic events to come and Zhivago agreed, "I, too, think that Russia is destined to become the first socialist state since the beginning of the world."

* * * * *

Dr. Zhivago had resumed his duties at his old hospital in Moscow, but it was very difficult to work with no light on dark days and no fuel even to boil water. Everyone was uneasy and fighting could be heard in the distance. Soon it spread to the section where Yurii's family lived and they were all barricaded inside for several days. He could not go to the hospital and there was no milk for little Sashenka.

Meanwhile, the official proclamations declared, "Dictatorship of the Proletariat Established in Russia."

* * * * *

The severity of that winter had been foretold and yet it was not as terrible as the two that followed, 1917 and 1918. No medicines, no heat, little food. Finally, when his family was on the verge of starvation, Yurii was struck with typhus and was unable to care even for himself. In his delirium he asked for pen and paper and wrote a remarkable poem entitled "Turmoil."

When he got better, Tonia convinced him that they must leave the city and in April they went to Varykino, a former estate of her grandfather's near Yuriatin. They traveled there in a freight car which was designated as a special coach and was, indeed, comfortable accommodation for these days. At certain stations along the way, they stopped to barter something for food—a small embroidered towel for half a roasted hare was a good bargain, they thought.

* * * * *

It was a new world and a new life for them in the country. Zhivago gave up the full-time practice of medicine to return to the soil. With a small plot of ground and a two-room annex allotted by the former steward of the estate who was now in charge, the family was able to live much better than they could have in Moscow. They stayed out of politics and had little interest in which faction dominated. During the long winter evenings, beside the kerosene lamp, Yurii was happiest when he had time to read and to write. Tonia became pregnant again and Sashenka grew apace.

"I should like to be of use as a physician or a farmer and, at the same time be able to write some scientific or literary work," he confided to his wife. He became a great admirer of Pushkin and Chekov and worked on his poetry long into the night. He went frequently to the Yuriatin public library, where he once saw Lara Antipova but she left before he could speak to her.

A few weeks later he decided to stop at her flat on his way home. They saw each other often after that, and, before two months had passed, he stayed the night with her, telling his family he had been detained in Yuriatin on business.

This was the beginning of his ordeal in which he was pushed to the very edge of madness by the weight of his guilty conscience. Even as he had decided to end his struggle by confessing all to Tonia and renouncing Lara, his problem was solved for him. He was kidnapped by partisans and impressed into military service.

* * * * *

Almost two years passed while Dr. Zhivago was in the Siberian forest, fighting typhus and dysentery and ministering to the wounded. During that time all kinds of rumors ran through the camp, one time that the Whites were winning, then that the Reds were victorious. First this town and then that town was reported destroyed. Yurii heard that Varykino had been raided and was deserted, that Yuriatin had been razed.

When he could bear the uncertainty no longer, he determined to escape on the skis he had buried at the edge of the woods. After days and nights of trekking across the frozen steppes, he arrived in Yuriatin exhausted and in rags. He went to Lara's and she nursed him back to health. He learned his wife and children had been sent to Moscow unharmed and he planned to join them as soon as he could, but for the present he took a temporary post lecturing at the Medical Institute. Lara and her daughter drew closer to him and he grew to love them deeply. Pasha, who was still alive and a top administrator in the partisan government, was often in the vicinity of Yuriatin but, heavily disguised, he kept his distance not wishing to reveal his identity.

* * * * *

Two or three months went by before Zhivago began to feel that there was wide-spread hostility to some of the ideas he set forth in his lectures at the Institute. Evidently he was considered a political deviationist. Everybody was confused these days, afraid to talk and afraid to listen. He was not quite sure what anyone thought.

Quite unexpectedly, just as he was about to resign and join his family in Moscow, he received a letter from Tonia. It had been five months on the way and brought news of their exile to Paris. Knowing they were gone, he was persuaded to drop out of sight with Lara and move to Varykino. They borrowed a horse and sleigh, which they packed full of potatoes and other necessities for the long winter. But they found no peace in the country either. They still felt spied upon and at night the wolves howled ominously from the edge of the clearing.

After they had been in their rural retreat barely two weeks, Komarovsky appeared. He was to be Minister of Justice in the new Cabinet, he said, and claimed to have come to warn them of their impending arrest. According to him, Lara's husband had been killed and the authorities were looking for her. Yurii would be implicated, he pointed out, for sheltering her. He urged them to go with him to the Far Eastern Republic where he had official duties and where they could escape from Russia. Yurii refused but Lara went, for her daughter's sake, believing that Yurii would follow as he promised.

* * * * *

It remains to tell the story of the last decade of Zhivago's life in which he went to seed intellectually and developed the heart condition that finally killed him.

In the spring of 1922 Zhivago and a waif of a boy called Vasia, who had attached himself to him, arrived destitute in Moscow. Through old friends of the doctor, the boy was able to study printing and, as part of his practice, he set up some of the booklets that Zhivago had written. But he didn't always agree with the ideas they contained and, as he matured in the new society, he agreed less and less. Vasia and Yurii parted company, the older man moving in with Gromeko's former porter, who had risen in the world and had rooms to rent. The porter's daughter, Marina, became Yurii's common-law wife and bore him two daughters. One day Zhivago did not return home and there was great consternation over his disappearance.

* * * * *

Strangely enough he had not gone far but lived for awhile in the neighborhood. On the first day he was to report for duty on a new job at a hospital, he had a fatal heart attack on the trolley.

His half-brother, Evgraf, a mysterious figure, a kind of guardian angel, who seemed always to turn up unexpectedly at crucial moments of the doctor's life to help him, appeared suddenly to take charge of the funeral arrangements and sort out Zhivago's papers. Among them were many literary prose pieces and poems which were collected and published posthumously, so that finally Zhivago's wish to be a writer was fulfilled.

DON QUIXOTE

by

MIGUEL DE CERVANTES

CONDENSATION BY NATHAN HASKELL DOLE

MIGUEL DE CERVANTES SAAVEDRA, dramatist and novelist, was born in 1547, the son of a Spanish druggist and surgeon. He died in Madrid in 1616, ten days before Shakespeare's death.

As a youth Cervantes went to Italy, where he served as a private in the army. In a naval battle off Greece he was thrice wounded, his right hand being permanently maimed. While returning to Spain he was captured by pirates and taken to Algiers, where he was held as a slave for five years.

After his ransom he wrote many plays. They brought him more fame than fortune, and he added to his responsibilities by wedding, at the age of thirty-seven, a girl of nineteen. It was evidently a marriage of love, as her dowry consisted only of "five vines, an orchard, some household furniture, four beehives, forty-five hens and chickens, one cock, and a crucible." As he could not live by his pen, Cervantes secured a minor governmental position; but he was in constant difficulties because of pressing debts and his unbusiness-like habits. He was thrown into prison for debt; released, he sank into abject poverty.

Part of "Don Quixote" was probably written in jail. This novel, a magic mirror that reflects nobles and kitchen wenches, barbers and ladies of high degree, all the varied life of a brilliant period, is considered by many to be the world's greatest humorous masterpiece. The wonder of it is that it was written by a man nearing his sixtieth year, who had all his life been poor, who had known little except misfortune. "Children turn its pages, young people read it, grown men understand it, old folks praise it."

In the sixteenth century romances of chivalry, written in absurd, exaggerated style, were extremely popular in Spain.

A dignified gentleman by the name of Quixada, who lived between Aragon and Castile, went crazy over these foolish books, which he spent all his substance in buying. His brain was stuffed with enchantments, quarrels, battles, challenges, wounds, magic slaves, complaints, amours, torments, giants, castles, captured maidens, gallant rescues, and all sorts of impossible deeds of daring, which seemed to him as true as the most authentic history. Every inn-keeper was a magnate; every mule-driver a cavalier.

He decided that for his own honor and for the service of the world he must turn knight errant and jaunt through the world, redressing wrongs, rescuing captured princesses, and at last winning the imperial scepter of Trapizonda.

He changed his name to Don Quixote de la Mancha, got himself dubbed knight by a rascally publican whose inn he thought was a castle with four turrets crowned with pinnacles of glistening silver. In order to carry a full purse he sold one of his houses, mortgaged another, and borrowed a goodly sum from a friend. When his practical housekeeper and his pretty niece, together with his neighbors, the barber and the curate, thought to cure him by burning his books, he was persuaded that his library had been carried away by a necromancer, and became crazier than ever. He scoured up a rusty suit of mail which had belonged to one of his ancestors, mended the broken helmet with a pasteboard vizor, patched with thin iron plates, and thus accoutered set forth on his old hack Rocinante, whose ribs stuck out like the skeleton of a ship, accompanied by a rustic named Sancho Panza, persuaded into serving as his squire.

Their departure was a brave spectacle: the tall, cadaverous, lantern-jawed knight, mounted on his bony nag, wielding his long lance and carrying his sword, his eyes gleaming with enthusiasm and dreaming of his beautiful mistress, whom he called Dulcinea del Toboso; the short, squat, paunch-bellied, long-haunched servant with a canvas wallet and a leathern bottle, mounted on the diminutive ass, Dapple.

On the plains of Montiel stood a score of big windmills. Don Quixote took them for outrageous giants and prepared to do battle against them, and, despite Sancho's protests that their huge arms were only vanes, he plunged the rowels into Rocinante's thin flanks and with couched lance dashed off to the encounter. The wind blew violently and the knight and his steed were whirled away into the field, where they lay motionless and as if dead; his lance was smashed to flinders. Sancho hastened to the aid of his master and found him unable to stir; but he was soon ready to go on again.

Their next adventure was with two monks riding on mules as big as dromedaries, in company with a coach in which sat a lady escorted by men on horseback. Don Quixote imagined that adventurers had captured a princess and in the haughtiest terms bade them release her. Then without further parley he drove against the monks, one of whom ran away, while the other fell off his mule. Sancho nimbly slipped from his ass and began to strip the luckless man; while he was engaged in this legitimate appropriation of the spoils of battle two muleteers of the train overset him, tore out his beard by handfuls, mauled him, and left him senseless. Don Quixote engaged in a terrific combat with one of the lady's guard, who sliced off half of his helmet and one of his ears. Undaunted, the knight pressed the combat to victory, but just as he was about to give the finishing stroke, the frightened lady begged him to desist, and he complied on condition that the defeated opponent should go and present himself before the peerless Dulcinea, who was in reality a buxom woman known through all La Mancha for her skill in salting pork and who had never deigned to look at her amorous neighbor.

A few days later, bruised and battered in untoward adventures, they came upon a flock of sheep which Don Quixote conceived to be a prodigious army composed of an infinite number of nations led by mighty kings. He spurred like a thunderbolt from the top of a hillock, shouting his battle-challenge, putting the hapless sheep to flight and trampling both the living and the slain. Impatient to meet the commander of the enemy, he shouted:

"Where, where art thou, haughty Alifanfaron?"

At that moment the shepherds rallied in defense of their flocks and overwhelmed the unlucky knight, first with stones and then with cudgels, leaving him in a desperate case, with nearly all his teeth knocked out or loosened, and his ribs half broken.

Did this adventure discourage him? Not at all. It was all a part of chivalry. He and Sancho rode on in dolorous discourse. They were overtaken by night and had no shelter or food. Suddenly appeared a band of about twenty horsemen, all in white robes, with torches in their hands and followed by a hearse draped in black. It was the funeral of a gentleman of Segovia. Don Quixote took it to be the train of some knight either killed or desperately wounded, and, assured that it was his duty to avenge the misfortunes of a brother-in-arms, halted the cortège and demanded an explanation. The replies of the clergymen failed to satisfy him and he flew at them in high dudgeon. Encumbered by their long robes, they became easy victims and all took to flight.

They possessed themselves of the edibles deserted by the clergymen, but, unfortunately, had nothing to drink, nor did they dare stir from the forest because of the awful clamor made by a fulling-mill which Don Quixote supposed to be enchantment.

The next morning they met a barber riding on an ass and wearing his brass basin on his head to save his hat from the rain. Don Quixote recognized this as the golden helmet of Mambrino, and flew at his enemy as if he would grind him to powder. The barber fled, leaving his helmet, which Sancho appropriated, though it seemed to him merely a common dish.

They came to another inn. In the night Don Quixote, while sound asleep and dreaming, enjoyed the most famous battle of his career. Dressed in a short shirt which exposed his lean, long, hairy shanks, and wearing a greasy red nightcap, with a blanket wrapped around his left arm for a shield, he was repeatedly plunging his sword into the plump bodies of several giants. Their blood flowed across the floor in wide, crimson streams.

Imagine the wrath of the worthy inn-keeper at discovering that his famous guest had disemboweled all his wine-sacks, which were made of goat-skins with the heads left on.

After this Don Quixote was got home by the curate and the barber; but he broke loose again. First he visited his Dulcinea, but came away convinced that through more enchantment she had been changed into a blubber-cheeked, flat-nosed country wench, the pearls of her eyes into gall-nuts, her long golden locks into a cow's tail, and her palace into a hut.

He had adventures with strolling actors and lions; he attended the rich Camacho's wedding; he explored the deep cave of Montesinos; he rode on a magic bark and visited the nameless duke and duchess through whose complaisance Sancho was granted his ambition to rule over an island and did it with wisdom worthy of Solomon. Many more adventures followed, but at last Don Quixote returned to his home and recovered his senses on his death-bed, dying as a lovable, high-minded, noble-hearted gentleman.

Cervantes's masterpieces is not all satire. Don Quixote has lucid moments; Sancho's simplicity veils common sense, often expressed in witty proverbs. There is occasional coarseness, but not so much as in Shakespeare. The chief fault is its treatment of insanity, in its author's fondness for cruel and brutal practical jokes, which may perhaps explain the maintenance of bull-fighting as the national amusement of Spain.

THE EGOIST
by
GEORGE MEREDITH

CONDENSATION BY MARGARET GILLETT

GEORGE MEREDITH (1828–1909) was born in Ports-mouth, Hampshire, the son of a naval outfitter. When he was five, his mother died. He received his early schooling in his birthplace, but later he studied in Germany. When he returned to England, he took up law for a time in London but soon turned to journalism to eke out a meagre living by his pen. In 1849 he married the daughter of the novelist Thomas Love Peacock, a step which brought some relief to his poverty.

Meredith published his first volume of poems (1851) while he was editing a small newspaper, and a few years later his first prose, an Arabian tale, full of extravagant humor, entitled "The Shaving of Shagpat" (1855). But he was not an easy man to live with, and shortly after the publication of his first important novel, "The Ordeal of Richard Feverel" (1859), his wife left him.

Successive, for the most part unsuccessful novels appeared at two or three year intervals for the next two decades. Among these was "Vittoria, or Emilia in Italy" (1867), which drew on his experience when he went there in 1866

*as a war correspondent for the "Morning Post." From 1860
on he was a professional journalist, and for two years, until
his second marriage, he shared a house in Chelsea with
Swinburne and the Rossettis. "The Egoist," which vies with
"The Ordeal of Richard Feverel" as his best novel, was
published in 1879. An example of Meredith's most fastidious
writing, it is also a study of the Comic Spirit as he had outlined it previously in his famous lecture of 1877. His other
well-known novel, "Diana of the Crossways" (1885), developed the question of feminism, which was receiving a
good deal of public attention in England at that time.*

*Although Meredith wrote constantly, he could not rely
solely on his books for his income and he served for a long
period as a literary advisor to Chapman and Hill, publishers. In this position he was able to help Thomas Hardy
get started on his writing career.*

Comedy is a game played to throw reflections upon social life
and the humorist often alludes to the biggest book on earth, the
"Book of Egoism." Concerning pathos and pity, on the other hand,
The Egoist surely inspires them and has for his epitaph, "Through
very love of self himself he slew."

*   *   *   *   *

There was an ominously watchful anxiety over the infancy of
Willoughby Patterne, the Egoist-to-be, and the scoundrel imps, pets
of the Comic Spirit, danced round him in glee.

When he grew to young manhood, Sir Willoughby became the
impeccable cavalier of the finely turned leg. He had received the
domestic education of a prince with allegiance only to himself. Under
the fond eye of a doting mother, he cultivated himself and had a
passion to excel in sports. Women adored him and he often engaged
in exquisite repartee with them, always retaining himself eminently
and correctly poised.

Everyone of importance in the county was deeply concerned
over who would be his wife. One faction supported Constantia
Durham, wealthy, healthy, and beautiful; another favored Laetitia
Dale, pretty, witty, and a poetess, though a portionless one. For the
moment, Sir Willoughby preferred to be free to bow on the one
hand to Constantia, the stately rose, and on the other to Laetitia,

the modest violet. However, it was not long before the handsome, arrogant youth was engaged to the lovely Miss Durham. This left Laetitia, a paragon of constancy, to worship her prince from afar.

Shortly after the bethrothal was announced, Laetitia and Sir Willoughby met accidentally in the park, where he escorted her in his most gallant manner. In the course of conversation, she inquired casually about Miss Durham's health.

"Durham?" he replied. "There is no Miss Durham to my knowledge."

To this, Laetitia could merely wonder if the young man was mad, that is, until she learned the lamentable fact that Miss Durham had indeed jilted her lover only two days before and run off with another suitor. For some months following this event, a homely courtship of Laetitia ensued. Then, quite unexpectedly, Sir Willoughby left, at his mother's behest, for a tour of the world. That was another disappointing surprise for the county, since everyone had eagerly awaited the second wedding announcement.

During the next three years, the gay young lord wrote incomparable letters home about his travels in America, Japan, China, Australia, and other far-away places—elegant letters, full of placable flicks of the lionly tail addressed to Britannia the Ruler. Laetitia waited patiently for her lover's return. Had his mother objected to her? Is that why she had sent him away? She could not help asking herself these questions.

Upon his return, Sir Willoughby requested an interview with her father, and Laetitia's heart leapt with expectation. But their conversation turned out to be only about their tenant-landlord relationship and the proposal to lodge the twelve-year-old son of a poor cousin at the Dale Cottage. The coming of Crossjay Patterne, a boy with the sprights of a dozen boys in him, brought a real and sunny pleasure to Laetitia. His antics distracted her from her anxious worry over her lord's silence.

Gradually rumor spread through the country that Sir Willoughby had been seen frequently with the beautiful daughter of a scholar-clergyman, Rev. Dr. Middleton. This was during the very period when Laetitia was often at the Hall, helping to nurse Lady Patterne, who was ill. She had noticed that Sir Willoughby's manner toward her had altered to that of a dear, insignificant friend. He even went so far as to ask her to give him her opinion of a "Miss Middleton" whom he would bring to her for her appraisal. When he spoke to her

in a personal way at all it was to praise the beauties of Platonic
relationships between men and women.

"Wives are plentiful, friends are rare," he said, and Laetitia swallowed her thoughts as they welled up in her. "You are my most
valuable tenant," he went on, as he squeezed her hand.

His ailing mother also confided in Laetitia. "Promise me you will
always be good to him," she breathed; "he has such faith in you.
You are, he says, his image of the constant woman." And with a
wry smile Laetitia promised.

Miss Clara Middleton was duly introduced to the county and de-
fined by the social arbiter as "a dainty rogue in porcelain." This
displeased Sir Willoughby, unable to accommodate himself to the
"rogue" part of the portrait of his ladylove. To his mind she was
essentially feminine—in other words, a parasite to cling to him and
a chalice, from which he could draw refreshment. The lovers sometimes had words about their roles, and the husband-to-be was disturbed that his Clara preferred to be herself, a separate entity. However, in spite of her passion for independence, she finally consented
to be engaged.

In the winter of the new year, Lady Patterne died. After an appropriate interval, Sir Willoughby invited Clara and her father to
come for a visit to the Hall so that his affianced could become acquainted with his aunts, the ladies Eleanor and Isabel, who would
continue to reside there with the newlyweds. This visit was a revelation to Clara—not so much of the aunts but of her future husband.
Every word he uttered, she discovered, concerned himself, and she
felt as if she were condemned to a life of idolatry. He became for her
the very petrification of egoism, herself his helpless prey. It was
obvious he intended to possess her every thought and feeling, to
leave her nothing of herself for herself. She hated it and grew to have
only revulsion for him. She foresaw their love-season as a carnival
of egoism for him. She asked to be released from their troth, and
urged him to marry Laetitia Dale, but Sir Willoughby thought her
request only a childish humor and disregarded it. Dr. Middleton,
mellowed by his host's good wine and impressed by his wealth, of
course supported him.

Meanwhile Sir Willoughby had planned to marry off Laetitia to
his dependent cousin, Vernon Whitford, Crossjay's tutor, so that
both might remain on the estate to minister to his needs. He would
assign them a cottage and "Old Vernon" could manage the property.

In the "Book of Egoism," it is written: "Possession without obligation to the object possessed approaches felicity." And so it is with a man's possession of an adoring female's worship.

But things did not come off quite as Sir Willoughby planned. He heard the sound of the shuttle of deceit without seeing it. Although he refused to *know* that his prospective bride was trying to escape his grasp, he sensed it. After all, he had been the victim of a runaway before! Clara's calm resemblance to Constantia was ominous. His fears were at last confirmed when he learned of her abortive attempt to go to London to visit a friend. Frantically, he confided in Laetitia Dale. To soothe his wounded vanity, he proposed to her, claiming to be free. She declined. She told him she had no longer any heart to give. It had been withered by the years of neglect. But she promised to keep his declaration a secret.

It so happened that young Crossjay unintentionally overheard the entire conversation and was so upset, because of his devotion to Miss Middleton, that he asked his tutor what to do. His tale only added to the general confused gossip that Vernon knew was circulating throughout the county—gossip which had linked Clara's name with that of Colonel DeCraye, who was to have been best man at her marriage to Sir Willoughby.

By this time the prospective groom was desperate to insure himself a bride, and he made every effort to keep both ladies entangled so that he might hope to end up with at least one of them. He thought with horror of the ridicule of the county at his being jilted a third time. At last, after much maneuvering, and aided by the persuasion of her invalided father, he was able to prevail upon Laetitia to submit. At the same time he promised Clara her freedom if she would agree to marry cousin Vernon and remain on the Patterne estate. She agreed, and the conclusion seemed strangely felicitious for all concerned—with the possible exception of Sir Willoughby, who had not only lost his admirers but had acquired a cold and severely critical wife in Laetitia.

The Comic Muse looks on the outcome with compressed lips while her imps cavort in their scoundrel revelry.

FAR FROM THE
MADDING CROWD
by
THOMAS HARDY

CONDENSATION BY ALFRED S. CLARK

THOMAS HARDY was born June 2, 1840, in Dorset-shire, England. He died January 11, 1928. In his youth he read much and cherished the dream of becoming a poet, but he studied and practiced architecture as assistant to a London architect, winning a prize for design. The fine proportion and solidity of structure in his novels were probably somewhat due to his architectural training.

For five years he assiduously practiced writing poetry, but when he was twenty-seven he turned definitely to fiction. His first story was accepted two years later, but upon the advice of George Meredith he decided not to publish it. His first novel, "Desperate Remedies," appeared in 1871.

During the next twenty-five years he published fourteen novels and two volumes of short stories.

"Under the Greenwood Tree" (1872) he "never surpassed in happy and delicate perfection of art." In this and his next novel, "A Pair of Blue Eyes" (1873), begins to show itself that strain of deep irony which is so potent throughout Hardy's writings.

"Far from the Madding Crowd" (1874) was his first popular success. In it is revealed Hardy's superb power of depicting nature as symbolic background for his characters, an organic part of the action of his story. This was the earliest of what he called his novels of character and environment, which included "The Return of the Native," "Tess of the D'Urbervilles," his masterpiece, and "Jude the Obscure." Not until he was fifty-eight years old was his first volume of verse published, and he was sixty-four when

*the first part of his stupendous epic poem, "The Dynasts,"
startled the literary world.*

*Hardy has been reviled by critics and public as a pessi-
mist, determined to look upon the dark side of life. Careful
reading reveals him dispassionately true to the realities of
life. He depicts with matchless skill the struggle of human
beings against fate—the fate of an inner weakness or a cruel
and inescapable circumstance.*

*He paints these struggles with a background of nature
which is beautiful or sinister, gentle or ugly, but is always
inevitable and organic. Yet his own "solitary, brooding,
strongly colored mind" dominates men and landscape.*

*The rustics of Hardy, comparable only to Shakespeare's,
seem to grow out of the very soil of that half-imaginary
Wessex which he has made famous. Their humor and quaint
wisdom constitute a kind of Greek chorus in the Wessex
books.*

Before Bathsheba Everdene came to Weatherbury as mistress of
the manor-house time seemed to have forgotten the village. The
smock-clad shepherds in the thatch-roofed cottages might have
been, as far as appearances went, their own ancestors of four centuries before. Little happenings seemed tremendous. The pulling
down of a hovel was a stirring event; the transformation of a well
into a pump shook Weatherbury like a revolution.

The stir of the great world without, its romance and passion and
tragedy—these came to Weatherbury—with Bathsheba. There was
a new arrival to be discussed, a great-boned, ruddy-faced shepherd,
Gabriel Oak, who beat out a fire that menaced the wheat-ricks and
who remained to work for Bathsheba. Fanny Robin, a servant, disappeared, lured by a soldier's red coat. These were things to agitate
the heads of the rustics who gathered at nightfall in the old malt-
house to drink and to moralize.

Their heads would have wagged even more had they known that
Gabriel Oak, only a few weeks before, had been his own master, and
had vainly urged Bathsheba, then a penniless maiden, to marry him.
Things that had seemed commonplace enough had abruptly reversed
their places in the world. A man had died in Weatherbury; a dog
had driven to death a flock of sheep. These were but the inevitable
tragedies of life, and yet the one had suddenly made Bathsheba an

heiress; the other had driven Gabriel out upon the highways to seek work. Chance or fate had kindled a fire, Gabriel had saved the wheat, and the two lives that had been flung so far apart were brought near again.

The pain of seeing another win her whom he loved would be intense, but Gabriel preferred even this to life where he could not see her. He knew that this must happen. Bathsheba was young, beautiful, wealthy, but rarer than these was her high spirit. "She was the stuff of which great men's mothers are made. She was indispensable to high generation, hated at tea parties, feared in shops, and loved at crises." This spirit, however, was to flame more brightly later, after her impetuosity had plunged her into the crises that were to prove her worth.

In all Weatherbury, one man alone was heedless to her charm. This was William Boldwood, "the nearest approach to aristocracy that this remote quarter of the parish could boast of." She resented being ignored and, in a moment of thoughtlessness, sent him a valentine that fanned into flame passions that Boldwood had hidden from the world.

At the shearing supper held in the great barn Gabriel could see that Boldwood's suit was prospering. He was madly in love, she no longer discouraged him. Neither Bathsheba nor Boldwood was thinking then of a song she had sung earlier that evening, when "the shearers reclined against one another as at suppers in the early ages of the world." Yet afterward how often were they to recall with a shudder the words that Bathsheba had so lightly sung:

> For his bride a soldier sought her,
>   And a winning tongue had he:
> On the banks of Allan Water
>   None was gay as she.

That very night the soldier came into her life, came as she walked about the farm to see that all was secure. Her skirt was caught as she trod fearfully through a growth of high firs; she heard the mutter of a man's voice. A dark-lantern revealed a spur entangled in her skirt, a young and slender man clad in brilliant brass and scarlet. It flashed like a gleam of romance in gray days, that scarlet coat that was afterward to be remembered as so sinister a portent.

The man was Sergeant Troy, a light-hearted scoundrel whose ready flattery sounded sweeter in Bathsheba's ears than the stammering longing of Gabriel or Boldwood. He courted her romantically, wooing her with his sword. She stood, a few days later, in a hollow of ferns and about her flashed his whirling, edged weapon, slashing so close to her that she could hear its sharp hiss as it carved out in the air her lissome figure. And when he turned to leave her he stooped swiftly and kissed her on the lips.

Gabriel tried to warn Bathsheba, but she scorned his reproaches. So he bore silently with his grief and he did not tell her that Troy had beguiled little Fanny Robin away from Weatherbury. Boldwood, whose heart had never before beat faster at a woman's approach, could not so control his anger. He shouted maledictions upon the man who had robbed him of all that had made life joyous. His madness precipitated that which he most dreaded, Bathsheba's marriage to Troy.

The hasty marriage led swiftly to sorrow, inevitably to tragedy. Troy celebrated the wedding by a revel in the barn where he and all the jovial rustics were soon hopelessly befuddled. Gabriel dared not drink with them. The creeping things of the night and the huddled sheep had warned him of a nearing storm, and in the fields the high ricks of wheat and barley lay uncovered.

The moon vanished and the wind subsided; on far horizons baleful fires fluttered. The mutter of distant thunder rolled into a sharp rattle. The flashes grew bright as he worked to protect the grain. Then Bathsheba was with him, and their laboring forms were outlined in black by the green snakes of fire that darted venomously earthward. As she trembled with fright, Gabriel felt her warm arm tremble in his great, sheltering hand. She was another man's wife; she did not love him; but there was solace in the strange ways of fate that had brought her nearer to him than when her heart was free.

Tragedy came when Fanny Robin crept home to die. Her body, with that of her child, was brought back to the house where she had worked. Standing by the coffin, Bathsheba learned that Troy had never loved her as he had this girl who had borne death and shame for him. He fled from Weatherbury and word was brought to Bathsheba that he had been swept out to sea and drowned.

The seasons rolled on and sorrow gave to Bathsheba's face a seriousness that added to her charm. Boldwood dreamed again and he was made happy by a promise, although six years must pass before its fulfillment.

To celebrate his joy, he planned a Christmas Eve party, more than a year after Troy had disappeared. And it was on this night that Troy chose to reappear, striding like a specter among the merrymakers. As he advanced upon her, Bathsheba stood like a stricken thing, half convinced that delusion had enthralled her. But there was nothing ghostly in the rough command that he shouted at her nor in the brutal grip that he took upon her arm. Then only did she stir, but she could not speak. A strangled scream was heard, then a deafening roar. Some eyes were upon Troy, pitching forward and never to rise again; others upon Boldwood, standing with a smoking gun in his hands.

Not until the next August, long after it was known that Boldwood was to be imprisoned for life, was Bathsheba able to walk as far as the village street. Fate had been hard to her. Of three men who loved her, one had been killed by another who would never stride in the daylight again. And now word had come to her that Gabriel—honest, sturdy Gabriel—whom she had found the one man in the world who did not fail her in her need, was leaving her. She sought him in his humble cottage and he confessed that he was going because people were coupling his name with hers. "Such a thing as that is too absurd—too soon—to think of, by far!" she cried. When he agreed with her that it was "too absurd," she insisted that she had not said that, but "too soon." Even then minutes clicked away before Gabriel could realize that what he had so long sought was to be his.

Their lives, in calm and storm, had been so close that, after the wedding, the rustics marveled at his easy way of speaking of my "wife." They agreed that he did not say the words as chillingly as might a man who had been married twenty years, but that that improvement would come later. Gabriel laughed aloud at that and Bathsheba smiled, for Bathsheba did not now laugh so readily as had been her wont when first she came among the simple folk of changeless Weatherbury.

FATHERS AND SONS
by
IVAN S. TURGENEV

TRANSLATED FROM THE RUSSIAN BY CONSTANCE GARNETT
CONDENSATION BY MARGARET GILLETT

IVAN TURGENEV (1818–1883), the first Russian writer to be widely read and admired in Europe, came from a family of provincial gentry. He studied at the universities of Moscow, St. Petersburg, and Berlin. In Berlin, where he published his first verses in 1838, he met radical political thinkers and became an enthusiast for European culture. In 1841 he returned to Russia and entered civil service for two years before he began to devote himself entirely to literature. Four years later he broke with his mother—their relations had been strained because of her tyrannical treatment of the serfs and his sympathy for them—and in 1850, when he inherited the family estate after her death, he freed them all.

Turgenev's first important work, "Memoirs of a Sportsman" (1852), sketches describing the human worth of the peasantry, appeared in the same year that he was exiled to his estate, for a time, as a result of his too liberal utterances on the question of landlordism. In addition to sketches, short stories, poems, and plays, Turgenev wrote several novels upon which his principal claim to fame rests. Among these, "Fathers and Sons" (1862), is probably the best-known today. He has been called the most Victorian of Russian novelists, and his influence has been noted on later writers as different as Henry James and Hemingway.

The author of "Fathers and Sons" spent most of his later life in Paris in a bitter mood, critical of his own people and his country. Part of his disaffection may have been the result of his frustrating infatuation with a singer, Mme.

*Viardot, a relationship which seems always to have remained
platonic. He revisited Russia in 1880, when he was over sixty
years old, but returned to France to die.*

It was May, 1859, and Nikolai Petrovitch Kirsanov eagerly
awaited his son's return from the university in Petersburg where he
had just been graduated. As the father stood, grey-haired and
rather bent, impatiently listening for the approach of the carriage,
he thought sadly of his wife who had died twelve years before.
"She did not live to see it!" he murmured to himself.

Arkady finally arrived, smiling boyishly to see his father, whom
he embraced warmly. He had brought his friend, Bazarov, a
premedical student, with him and his father welcomed the sombre
young man heartily. After the luggage was arranged and the passengers settled, the trio set out for home, a distance of about
twelve miles from the station.

When they had driven a while and exchanged the news since
their last letters, Nikolai remarked somewhat diffidently, "We shall
get on together splendidly, Arkasha; you shall help me in farming
the estate, if it isn't a bore to you."

"Of course," said Arkady as he took a deep breath of the sweet
country air, "but what an exquisite day it is today!"

A quarter of an hour later they drew up before the steps of a new
wooden house, painted gray, with a red iron roof. This was Maryino
or, as the peasants called it, Poverty Farm. In the drawing room they
were greeted by Arkady's uncle, Pavel, a man of medium height
and middle age, with a very elegant, cosmopolitan manner. He
shook hands with Arkady and kissed him, but he did not extend
his hand to Bazarov when they were introduced, obviously not
wishing to touch such an unkempt fellow.

Immediately after supper the four separated and the two young
men retired early, exhausted after their hard journey. The next
morning, while Bazarov was out looking for frogs for his natural
science study, father and son met on the terrace where the samovar
was already boiling. Nikolai was in some confusion. He had not yet
told his son about his new baby brother, although, of course, Arkady
knew that the girl, Fenitchka, was not installed in the main house.
When she did not join them at morning tea, Arkady went to look
for her and soon returned with the announcement: "We have made

friends, Dad!" And, as he flung himself on his father's neck, added, "But why didn't you tell me I had a brother? I should have kissed him last night, as I have kissed him just now." At that moment she appeared, a young woman with a white, soft skin and red, childishly pouting lips. She brought a large cup of cocoa for Pavel, said "Good morning" in a resonant voice, and moved gently away.

Pavel joined them first and, shortly after, Bazarov returned from his frog-hunting expedition and began rudely drinking tea in silence. Arkady's father spoke at last and the conversation gradually broadened out to a critical appraisal of Russian and German science. Bazarov favored the German and Pavel took exception to the young man's lack of patriotism and general nihilistic attitude, which he considered impudent and downright irreverent. Bazarov, on the other hand, did not conceal his contempt for the "provincial aristocrats" who were just old fogies from another era. Arkady tried to defend his uncle, accusing his friend of being too hard on the older generation, and later, in an effort to explain Pavel's outlook, he told his uncle's story—how he had abandoned a brilliant military career for love of Princess R—, whose death had brought an end to his hopeless passion, leaving him so distraught that he withdrew from society to live at Maryino with his recently widowed brother. But Bazarov was not particularly impressed with this tale, which seemed to him a bit ridiculous. The two gray-haired men struck him as absurd, self-indulgent romantics.

An uncomfortable and strained fortnight passed at Maryino. Bazarov seemed to ignore the social amenities of the main house but found great popularity with the servants who thought the visiting "doctor" was wonderful. With his ministration to her baby, he even won Fenitchka's confidence. But Arkady's uncle and father both considered him a baleful influence on their boy. They feared Bazarov would persuade him to renounce poetry and art—everything civilized in fact—for science and its earthiness. Angry arguments ensued in which youth confronted age. "I've told you already, uncle, that we don't accept any authority," put in Arkady. To which Bazarov added: "At the present time, negation is the most beneficial of all—and we deny—"

"Everything?" Pavel inquired.

"Everything!" Bazarov repeated with indescribable composure.

The tension was relieved when the two young men decided to

make a holiday jaunt to X—, a town where Arkady had an illustrious relative, a visiting official from the capital, whose presence there would insure them a gay time.

At a ball given in his honor by the governor, the official introduced them to Mme. Odintsov, a ravishing beauty and a widow with a sizable fortune. Even the imperturbable Bazarov was captivated. They were thrilled when Anna Odintsov invited them to visit her at her country place near X—, where she was evidently quite bored living with her sister and an elderly aunt. When the guests arrived, they were introduced to both sister Katya, a girl of eighteen, black-haired and dark-skinned with a round, pleasing face, and Mme.'s aunt, Princess H—, a thin little woman with a pinched expression and a cap covered with yellow ribbons. Fifi, a large, graceful greyhound, with a blue collar, completed the company.

Anna Sergyevna Odintsov was a curious creature. As Bazarov described her, she was "a female with brains." She led a completely ordered existence and, during the two weeks of their stay, the young men were required to adhere strictly to her daily schedule. Little by little Bazarov realized he was falling in love with Anna, a condition quite unbelievable for him who prided himself on being beyond such human frailty. Arkady, left with Katya, was at first depressed to find himself cut off from both his hostess and his friend. He felt, too, that his relationship with Bazarov was changing in a baffling way that dismayed him.

Finally Bazarov could stand it no longer. He confessed his passion to Mme. Odintsov, who was alarmed by his ardor and had no mind to sacrifice any of her independence. She made no effort to detain him when he said he must leave at once to visit his parents, whom he had not seen for three years. Arkady, still his avowed disciple, went with him and the pair spent two restless days with the old folk before abandoning them to return impulsively to Anna's. She received them so coolly that they were embarrassed, made excuses, and went on to Maryino the same day.

Nikolai was delighted to have his son back, but Uncle Pavel bristled more than ever at Bazarov's modern thinking and, when he saw the upstart kiss Fenitchka one day in the garden, he demanded a duel with pistols. Bazarov could not decline the older man's challenge even though he considered dueling foolish, quaint, and even dangerous. But the result of the early dawn meeting was, fortunately, not fatal. Pavel received a wound in the leg and his adversary made an abrupt departure from Maryino.

A few days before the duel, when he thought his friend was absorbed in his nature study, Arkady, who had developed a tender regard for Katya, had made a clandestine visit to her. He was very much surprised, then, when Bazarov turned up suddenly at Anna's and told of his feudal encounter with Pavel. But Arkady was so involved in his own affair that he gave only passing notice to his friend's report. Katya filled his mind and heart. He was stunned when she accepted his proposal but received little sympathy from Bazarov who had made no progress with Anna. In a cloud of misunderstanding the truculent scientist took his leave of the lovers and what he considered his own hopeless predicament.

Bazarov's parents were overjoyed at his unexpected return but hardly dared speak to him in his melancholy state. Time grew heavy on his hands and, in order to distract himself from his despair, he began to assist his father in his medical care for the peasants. In his depressed frame of mind he carelessly cut his finger while performing an autopsy and died several days later from the infection.

Six months passed by and winter arrived. A double wedding took place at Maryino. Arkady was married to his Katya at the same time that his father's alliance with Fenitchka was regularized. After the ceremony, Uncle Pavel, dapper as ever, went abroad for his health. As the story draws rapidly to a close, Anna, who finally visited Bazarov on his death bed, has recently married a very clever lawyer, cold as ice. The Kirsanovs, father and son, live at Maryino and manage the property in partnership, planning together for their children. Bazarov is buried in a little cemetery near his home and his old parents visit his grave as often as their aging legs permit. Although they never understood their son, they know that no matter how passionate, sinning, and rebellious the heart hidden in the tomb, the flowers growing over it tell of eternal reconciliation and of life without end.

FILE NO. 113
by

ÉMILE GABORIAU

CONDENSATION BY ISABEL ANDERSON

*ÉMILE GABORIAU was born in Saujon, Charente In-
férieure, November 9, 1835. He died in Paris, September 28,
1873.*

*Gaboriau is an admirable example of a man who arrived
by finding out for himself what his real job was. Lawyer's
clerk, volunteer in a cavalry regiment, he was writing with
modest success pieces from life as it came before his eyes,
when, bang! he wrote "L'Affaire Lerouge" in 1866. He suddenly became a European, indeed an international, character
as the great master of the detective story. As has been the
case with Sherlock Holmes, readers were not content with
the printed page, but demanded to see upon the stage
the personages who had excited their wild enthusiasm in a
career of crime. "Le Dossier No. 113," "Monsieur Lecoq,"
"La Corde au Cou," "La Dégringolade," "Le Crime
d'Orcival," "Les Esclaves de Paris," "L'Argent des Autres,"
are some of the books which have revealed the mysteries of
crime, the procedure of the police courts, the pursuit by
ingenious sleuths, and all such processes as give a thrill of
delight to that very great body of humanity ranging from
grave to gay who take pleasure in a good detective story.*

"An exceptionally daring robbery—prominent bank entered—
huge sum taken!" were the head-lines in a Paris paper.

In following up this extraordinary case the mystery deepened,
unheard-of crimes were unearthed, and thrilling situations occurred
which baffled even the celebrated detective, Lecoq. It appeared that
upon opening the safe one morning the cashier startled the clerks by
crying out, "I have been robbed!" They gathered about, but,
strangely enough, upon inspection the safe showed only a scratch,

but no sign of having been broken open, although the 350,000 francs were missing that the cashier said he had placed there the day before, in order to pay Count Louis de Clameran, a friend who had been left a legacy by his brother Gaston. M. Fauvel, the president of the bank, and M. Prosper Bertomy, the cashier, were the only persons who possessed keys to the door and were credited with the knowledge of a word which made up the combination. Although their relations had been like those of father and son, each now accused the other of taking the money.

The clerks were interviewed by the police, and search was made of the apartment over the bank, occupied by the president, his wife, and beautiful niece, Madeleine, whose engagement to the cashier had been mysteriously broken off—it was suspected she preferred Mme. Valentine Fauvel's handsome nephew, Raoul Lagors. The president's record was good, but suspicion was directed toward the cashier, as he had been living extravagantly. His arrest followed, although he protested his innocence. During the inspection of the bank and the apprehending of the cashier he was seen to scribble a line hurriedly and throw it to a clerk. The latter was shadowed to the cashier's apartment and the note procured. It was addressed to Mme. Gypsy, informing her of his arrest and advising her to hide. During the examination at court Prosper remembered that he had been indiscreet the previous night in saying to Gypsy, when perhaps he might have been overheard by the count and Raoul, that he had reason for constantly thinking of her at his work when she accused him of not thinking of her any longer. The word Gypsy opened the safe. For lack of sufficient evidence Prosper was released and the case filed in No. 113.

On Prosper's return to his apartment, Gypsy had gone, but a note addressed in small printed letters was delivered to him, containing money. The clever Lecoq, now living with Prosper, under the guise of an old friend of his father's, revealed that the printed letters had been cut from a prayer-book. Surely there was a woman in the case! Later a torn prayer-book was discovered hidden in Madeleine's room. Did she love Prosper and think him innocent and in need of money? Yet soon after that, to the surprise of every one, her engagement was announced to the old Count de Clameran. The reason for this was that Madeleine, by chance, overheard a conversation between the count and her aunt. The old count threatened to tell of the family skeleton if she did not consent to the marriage.

Madeleine appeared and said she would marry him to keep the secret and the honor of the family name. On learning of Madeleine's engagement, Prosper, who really had always loved her, became very angry, and, thinking there must be a sinister motive for Mme. Fauvel's allowing it, wrote an anonymous letter to M. Fauvel, telling him to watch his wife.

Lecoq noticed that the good-looking Raoul still continued his frequent visits to the house. Did it mean that he was perhaps not the nephew, but the lover of Mme. Fauvel? Disguised, the great detective attended a masquerade ball and made insinuating remarks to Mme. Fauvel concerning Raoul which caused her to faint, and when he spoke of money matters, Count Louis turned pale. Returning home that night, the detective was followed by two men and stabbed, but, fortunately, not killed. Lecoq, thinking he recognized the count and Raoul, decided that they realized the police suspected them of robbing the bank, and also that there must be an even greater mystery to unravel that had caused them to become would-be assassins. Records were looked up and an amazing story came to light.

Lecoq discovered that years ago, Mme. Fauvel, then Valentine de Verberie, had been engaged to the count's brother, Gaston. In defending her name at a country inn, Gaston had killed a man and fled to America, although he was thought to have been drowned while escaping. A son was born to Valentine and given away by her mother. Later she had married Fauvel, who was told nothing.

The story was never unearthed until Count Louis had squandered the family money and by mere chance had heard of the child's existence from an old nurse. He made inquiries. Not long after this the count introduced a young man to Mme. Fauvel as her son, to serve his own ends and to extract hush-money. This young man was called her nephew and proved to be Raoul Lagors.

The situation became even more complicated. Gaston returned from America immensely rich, not knowing of the existence of her son, but determined to see his old love Valentine once more. Louis, however, realized that for his own ends Gaston and Mme. Fauvel must never meet. He joined Gaston in the south of France and got into his good graces. Gaston made a will leaving everything to Louis; then poor Gaston became mysteriously ill and died. Louis returned to Paris rich.

Madeleine seemed to wish to delay her marriage. The count feared she still loved Prosper, so he promised Raoul a large sum if he would in some way ruin the cashier's reputation, thinking thus to hasten his own marriage, as he really was in love with Madeleine. The moment came when Raoul overheard Prosper telling Gypsy he constantly thought of her at the bank. He then went to his mother and said he would shoot himself if he did not have a large sum of money that very night to pay a gambling debt. She got for him the key to the safe. The poor lady had already given him all her money and jewels and had nothing left to bestow. At the last moment she tried to stop him, hence the scratch that was discovered later. When she inquired how he knew the word that made up the combination, Raoul said that Prosper had given it to him and they were to divide the money between themselves.

Owing to the anonymous letter, M. Fauvel intercepted his wife's mail, and one day found a letter from Raoul asking her to go to his villa. M. Fauvel followed, and, on entering and seeing his wife in the arms of the young man, pulled out his pistol to shoot, but fortunately it did not go off, as Gypsy, who had become Madeleine's maid, under Lecoq's instructions, in order to watch the house, had taken out the bullets. At this point the great detective appeared and told the banker the whole story. He then demanded the 350,000 francs which had been stolen and Raoul returned the money; and what was more remarkable still, Lecoq showed them papers that proved Raoul was not Mme. Fauvel's son, after all—her son had died—and the imposter was the son of a jockey hired by the count to play the part so as to secure money from Mme. Fauvel at the time when the count was poor, before Gaston had died.

During the conversation Raoul had made his escape, but no one cared, for the Fauvels naturally wished to keep the story secret, and it ended happily, for M. Fauvel forgave his wife her early indiscretions. Lecoq was just about to arrest the count for his many crimes when the wicked old man went insane and kept repeating constantly that his brother Gaston was poisoning him. Strange to relate, the great Lecoq married pretty Mme. Gypsy, whom he had known and loved for years. Prosper, of course, married Madeleine, and M. Fauvel retired from the bank. The firm is now called Prosper Bertomy and Company. This amazing record of crime still remains in the police court in Paris and can be found in File No. 113.

THE FOUR HORSEMEN
OF THE APOCALYPSE*

by

VICENTE BLASCO IBÁÑEZ

CONDENSATION BY ALICE G. HIGGINS

VICENTE BLASCO IBÁÑEZ was born in Valencia, Spain, in January, 1867, the son of a dry-goods shop proprietor. He died at Mentone, France, on January 28, 1928. He attended the University of Valencia and received a degree in law. He was against the established order from his college days. As a result he received the first of a series of imprisonments when he was eighteen—for a sonnet against the government. He passed periods of exile at Paris and in Italy, alternating with stays in prison. One of his protests was against the measures pursued by the government in suppressing the Cuban insurrection. He founded a republican newspaper, of which he was editor, reporter, and reviewer. He established a publishing-house to introduce to Spain the great works of European literature at popular prices; this was but one of the attempts he made, sometimes at the risk of his life, to bring his country into the current of modern thought. He was elected to the Cortes, and became the leader of his party.

In his novels he began in the usual Spanish way with pictures of local provincial life with the types and the pictures of which he was familiar. But he dealt not merely with pictures; his stories all have an object in which their strenuous author is greatly interested. He lacked restraint, his passion for independence was without bounds, he carried his admiration for the realism of Zola to limits which shock our more restrained habit of mind, but despite the opposi-

* Printed by permission of, and arrangement with, E. P. Dutton & Co., New York, authorized publishers. Copyrighted, 1918.

tion which he encountered at home and abroad, the author
of "The Four Horsemen of the Apocalypse" was one of the
most widely read of contemporary writers.

In 1870 Marcelo Desnoyers was a lonely lad of nineteen years, living in Marseilles. A popular manifestation in favor of peace, at the first news of war with Prussia, influenced him to leave the country and he made an unforgettable trip to South America, where, after many failures and a laborious existence, he became an employee of Madariaga, the centaur.

Don Madariaga's fortune was enormous. He had gained his first money as a fearless trader, and with his earnings had bought vast tracts of land, devoting them to the raising of cattle. Though he had a capricious and despotic character, he nevertheless felt a certain fondness for his new French overseer. One morning Desnoyers saved his life.

"Thanks, Frenchy," said the ranchman, much touched. "You are an all-round man and I am going to reward you. From this day I shall speak to you as I do to my family."

Desnoyers soon married Luisa, Madariaga's elder daughter, while a young German, Karl Hartrott, a recent arrival at the ranch, married Elena, her younger sister. Seated under the awning on summer nights, the ranchman surveyed his family around him with a sort of patriarchal ecstasy.

"Just think of it, Frenchy," he said, "I am Spanish; you, French; Karl, German; my daughters, Argentinians; the cook, Russian; his assistant, Greek; the stable boy, English; the kitchen servants, natives, Galicians, or Italians; and among the peons are many castes and laws. . . . And yet all live in peace. In Europe, we would have probably been in a grand fight by this time, but here we are all friends."

Julio, the son of Desnoyers, was the favorite grandchild of Madariaga. "Ah, the fine cowboy! What a pretty fellow you are!" he would say. "Have a good time, for grandpa is always here with his money."

One evening the Patron's horse came slowly home without its rider. The old man had fallen on the highway, and when they found him, he was dead.

The Hartrotts moved to Berlin at once and the Desnoyers went to Paris, each household in possession of an enormous fortune. Besides establishing his family in an ostentatious house in Paris, Desnoyers bought a castle, Villeblanche-sur-Marne, a mixture of palace and fortress, where he could put his rapidly accumulating purchases of paintings, furniture, statues—all those things which he carried away from the auctions which it had now become his habit to frequent.

The only disappointment in Desnoyers's new life came from his children—his daughter Chichi because of her independence, and Julio because of his aimless existence. Julio has had to make a trip to South America in order to realize on a bequest from his grandfather, so that he might marry the fascinating and frivolous Marquerite Laurier, with whom he had become infatuated.

Suddenly the cloud of war cast its shadow over this family. The self-sufficient Dr. Julius von Hartrott said to his cousin, "War will be declared to-morrow or the day after. Nothing can prevent it now. It is necessary for the welfare of humanity."

On the eve of mobilization Tchernoff, a friend of Julio's, had a vision in which he saw the Apocalyptic Beast rising out of the sea. Four terrible horsemen preceded the appearance of the monster, and these scourges of the earth, Conquest, War, Famine, and Death, were beginning their mad, desolating course over the heads of terrified humanity.

Julio, being an Argentinian, was exempt from military service and had hoped to continue his life as though nothing were happening. His inamorata, however, from a woman infatuated with dress was gradually transformed by her desire to serve. The war had made her ponder much on the values of life, and her sense of duty to the husband whom she so greatly wronged sent her back to his side when she heard that he had been severely wounded. To Julio she said, "You must leave me. . . . Life is not what we have thought it. Had it not been for the war we might, perhaps, have realized our dream, but now! . . . For the remainder of my life, I shall carry the heaviest burden, and yet at the same time it will be sweet, since the more it weighs me down the greater will my atonement be."

The vanquished lover said good-by to Love and Happiness, but this repulse gave him a new impetus to fill the vacuum of his empty existence.

When Paris was threatened and refugees told of the wholesale sackings of their homes, Don Marcelo began to fear for his castle, and went to Villeblanche, arriving in time to witness the discouraged exhaustion of the French army's retreat. Closely following were the invading Germans shouting joyously, "Nach Paris!"

Villeblanche became the camping-ground for a regiment and its bewildered proprietor was subjected to innumerable indignities, saw his most choice possessions looted, and was the powerless witness to the murder of prominent civilians of the village. A young officer arrived who introduced himself as Captain Otto von Hartrott. He explained with true German callousness the ruin and plunder of his uncle's castle by saying to him, "It is war. . . . We have to be very ruthless that it may not last long. True kindness consists in being cruel, because then the terror-stricken enemy gives in sooner, and so the world suffers less."

For four days Don Marcelo lived through a period of stupefaction slashed by the most horrible visions. The village was reduced to a mass of ruins before his eyes, and his household suffered unspeakably from the bestiality of the carousing officers. A war hospital was established on the estate, but moved on under the stress of battle, though the banner of the Red Cross remained to deceive the French about the artillery which was installed in the park. When a French aeroplane discovered this piece of treachery, Don Marcelo found himself in the heart of a furious battle. The cannonading of the Germans and the bursting of French shells terrified him until at last he saw at the foot of the highway near his castle several of the attacking columns which had crossed the Marne. They rushed forward unmoved by the deadly fire of the Germans, and he realized his beloved French were driving back the Teuton horde.

Only ruins of his once beautiful estate were now left him and he said farewell forever to Villeblanche. After his return to Paris a young soldier of the infantry called to see him. It was his son Julio, never so distinguished-looking as in this rough, ready-made uniform. Their reconciliation was complete.

With his son on the battle-field Don Marcelo lived through months of anxious suspense. Through the influence of a friend he was able to go to see the young hero. It was a tortuous journey through the zigzags and curves of the trenches, while bullets buzzed like horseflies through the air, and on through dark galleries and subterranean fortifications until he reached the outer intrenchment line.

Desnoyers hardly recognized his son on account of his changed appearance, but in spite of his hard life Julio had found content in comradeships such as he had never known. For the first time in his life he was tasting the delight of knowing that he was a useful being. As his father left him, hope sang in his ears: "No one will kill him. My heart, which never deceives me, tells me so."

Julio became a sergeant, then a sub-lieutenant, and for his exceptional bravery received the Croix de Guerre, the military medal, and finally was among those proposed for the Légion d'Honneur. One afternoon during the Champagne offensive, Desnoyers, still cherishing the fond illusions of hope, returned to his home in gay spirits to find the dreadful news awaiting him. Julio, his son, lay dead on the field of honor.

When he went to the burial-fields to find his son's last resting-place he recalled Tchernoff, the dreamer, and the four terrible horsemen riding ruthlessly over his fellow-creatures whom he saw in his vision, and the prophecy which he then made:

"No, the Beast does not die. It is the eternal companion of man. It hides, spouting the blood forty . . . sixty . . . a hundred years, but eventually it reappears. All that we can hope is that its wounds may be long and deep, that it may remain hidden so long that the generation that now remembers it may never see it again."

GIL BLAS

by

ALAIN RENÉ LE SAGE

CONDENSATION BY NATHAN HASKELL DOLE

ALAIN RENÉ LE SAGE, author of one of the world's most remarkable books, was born December 13, 1668, in a small town of western France. He died, nearly eighty years later, in 1747.

Unlike many men of genius, Le Sage did not go through life doing spectacular things. His father, who held some responsible legal positions, left a considerable fortune when Le Sage became an orphan as a child. His guardians either

*stole or invested with criminal carelessness the lad's money,
but he was given a good education and was admitted to the
bar. Fees came in slowly and Le Sage faced extreme poverty.
Yet he dared to marry and turned to the stage for means
of support.*

*For years he wrote, never really successful, but never
actually in want. He was nearly forty years of age when a
comedy gave him a Parisian reputation, and a novel made
him known to France. The first two parts of "Gil Blas" were
published in 1715, but they were not liked so well as his
earlier story. Le Sage, however, knew how good it was, and
he labored over it as devotedly as a great sculptor over a
block of marble. The third part was not published until
1724, and not until 1735 was the last part put forth. During
these twenty years he had also turned out play after play,
and numerous books. He did not cease to write until after
his seventieth birthday had passed.*

*Outside of France Le Sage will always live because of his
one book that ranks among the world's masterpieces. "Gil
Blas" is life itself, an animated picture of Spain in its most
colorful period. "It is a work," says Sir Walter Scott,
"which renders the reader pleased with himself and mankind, where faults are placed before him in the light of follies
rather than vices, and where misfortunes are so interwoven
with the ludicrous that we laugh in the very act of sympa-
thizing with them."*

Gil Blas, the only son of an old soldier, had reached the age of
seventeen when his uncle, the village priest, who had taught him
a little Latin, Greek, and logic, sent him off with forty ducats and
a bad mule to study divinity at Salamanca.

His adventures began immediately. At his first stop he was
cheated out of his mule; as he was eating his dinner a wily flatterer
invited him to be his guest and showed his gratitude by the good
advice never to be taken in by praise. He had to pay an exorbitant
reckoning and went on his way, "giving to as many devils as there
are saints in the calendar, the parasite, the landlord, and the inn."

He soon fell into the hands of bandits, who made him join them
on their raids. In one of them they captured Doña Mencia, wife
of the Marques de la Guardia, and brought her to their cavern.

Gil Blas pretended to be ill and escaped with the grateful lady. He was arrested as one of the bandits, and as he was wearing clothes recognized by one of their victims, and his pockets were full of money, he was thrown into jail. After several weeks' imprisonment his innocence was established, but the jailer had robbed him of everything.

At Burgos he sought out Doña Mencia, who presented him with a hundred ducats and a costly ring.

He bought a pretentious outfit for twice its value and decided that instead of becoming a licentiate, "he would make his way in this world rather than think of the next." A second gift of a thousand ducats from Doña Mencia confirmed him in his resolve.

He bought two mules and, hiring a servant, set forth for Madrid. His servant conspired with several rogues to make a fool of him. One of them, Camilla, pretending to be related to Doña Mencia, invited him to hired lodgings as if to her own home, and there he was feasted and flattered. As a mark of special favor she exchanged her ruby ring, which she declared was worth three hundred pistoles, for his, and procured him an invitation to a great country-seat for hunting and fishing.

But when he arose in the morning his servant, his two mules, his portmanteau, and Doña Mencia's pretended relatives had vanished. The ruby ring was a cheat.

Fortunately he fell in with a boyhood friend, Fabricio, at Valladolid and by his advice became a servant to a clergyman, the Canon Sedillo, at whose house he led an easy life. The canon soon died, leaving him his worthless library and the good fortune of becoming assistant to his physician, the famous Doctor Sangrado. Under him Gil Blas became particularly proficient in his method of practice, which consisted of nothing but blood-letting and "drenchings of water." He declared that he made as many widows and orphans as the siege of Troy; one of his victims was the betrothed of a giant Biscayan, who threatened him with dire vengeance, and he fled to Madrid, where he became valet to a mysterious and wealthy Don Bernardo, his only duty being to keep the wardrobe brushed and to tend door. But he happened to fall in with Rolando, captain of the brigands; and Don Bernardo, seeing him in such suspicious company, dismissed him with six ducats.

From one reason or another he kept changing employers; he served now a dissipated hidalgo, then an intriguing actress, then an aged libertine whose daughter, in gratitude for aiding her to win back her recreant lover, Don Luis Pacheco, gave him a hundred pistoles, and, on her father's death, got him a place with still another aged roué, Don Gonzales, whose dressing operations, when he arose at noon, reminded him of the resurrection of Lazarus.

Here again he acted as intermediary in a love-affair, but when he told his infatuated employer that he was being duped he was turned off, though given a recommendation to the Marquesa de Chaves, reputed the cleverest woman in Madrid, because she was as solemn as an owl and rarely spoke. Her salon, called "The Fashionable Institution for Literature, Taste, and Science," was the resort for wits and notables of Madrid.

Here again he had easy work, but, getting into trouble about a girl, was compelled to leave the city. On his way to Toledo he rescued a young nobleman, named Don Alfonso, from arrest. They became friends, and after Don Alfonso reached his home he and his father became Gil Blas's patrons, placing him as secretary to their relative, the Archbishop of Granada, who was inordinately vain and as broad as he was long.

Gil Blas praised his sermons and was regarded as a young man of excellent judgment until after the prelate's mind was affected by apoplexy and his homilies became discordant ravings. Gil Blas obeyed the archbishop's command to tell him if he fell short in his preaching and was ignominiously packed off. Reduced to extremities once more, he posed as the brother to a disreputable actress and thus secured the position of secretary to a Portuguese grandee, the Marquis de Marialva. The trick was discovered. He returned to Madrid, and after many amusing and not always creditable adventures was appointed under-secretary to the Duke of Lerma, prime minister to the king. His duties may be gaged by his comment, "One makes a merit of any dirty work in the service of the great."

His experiences with the upper and the lower world, with actors, poets, libertines, physicians, bandits, adventurers, and hidalgos and their servants, had sharpened his wits, and his native ability and smattering of education gave him growing influence. He was courted, flattered, and bribed; his conceit and avarice became colossal.

He declared that "a court had all the soporific virtues of Lethe in the case of poor relations" and confessed that "every trace of his former gay and generous temper had disappeared."

Pride came before a fall. Having been employed to procure

a questionable mistress for the heir-apparent, he was arrested by the king's orders and thrown into the dungeon of Segovia. The prince intervened, but he was exiled from the two Castiles. All his property was seized and his mercenary engagement to a wealthy jeweler's daughter was broken.

Then his friend Don Alfonso, whom he had got appointed as governor of Valencia, presented him with a small estate near that city.

On his way thither he stopped at his birthplace and found his uncle a mental wreck and his mother worn out in caring for his dying father. He gave his father a pompous funeral, and settled an annuity on his mother, but the townspeople were so indignant with him for his neglect of his family that they threatened to mob him.

Glad to escape with his life, he reached Valencia, where he was received at his new home by seven or eight servants provided by Don Alfonso. He got rid of most of them and lived frugally, marrying Antonia, daughter of his farmer, Don Basilio. But his idyllic happiness ended with the death of his wife in childbirth.

Soon afterward the crown prince came to the throne and offered him a place of high responsibility. Gil Blas, who had learned wisdom, replied that "all he wanted was a good situation where there was no inducement to violate his conscience, and where the favors of his prince were not likely to be bartered for filthy lucre."

He was made confidant to the prime minister, who intrusted him with the education of his illegitimate son and heir. This brought him a title.

After some years when the duke lost the king's favor, Gil Blas followed him into retirement, and on his death was remembered with a bequest of ten thousand pistoles. He returned to his beautiful estate, made a second marriage, and lived, happy and respected, training his children wisely and confiding to his memoirs all his errors, crimes, joys, and sorrows, together with his opinions of literature, society, and the stage. His narrative is interspersed with long and fascinating stories related by various characters whom he had met; these and his own adventures furnish a vivid picture of the romantic Spain of the seventeenth century.

Gil Blas is one of the wisest and most amusing of romances, and though it is not free from the coarseness permitted at that time, vice is not depicted attractively and its teaching is generally moral.

GULLIVER'S TRAVELS

by

DEAN SWIFT

CONDENSATION BY JAMES B. CONNOLLY

JONATHAN SWIFT, the great Dean of St. Patrick's, who ranks among the mighty satirists of all ages and all lands, was born in Hoey's Court, Dublin, November 30, 1667. He died October 19, 1745.

This most brilliant wit, genius, hater of rascality, master of irony and invective, and true Irish patriot, was born to poverty and dependence; he started life embittered and he ended "dying of rage like a poisoned rat in a hole," to use his own expression. His life was a failure, though he played a mighty part. "Good God! what a genius I had when I wrote that book!" he said when he later reread the "Tale of a Tub," and the world has agreed with him. Yet failure ever tracked him. He never received the preferment in the Church which his ability would have brought another; by his political pamphlets he largely formed the public opinion of his time, yet that was the end of it for him; he had the strongest attachments for two women, Stella, to whom the famous "Journal" was written, and Vanessa, but little happiness came to him. "To think of him," said Thackeray, "is like thinking of the ruins of a great empire."

"Gulliver's Travels" (1726), though a satire on courts and statesmen, has survived its temporary and local purpose, and, especially in the first two parts, is considered to be one of the great possessions of literature.

I was of a Nottinghamshire family and educated at Cambridge. Likewise was I educated in medicine, and, preferring a ship's surgeoncy to any preferment ashore, it came about that after several deep-sea voyages I found myself surgeon of that ship, the *Antelope,* which was wrecked in a violent storm on a coast northwest of Van Diemen's Land.

Of all the ship's company I alone escaped to the land, where, in utter exhaustion, I lay down and fell asleep. I awakened to find myself bound hand and foot and surrounded by swarms of the tiniest human creatures. They brought me food and drink and conveyed me to their capital, where the king, of a majesty a full half-inch taller than any of his subjects, came with his court to view me.

In time I learned that I was in the kingdom of the Lilliputians. By them I was kept a long time in captivity. Being ultimately satisfied of the harmlessness of my intent, I also adding my word of honor to do them no injury, they released me, and set aside six professors of education to teach me their language. For my bodily sustenance they allowed me a quantity of meat and drink sufficient for 1724 of their own people; for so, being exact in their mathematics, they estimated the proportions of my bulk to theirs. Three hundred cooks and 120 waiters were named to dress my meals, 200 seamstresses were apportioned to make my linen, and 300 tailors for my outer clothing.

With my wants thus attended to, I was desirous to be of service to them. My first service was not to damage their people or their property as I walked abroad, a most likely danger when the men were of such size that I could secrete two or three of them in one of my coat pockets. In walking the streets, were I to step heavily, there was danger of my shaking down large buildings; or, by not having an eye below me, I could easily tread to death half a dozen of their cattle.

One day the king, who was most friendly to me, came to me in great trouble. The Emperor of the neighboring kingdom of Blefuscu had threatened to lay waste the kingdom of Lilliputia. The Blefuscuan navy, consisting of fifty great ships of war, was even then about to set sail; but I, by wading and swimming, reached their chief harbor where they were yet at anchor. With my pocket-knife I cut the cables of their fifty ships of war, and then, tying each ship to a piece of twine, I drew them after me to dry land, and so compelled the capitulation of Blefuscu.

While this deed redounded to my glory, it also raised me up powerful enemies, one being the high admiral of the Lilliputian navy. Had I wished, I could have crushed them and their entire kingdom under my boots, but there was my pledged word not to harm them. So when by secret intrigue they had me tried and condemned to the loss of my eyes, there was nothing left me but escape. I went to Blefuscu, where I was given a great reception and where they would have me stay; but I was weary of kings and princes, and told them that I desired nothing except that they would provision for me a boat, which I had found drifting on the shore, and allow me to go my way.

They stored the boat with the carcasses of 100 oxen, 300 sheep, with cows, bulls, and as much ready-dressed meat as 400 cooks could provide. Being thus protected against famine, I set sail on the third day and was picked up by an English merchant captain, who deemed me crazy when I told him my story. Not until I had taken several head of cattle from my pockets would he believe me. To my great grief, one of the ship's rats carried off one of my sheep on the way home.

On reaching home I learned that my uncle John had died and left me his estate near Epping, and the same being sufficient to keep my family from want, and the lust to wander being still quick within me, I set off to sea once more, this time in the *Adventurer,* bound for Surat.

On this voyage, after a great tempest, we put into a strange bay for water. Rambling on the shore, I became separated from my companions and fell into the hands of some natives of Brobdingnag, colossal men, of whom hardly one was under sixty English feet in height.

I was here put on exhibition, and, my fame reaching the ears of the king and queen, they commanded my presence at court; and thither I was brought, in charge of the daughter of one of my captors, a little girl named Glumdalclitch, nine years of age and small for her years, being not above thirty feet in height.

In the train of their Majesties, I traveled all over the kingdom, which was 6,000 miles in length by 3,000 to 5,000 in breadth. The capital city was 54 miles in length by 45 in breadth, a wonderful city where the king's palace was 7 miles around and the chief room therein 240 feet high, and broad and long in proportion. The king's stable was also a goodly building, housing 500 horses, noble creatures of a height of from 54 to 60 feet.

Of the Lilliputians, I used to say that they were people without a blemish in their persons, and the Brobdingnagians coarse beyond description; but later reflection induces me to think that the Lilliputians had blemishes proportionate to their size, the same being too tiny for me to estimate; and that possibly the Brobdingnagians appeared more vulgar than they truly were, their colossal proportions magnifying every defect. In some matters these large people were at least larger-minded. Thus, in the matter of whether it was proper to break an egg on the little or big end—which had almost split the Lilliputian kingdom in twain—as to that matter the Brobdingnagians would have lost little sleep. I judge this from a comment by the Brobdingnagian king on a political matter which I spoke of in connection with my own country—England. "It is tyranny," he said, "for a government to require those who hold differing opinions to change or not to change them."

His Majesty was much interested to hear of England; whereat I related at length her history, which astonished him. He protested that it seemed no more than a sequence of conspiracies, murders, revolutions, banishments, the worst effects that avarice, faction, hypocrisy, hatred, lust, malice, and ambition could produce. "What a pernicious race of odious vermin to be allowed to crawl upon the earth!" he said; which injurious judgment of my noble and beloved country pained me exceedingly.

Now, while I had become a favorite of a great nation, it was upon such a footing as ill became the dignity of humankind. I wished to be once more with people of my own mind; also I longed for a whiff of that sea which looked toward my own land. In response to my entreaties, I was taken to the seacoast. My little nurse Glumdalclitch being ill, I was put in charge of a page, who left me alone on the shore while he sought for birds' eggs. While thus alone, the traveling-cabinet in which I lay was seized by a great bird who took it far out to sea and then let it drop, almost at the exact moment that an English ship happened by to pick me up. Thus was I singularly rescued and brought once more safely to England.

I made other voyages and had divers adventures, a most singular one being that of my rescue from a desert continent by the people of an island which flew in the air, the same being made to rise and fall by means of an immense loadstone. The people of the flying island held themselves as a superior race, for no greater reason that I could see than that they had one eye turned inward and one turned upward.

A later voyage took me to the country of the Yahoos and the

Houyhnhnms. These Yahoos, being servile attendants to the Houy-hnhnms, were of disgusting habits, and so much resembled human beings that the wise and virtuous Houyhnhnms took me also for a Yahoo even to the end of my stay with them, a judgment which grieved me much.

The Houyhnhnms, who had the forms of horses, had the most sensible laws of any creature that I ever lived with. Their abhorrence of many of our human habits was so deep that I came in time to have a contempt for my own species and wished that I, too, were a Houy-hnhnm and be allowed to remain with them; but they banished me from their kingdom as one who might set up for a leader of the Yahoos and so some time give them trouble. They allowed me to build and provision a boat, and so I paddled off and in time reached England, where my wife and children were very glad to see me.

THE HEART OF MIDLOTHIAN
by
SIR WALTER SCOTT

CONDENSATION BY THURMAN L. HOOD

WALTER SCOTT was born in Edinburgh on August 15, 1771. His father was a lawyer, the first of the Scott line to leave the open country for the town.

Scott's education as a romance-writer began while he was a child. It can be traced even to his cradle, for he was sung to sleep not with lullabies, but with the lilting songs of the exiled Stuarts. As soon as he could understand stories, his grandmother and aunt poured into his eager ears tales of border warfare and old Scottish ballads.

He was a sickly child, and this resulted in a permanent lameness. But as a boy he so far overcame this handicap that he was always in the thick of school-boy fights, and none of his comrades could climb better than he the steep slopes of the Castlerock.

For a man who wrote such a prodigious amount, Scott was surprisingly late in getting started. He was thirty-four years old when his first original work appeared, "The Lay of the Last Minstrel." From that moment until his death, on September 21, 1832, he was, with the possible exception of Byron, the most popular writer in English.

When the public seemed to be tiring of his long romances in verse, he turned to novel-writing, and in 1814, when he was forty-three, he came into his career of greatness with "Waverley." For eighteen years novel after novel followed in rapid succession, stirring romances of history or colorful tales of Scottish life. They were all published anonymously until the financial disaster of 1825 made it seem wise to reveal the author's name.

"Waverley," "Ivanhoe," "The Heart of Midlothian," and "Kenilworth" are representative of Scott at his best. But "Old Mortality," "Quentin Durward," "The Talisman," "Guy Mannering," "The Fortunes of Nigel," "The Antiquary," "St. Ronan's Well," "Rob Roy," and, indeed, others have all been ranked as favorites among the innumerable admirers of the romances written by "the Wizard of the North."

Scott's struggle to pay his debts was as heroic as anything in his most heroic novel. He was fifty-five years old when the printing firm in which he was a secret partner failed and left him responsible for debts of $650,000. His wife died a few weeks later; he himself faced a probable mental breakdown, as he had had a slight attack of aphasia, an inability to remember the meaning of words. Yet he refused to go through bankruptcy, although he had had no part in incurring this mountainous debt. All that he asked from his creditors was time. This secured, he buckled sternly to his task.

He wrote doggedly and well, if not with the old fire. In two years he had paid off more than $200,000. To make money more quickly he turned from novels to a "Life of Napoleon," which brought him nearly $100,000. His last year was made happy by a merciful hallucination. He conceived the idea that he had paid every creditor in full. About $250,000 actually remained unpaid at his death in

1832, but this was reduced by insurance to $150,000. This, too, was paid from copyrights, and fifteen years later the last claim was discharged. No one had helped him. He had paid in full by his own unaided labor.

The Heart of Midlothian, by many called the finest of the Waverley Novels, was published anonymously in 1818. It takes its name from the Tolbooth, or old city jail, in Edinburgh (pulled down in 1815), the "stony heart" of Midlothian, which reared its ancient front in the very middle of the High Street of the city.

On the afternoon of September 8, 1736, Reuben Butler, assistant-master of the school at Libberton, and licensed minister of the Gospel, found himself in unexpected trouble. First of all, he had become entangled with the crowd of good citizens of Edinburgh in the Grass-market, murmuring at the postponement of the execution of Captain John Porteous of the City Guard. They were still in the heat of anger from the events of the preceding day, when Porteous had ordered his men to fire, and had fired himself, upon the crowd, some of whom were attempting to cut down the body of "Scotch" Wilson, the famous smuggler. Several innocent citizens had been killed. Now that the chief offender seemed likely to escape, there was no knowing what the mob might do. The quiet young pedagogue would gladly have returned to Libberton. Then, to his consternation, he learned that Effie Deans, the younger and more charming sister of his sweet-heart Jeanie Deans, was imprisoned in the Tolbooth.

When he had last seen Effie, more than a year before, she had been a beautiful and blooming girl, the lily of St. Leonard's. Many a traveler past her father's cottage had stopped his horse on the eve of entering Edinburgh, to gaze at her as she tripped by him, with her milk-pail poised on her head, bearing herself so erect, and stepping so light and free under her burden that it seemed rather an ornament than an incumbrance. Now the poor girl, scarce eighteen years of age, lay in the Tolbooth, charged with child-murder.

The facts were that after working for a time in a shop in Edinburgh, the unhappy prisoner had disappeared for the space of a week, and then made her appearance before her sister at St. Leonard's in a state that had rendered Jeanie only too certain of her misfortune. But to all questions she had remained mute as the grave, until the officers of justice had come to apprehend her.

Before Reuben Butler could see her the Tolbooth was closed; and before he could escape from the city a crowd of rioters compelled him to return with them to the jail and administer the last rites to Porteous, whom they dragged forth to death.

The leader of the mob, a young man disguised in woman's clothes, seized a moment in the midst of the turmoil in the jail to beg Effie to escape. "For God's sake—for your own sake—for my sake, flee, or they'll take your life," was all that he had time to say.

The girl gazed after him for a moment, and then, faintly muttering, "Better tyne life, since tint is gude fame," she sank her head upon her hand, and remained, seemingly, as unconscious as a statue, of the noise and tumult which passed around her.

In the morning, on his way to see Jeanie and her father at St. Leonard's, Butler encountered in the King's park a young man of noble bearing, but strangely agitated, who bade him "tell Jeanie Deans that, when the moon rises, I shall expect to meet her at Nicol Muschat's Cairn, beneath Saint Anthony's chapel."

After attempting in vain to induce Jeanie to explain the message, he returned to visit Effie again, in the Tolbooth, only to be compelled, on his arrival there, to tell the whole story, lest he be convicted of guilt in the Porteous affair. And then he was sent home, under bail not to leave Libberton, nor to communicate with any member of the family of Effie Deans.

But if his experiences were to him incomprehensible, they were by no means so to the authorities. By piecing together his testimony with that of others, they rightly determined that the stranger in the King's park, the leader of the Porteous mob, and the father of Effie's child were one and the same person, namely, Geordie Robertson, comrade of Wilson the smuggler, and but lately escaped from the very prison in which Effie Downs was now confined. Accordingly, they planned to capture him that night at Muschat's Cairn. But before they could reach that place, Robertson had time to beg Jeanie to save her sister at the trial by testifying that Effie had disclosed to her her condition. Then he escaped.

Merely that slight falsehood would have removed the case of Effie Deans from under the letter of the cruel Scotch statute. But Jeanie, steadfastly, devoutly truthful, was utterly unable to placate her conscience in bearing false witness. Nor could the disappointment of Effie herself, whom she was at last permitted to visit in the strong-room of the prison, alter her resolution. "He wanted that

I suld be mansworn," she said. "I told him that I daurna swear to an untruth."

At the trial, when Jeanie was brought in to testify, Effie, in human weakness, cried, "O Jeanie, Jeanie, save me!" But when the solemn oath—"the truth to tell, and no truth to conceal, as far as she knew or was asked," was administered "in the name of God, and as the witness should answer to God at the great day of judgment," Jeanie, educated in deep reverence for the name of the Deity, was elevated above all considerations save those which she could, with a clear conscience, call Him to witness. And when the advocate came at length to the point of asking her, "what your sister said ailed her when you inquired," Jeanie could only answer, "Nothing." When the sentence was pronounced by the Doomsman, Effie's own eyes were the only dry ones in the court. "God forgive ye, my Lords," she said, "and dinna be angry wi' me for wishin' it—we a' need forgiveness."

The next morning found Jeanie Deans traveling alone and afoot on the long road to London "to see the Queen's face that gives grace," and beg for her sister's pardon. Her tartan screen served all the purposes of a riding-habit, and of an umbrella; a small bundle contained such changes of linen as were absolutely necessary. She had a few guineas, and a letter from Reuben Butler to the Duke of Argyle, whose grandfather had been under obligations of the deepest to the famous Bible Butler, grandfather of the poor assistant-schoolmaster, now sick at Libberton.

She passed luckily, on the whole, through so weary and dangerous a journey, and at length, through the intercession of the duke, secured the pardon which she sought.

Before she reached Scotland again, Effie had eloped with her lover, who was in reality George Staunton, son of an English nobleman. The sisters, who had last met when Effie was sitting on the bench of the condemned, did not meet again for many years, though Lady Staunton wrote sometimes to Jeanie—now Mrs. Butler, wife of Mr. Reuben Butler, pastor of Knocktarlitie.

Finally, by chance, Sir George learned that Meg Murdockson, who had attended Effie in her illness, had not murdered the child, as they had always supposed. He traced the boy to a certain troop of vagabonds, of which Black Donald was the chief. In an affray with Black Donald's men, Sir George was shot by a young lad called "the Whistler," who proved to be the lost son. The lad disappeared and escaped to America. Lady Staunton, overcome by the tragedy, after vain efforts to drown her grief in society, retired to a convent in France. Although she took no vows, she remained there until her death. But her influence at court accomplished much for the children of her sister Jeanie, who lived happily on in the good parish with which the bounty of the Duke of Argyle had provided her husband.

The Heart of Midlothian is notable for having rather fewer important characters, a smaller variety of incidents, and less description of scenery than most of Scott's novels. One of the most remarkable scenes in all fiction is the meeting of the two sisters in prison under the eyes of the jailer Ratcliffe. The interview of Jeanie with Queen Caroline is also most noteworthy. There is much humour at the expense of the Cameronian wing of the Presbyterian faith in Scotland. In this work also appears the strange character of Madge Wildfire, daughter of the old crone, Meg Murdockson. Into her mouth is put the famous song, "Proud Maisie is in the wood."

HENRY ESMOND
by
WILLIAM MAKEPEACE THACKERAY

CONDENSATION BY ANNIE D. HUBBARD

WILLIAM MAKEPEACE THACKERAY, son of a civil servant in India, was born July 18, 1811, in Calcutta. He died December 24, 1863, in London, where most of his life was spent. From 1840 on, his wife was insane, so there lived in his heart, as in that of the other great humorist of his time, Dickens, constant domestic sorrow.

Thackeray began in school-days rather to absorb life than to attain scholarship. He delighted even then to reproduce it in comic verse and caricature. At Cambridge, in Weimar, in Paris art-schools and London law-school, he went gaily on his way indolent in study, but eager in friendship, ardent in

*life. At twenty-one he owned and managed a London news-
paper; at twenty-five he was penniless, after scattering a
comfortable fortune. But he had bought experience invalu-
able to the young journalist, priceless to the novelist.*

*Thackeray's astonishing versatility was early realized. He
aspired to illustrate Dickens's novels; he wrote travel
sketches, stories, ballads, and burlesques.*

*"Barry Lyndon," his first notable novel, was the history of
a rascal; but in the most fascinating of feminine rascals,
Becky Sharp, Thackeray first brilliantly showed himself
master in the creation of living characters ("Vanity Fair,"
1846–48). "Pendennis" (1849–50) was, like Dickens's
"David Copperfield," in essence autobiographical. The need
of money drove Thackeray reluctantly to the lecture-field.
His course on Eighteenth Century Humorists, popular in
England and America (1851), prepared the ground for
"Esmond" (1852), his unsurpassed historical novel. "The
Newcomes" (1854), "The Virginians" (1859), and the un-
finished "Denis Duval," complete the list of his best novels.*

*"In the creation of living character, Thackeray stands
simply alone among novelists," says Saintsbury. Becky
Sharp, unscrupulous and fascinating; Colonel Newcome,
noble and lovable; Clive and Pendennis, natural young men
—all, from Barry Lyndon to Denis Duval, live and have a
being of their own. "Once created," says Thackeray, "they
lead me and I follow where they direct. . . . I have never
seen the people I describe nor heard the conversations I put
down. . . . I am often astonished myself to read it. . . .
It seems as if an occult power was moving the pen."*

*It was this very quality of a life outside his own mind
which made his characters so vivid to himself as well as to
his readers. He says: "I know these people utterly—I know
the sound of their voices." He even visited, after the publication of "Vanity Fair," the hotel in Brussels where Becky
Sharp had stopped.*

In the days when the Stuart was playing his losing game for
England's crown a sallow-faced, precocious boy was growing up,
half loved, half neglected, in Castlewood House, knowing all the
secrets of its hidden chambers, where cavalier and priest could hide

for a lifetime. Harry was reputed the illegitimate son of Thomas Esmond, Lord Castlewood, whose childless wife, herself an Esmond, had been a beauty and king's favorite once. After Viscount Castlewood had died, fighting for King James at Boyne Water, and King William's men had taken his lady prisoner, hiding in her bed, painted and powdered, resplendent in her brocade gown and gold-clocked red stockings—by her side the japan box holding the papers of the Royalists—another kinsman, Francis Esmond, had taken possession of the old house.

"O dea certe," little Harry Esmond said in his heart, when Rachel, the new Lady Castlewood, in her lovely girlhood, met him in the yellow gallery and there stirred in him the beginnings of a lifetime's devotion to her, to her beautiful children, Beatrix and Frank, and to his jovial new patron, Francis, Lord Castlewood. As a loved kinsman now, Harry had grown to manhood, when suddenly the smallpox, ravaging the neighborhood, destroyed for a time Lady Castlewood's beauty, and her gay husband's heart turned to lesser loves, though he still cared enough to be wildly jealous when Lord Mohun, a London blood, made love to her. The two men fought, and Francis, foully murdered by Mohun, on his death-bed made a written statement that he had long known from the priest who heard Thomas, Lord Castlewood's, dying confession that Harry Esmond had a right to the name he bore and was head of the house of Castlewood.

This paper, stained with the blood of his dear master, Harry burned, and vowed—thanking Heaven that he had been enabled to make the righteous decision—that his mistress should never know sorrow through him, and that little Frank should become Lord Castlewood in his father's stead.

Fate dealt hardly just now with Harry Esmond, for as he lay wounded and in prison as a result of his part in the duel, his dear lady, visiting him, chose to believe that he might have prevented her husband's death. Perhaps because she felt in her heart a tenderer love for him than she dared confess, she forbade him her home and even her friendship. The living of the parish church of Castlewood, long since promised him, was given elsewhere, and Esmond would have been penniless and friendless had not the old dowager, his father's widow, who had long cherished pique against the younger and fairer Lady Castlewood, summoned him to her new house at Chelsey. As he kissed her withered hand and saluted her as Marchioness, something in his assured bearing made her guess that he knew he was her husband's true son and chief of the house. Half frightened, she drew from him the story of his renunciation, and when he told her that his father's son would not aggravate the wrong his father had done, and asked only for her kindness, her worldly old heart was touched. Henceforth he was "Son Esmond" to her, and when her influence at court had procured him an ensign's commission she was proud of him in his laced scarlet coat.

Esmond served with some distinction under Marlborough abroad and was wounded at Blenheim, but the best thing his campaigning brought him was a chance encounter in St. Gudule's Church at Brussels with Father Holt, the tutor of his boyhood, who told him his mother's story. She had been of that very town, and a most tender, faithful creature. His father had deserted her, married her secretly, and again deserted her, and she had taken her broken heart to that convent. Esmond knelt by her grave, took a flower from the little hillock, and as he listened to the choir chanting from the chapel, realized afresh that love and humility were all that counted in life.

One great happiness had come to Esmond before this—he had seen his dear lady, her face sweet and sad in her widow's hood, in Winchester Cathedral, and when their eyes had met the time of estrangement was passed. Knowing now how her heart had followed him, he dreamed that they might be happy together, but she saw more clearly. When, in their house at Walcotte, Beatrix, the sixteen-year-old maid of honor, with a scarlet ribbon upon the whitest neck in the world, came to meet him, he forgot her mother. No other woman of her day was like her for beauty and wit, and for ten years he was her slave, kneeling with his heart in his hand for the young lady to take, while she looked far higher than the nameless and fortuneless colonel. "Yes," she said, "I solemnly vow I want a good husband. My face is my fortune. Who'll come? Buy! Buy!" While marquises and lords were coming, eager for her, Esmond bore the torments of a hopeless passion, and his dear mistress suffered with him.

At last a suitor worthy of the prize appeared—the Duke of Hamilton—much Beatrix's senior, wealthy, and second to none in the kingdom. Esmond had to accept his fate. The wedding gift he made her was a splendid string of diamonds his father's widow had given him. As she accepted it with a cry of delight, her bridegroom-elect, with a darkening face, told her he did not choose the Duchess of Hamilton should accept presents from gentlemen who had no right to the names they bore. Her mother, to whom the old dowager on her death-bed had maliciously told Harry's story, answered for her: "Henry Esmond is his father's lawful son and true heir. We are the recipients of his bounty, and he is the head of a house as old as your Grace's own." And Beatrix, from whom it had all been kept a secret, whispered to him, "Why did not I know you before!"

On the eve of marriage the duke died in a duel. Beatrix mourned him honestly, but Esmond dared hope for himself, and planned a bold move to win her love. All the Esmonds were heart and soul for the Stuart cause. Frank, the young viscount, who was fighting abroad, closely resembled the exiled chevalier. The two came together to Lady Castlewood's London house, the prince impersonating the viscount, and Frank, his valet, and were received with great joy. Stuart partisans came to the house by stealth and the plot spread like leaven. The maid of honor contrived an interview between the prince and Queen Anne, his sister, whose health was failing, and all hoped that she would proclaim him her successor. Then Beatrix's friends began to fear for her, as the prince, who had no respect for women, was infatuated with her and she listened to him. Against her will they sent her to Castlewood. Suddenly the queen was reported dying, and the prince could not be found. Beatrix had found means to tell him her whereabouts. Henry Esmond and Frank rode all night to Castlewood. Entering by the secret window, they found the prince and told him they came to avenge their dishonor. Taking from their old hiding-place the papers proving his birth and title, Esmond burned them before the prince, with the words: "I draw my sword and break it, and renounce you. Had you completed the wrong you designed us, I would have driven it through your heart." Frank, breaking his own sword, echoed him: "I go with my cousin. I'm for the Elector of Hanover. It's your Majesty's fault. You might have been king if you hadn't come dangling after Trix!"

The talk was scarce over when Beatrix entered the room. She turned pale at the sight of her kinsmen, and looked at Esmond as if she could have killed him on the spot. It did not pain him, for the love of ten years was dead.

As they rode back to London, the herald was proclaiming, "George, by the grace of God, King." Queen Anne had died that night.

The chevalier escaped secretly to France, where Beatrix joined him. Frank married a foreign countess, and Esmond's mistress was left alone. At last, as beautiful in her autumn as maidens in their spring, she listened to him and consented to become his wife. In their Virginia plantation they built a new Castlewood, and found there an Indian summer of serene happiness.

‿◁()▷‿

THE HORSE'S MOUTH*
by
JOYCE CARY

CONDENSATION BY MARGARET GILLETT

JOYCE CARY (1888–1957), Irish-born (Londonderry) writer, started to be a painter and spent three years studying art in Edinburgh and Paris, where he became obsessed with the work of William Blake. After his sojourn on the Continent, he returned to England and took his degree at Oxford in 1912. Still uncertain about his vocation, he volunteered for the Balkan War and later went to Africa, where he fought with the Nigerian Regiment in the Cameroons in 1915, was wounded, and finally was invalided home. His next assignment was in remote and isolated Borgu, as the only white administrator, but ill health forced him to retire from African service in 1920.

His first volume of short stories, published the same year, received little notice and it was not until 1932, when he was forty-four, that his first novel, "Aissa Saved," brought him success as a writer. Between 1941 and 1955, Cary produced two trilogies, the first one including "Herself Surprised," "To Be a Pilgrim," and "The Horse's Mouth," and the second, "Prisoner of Grace," "Except the Lord," and "Not Honour More." "The House of Children" (1941), one of his touching and vivid autobiographical novels of childhood,

* By permission of Harper & Bros., New York, and Michael Joseph, London, publishers of *The Horse's Mouth,* copyright, 1944, by Joyce Cary.

won the Tait Black Memorial Prize. Besides these, the author wrote three more novels about Africa and three less successful "chronicle novels." "Marching Soldier" (1945) and "The Drunken Sailor" (1947) are his books of verse. Cary also published several political studies anticipating the coming struggle on the "dark continent": "Power in Men" (1939), "The Case for African Freedom" (1941) and "The Process of Real Freedom" (1943). With "The Prisoner of Grace" (1952), he finally received full recognition on both sides of the Atlantic for his work as a novelist. His last novel, "The Captive and the Free," was published posthumously in 1959.

Critics of Cary's early writing detected the influence of the Russians and Conrad, whereas later evaluations, while admitting his right to a place in the Dickens tradition, put him in the post-Joyce generation with indebtedness to his fellow Irishman and to Proust.

A man of my age has to get on with the job. I had two and six left from my prison money, hardly enough for working capital. My old friend Coker might stake me to a few pounds. How much did I owe her now? I tried to figure it out as I made my way down on the Thames-side to The Eagle.

"So you're out, are you? Thought it was tomorrow." Coker's greeting was always cheerful. Sympathetic type. But not this time. She gave me the shake for fair. Shut the pub door in my face. Not opening time yet.

I went home to my studio then, an old boatshed down by the water wall. Quite comfy for a man of sixty-seven, fixed up like I had it before. Not too much damage done either. The kids had broken a few windows and mussed up my Fall a bit while I was away. Still that leg of Adam's was pretty good. I might beef up Eve a bit to balance it. Not now though.

Back to Coker's again. Maybe the red-headed horror's mood would be changed. Bar-maids are funny. She drew me a pint and waited for my shilling. Then she tossed me a pair of socks across the counter. When I finished my beer I went out and when I got to the corner I put the socks on. I felt better. Surrey all in one blaze like a forest fire. Great clouds of dirty yellow smoke rolling up. Nine carat gold. Sky water-green to lettuce-green. A few top clouds, solid as lemons. Far bank of the river like a magic island. Rheumatic old willows trembling and wheezing together.

I could do that, I thought. If I had the right colors, the paint, that is. And I thought for a spell about Sara Monday. The old Sara of twenty years ago. My Eve. The individual female She. When I got back to my semi-floating studio, the rain was coming down like glass bead curtains outside. I knocked up a little sketch of Sara as she is now, broad as a door and crumpled like a folded hammock. Quite a contrast to the Sara that old millionaire Hickson has. My Sara. Standing in the sun beside a flat bath. Right foot on a chair. Drying her ankle with a green towel. Eight by five. The formal composition was good. The old boy had got that one for a few quid. Sara needed the money. Worth at least fifty thousand.

Coker thought I should sue him for it but the poor old duffer hadn't been too bad. He had given me an allowance. Two pounds a week. No overtime. Until I went to the chokey and then he paid my bills, so I suppose he had a kind of right to it. But you don't know Coker. A bulldog. She wanted what I owed her and she kept after me to go with her to Hickson's. And I did, finally. But nothing came of it. His man called the coppers when they missed one of those little oriental what-nots in the reception room. I had unconsciously slipped it into my pocket. There were dozens of them around. I don't know how they missed it so quick. I got six months for that piece of carelessness.

But that stretch in the clink was good for me. Cured my cough and I learned some more Blake by heart. Great stuff. Large poetry. I like art big. While there, I also received a letter. From an admirer, you might say. Um-de-dump Alabaster, Esquire, M.A., art critic, plenipotentiary. Wanted to do my biography with reproductions of my major works. In color. Some of the boys from Ellam Street trying to pull my leg, I figured, and put it out of my mind.

Then Alabaster turned out to be real. A real kid just out of school. And oh so enthusiastic about art. My! He knew Hickson's collection like a book. Some crap about Hickson giving him support for the publication of his book about me Gulley Jimson, Life and Works. I didn't even listen. He was obviously broke. At least as broke and hungry as I was. So I took him to my hotel (commonly called a doss house, in parenthesis) for dinner. We arranged business details over our fish and chips.

"Excuse me, I am not in the art business. I am a critic." "Look, Professor, we're both broke. So why worry. You can have a sideline as my agent." His patron, Sir William Beeder, wanted another canvas like my Sara in the Bath that old Hickson had. All millionaires want nudes. Their virility's slipping. Lady Beeder paints, Alabaster told me. Imagine. Sky with clouds, grass with trees, water with reflection, cows with horns, cottage with smoke and passing laborer with fork, blue shirt, old hat. Lovely.

Anyway the Beeders invited me for tea. I gave it to them straight from the horse's mouth and I made a hit. Teedle-um-de-oh. 250 or 300 guineas. Some handsome figure like that. But at the moment I had no studio. Not even a painting. Coker and her savage old mother had moved into my aquapalace and cut up my Fall to mend the leaky roof. A minor difficulty. One must be philosophical about these little set-backs. Fortunately the Beeders went on a junket and left the key to their flat with Alabaster. They were considering having me decorate one wall, he said consolingly when he heard what had happened to my picture.

That flat had some nice walls. Beautiful, clean plaster surface. Smooth as a baby's skin. Of course I had to wait until some of the boy's high class friends came to pick him up for a long week-end. He wouldn't let me touch anything while he was there. I promised him I'd give the key to the porter just as soon as I had done the washing up. Lady Beeder's bed looked very soft. The silk sheets were positively slippery. After I had taken a few silver spoons that were lying loose in the drawer to the pawn shop, I was able to get the brushes and paint I needed and begin. The wall of the main room was just right for the Raising of Lazarus. Something I had wanted to do for a long time. The light was excellent just opposite the main entrance. I started with the feet. Enlarged.

Lady Beeder's first glimpse of those feet when she came in the door gave her a turn, it seems. And while Sir William was attending to her and they were both in shock, I managed to get out the side door. But millionaires can afford to be magnanimous. Sir William even sent me back my things. I had left too hurriedly to collect anything. They had returned unexpectedly.

Then came what art historians will probably refer to as my lean period. That was just before poor old Hickson died and left my Sara to the Tate Gallery. Of course Sir William wanted his nude more than ever after that. Alabaster wrote me about his eagerness and I went over to the Tate to make a study of Sara. It could have been a preliminary sketch which I only rediscovered recently.

I knew Sara herself had an early smaller one I had done before Hickson's but she wouldn't part with it. Liked to look at it and admire herself and think about the good old days. And she was wily. I had tried I don't know how many times to get it. Even the old tricks wouldn't work. She'd smooch back but wouldn't give an inch about the picture. So when I met her accidentally in the cemetery, I didn't have much hope. That is until she mentioned that her present husband was in the hospital. He was a seven-footer and I didn't like to tangle with him. It wasn't dignified. "Fell off the ladder," she said. I took her to the pub just outside the gates and ordered a couple of cans. Then I excused myself to see a man about a rose and beat it to her place to pick up my picture. But old Sara, the wise old barque, sailed in just as I was about to lay my hand on it. Screaming "police!" I had such a fright that I tapped her on the bonnet, unintentionally gave her a little push and she fell down the cellar stairs. I barely got out the back way as the big walrus-eyed copper came in the front.

A couple of days later it came over the wireless at The Eagle. Cokey always liked to listen to the police notices for social news. Mrs. Monday, the victim of a murderous attack on the tenth of the month, died today in St. (static) Hospital. Before she died, she became conscious for a short time, and was able to give a full description of her assailant. A young man of about six feet with red hair and mustache, dressed like a seaman. Spoke with a foreign accent. An anchor tattooed on his right hand. Large blue scar as if from gunpowder on left cheek. Cokey looked at me with disgust. She knew old Sara had diddled the authorities with her last breath. I took a long drink and my untattooed right hand trembled as I lifted the jug to my lips.

I guess I was pretty upset. I went back to my wall. The one I had found in the old abandoned chapel off Horsemonger's Yard. Twenty-five by forty it was. I'd always wanted enough space to do the Creation justice. Unfortunately it was condemned. The building, I mean. But before the Council had all the legalities unscrambled, I had started on my masterpiece. The whale was sketched in and looked grand, especially its right eye. The inward eye of a mystic which contemplates eternal joy. Straight out of Randypole Billy. Now the Leviathan smiled as the demolition crew arrived.

While I was thinking about Sara and feeling sad, the wall fell away from my brush. I couldn't believe it. I guess I tumbled right out of my painter's sling in surprise. But when I woke up at the hospital, the sister said I had had a stroke.

THE HOUSE OF THE SEVEN GABLES

by

NATHANIEL HAWTHORNE

CONDENSATION BY JOSEPHINE VAN TASSEL BRUORTON

NATHANIEL HAWTHORNE was born in Salem, Massachusetts, July 4, 1804. His early boyhood days were spent in Salem, but when he was fourteen years old the family moved to Maine. Here the young lad continued the solitary walks of which he was so fond, but in the wilderness, instead of the narrow streets of Salem. Even at this early date he had acquired a taste for writing, and carried a little blank-book in which he jotted down his notes.

After a year in Maine, Hawthorne returned to Salem to prepare for college. He amused himself by publishing a manuscript periodical, and at times speculated upon the profession he would follow in the future. He wrote to his mother, "I do not want to be a doctor and live by men's diseases, nor a minister to live by their sins, nor a lawyer to live by their quarrels. So I don't see that there is anything left for me but to be an author."

For some years Hawthorne lived in Concord, Massachusetts, in the old Manse, and wrote "Mosses from an Old Manse," "Twice Told Tales," and "Grandfather's Chair." He joined the Brook Farm colony at West Roxbury, but found that the conditions there suited neither his taste nor his temperament, and he remained but one year.

In 1846 Hawthorne moved again to Salem, where he had been appointed as surveyor of the custom-house at that port. He filled the position until a change of administration led to his retirement.

While at the custom-house he found, among some old papers, a large letter "A" embroidered on red cloth, and, speculating upon the origin and history of the letter, his imagination was so stirred that, upon his retirement from office, he wrote "The Scarlet Letter."

Soon after the publication of "The Scarlet Letter," Hawthorne moved to Lenox, Massachusetts, where he wrote "The House of the Seven Gables." On a European visit he spent some time in Italy, and during his stay there he sketched out one elaborate work, and prepared it for the press while living in Leamington, England. This was "The Marble Faun," the English edition of which was known as "Transformation, or the Romance of Monte Beni."

His shorter stories are remarkable for their originality. But in some of the longer stories he showed how deeply he pondered the great problems of life, in depicting the characters which move through his works. He inherited the gravity of his Puritan ancestors, and was said to be "a great anatomist of the human heart."

He died at Plymouth, New Hampshire, on the 19th of May, 1864, and five days later was buried at Sleepy Hollow, a beautiful cemetery at Concord where he used to walk under the pines when living at the old Manse. Over his grave is a simple stone, inscribed with the single word, "Hawthorne."

Of your courtesy, I beg you to call this tale a Romance, rather than a Novel; for it makes attempt to connect a bygone time with the present that is even now drifting away from us. It is a legend, bringing with it the Mist of the Past floating round each character and event—even round the old house itself.

Sometimes it drifts aside and you catch a glimpse of older days —days when Colonel Pyncheon, out of pure covetousness, despoiled old Wizard Maule of his house and little plot of land—days when Maule cursed the colonel for his sins and foretold, "God would give him blood to drink!"—days when Thomas Maule, son of the Wizard, built for Colonel Pyncheon, over his father's very threshold, the House of the Seven Gables.

On the day when Hepzibah Pyncheon trod her pride underfoot and opened the little cent-shop, built in the front gable of the old house, there were but few of the Pyncheon blood left. Judge Pyncheon, his son (who died abroad and enters not into this tale), Hepzibah and her brother Clifford, little Phœbe Pyncheon (who had come for a long visit) and a few cousins, were all. The race of Maule was supposed extinct—at least there were none known.

Long since Hester had let one of the gables to a daguerreotypist named Holgrave; and none others were in the old house save herself and Clifford (now pardoned out after serving sentence for the supposed murder of an uncle), and little Phœbe.

Judge Pyncheon was the great man of the town, but, despite his ever-ready smile and studied benevolence, he was not greatly liked. Hepzibah shrank away from him and Clifford shrieked when he would have forced his way in to see him.

Hepzibah and Clifford scarce left the house even for the garden; but Phœbe and young Holgrave met there often, and the kindly Mist made itself thin between them till they saw each other clear and their hearts drew close and love came to them—but so softly and sweetly they knew it not for love, but called it by that other sweet name—friendship.

Then Phœbe must needs go home—and with her went all the sunshine; and the Mist drifted back—and all the scant happiness that had come with her to Hepzibah and Clifford for a little, fled away.

When she had gone, the judge became even more determined to see Clifford.

"Cousin Hepzibah," he begged, with his most benevolent smile, "let me see Clifford."

"You cannot," said Hepzibah. "Since yesterday he hath kept his bed."

"What?" cried the judge. "Is he ill? Then I must and will see him. There is none who would so delight to promote his happiness and well-being. I beg of you to let me see him, Hepzibah."

"In the name of Heaven!" cried Hepzibah, her anger overcoming her fear, "give over, I beseech you, this loathsome pretense of affection for your victim. You let him go to prison under false accusation. You hate him! Say so, like a man! At this moment you cherish some black purpose against him in your heart! Speak it out! But never speak again of your love for my poor brother."

The judge's benevolent countenance became hard.

"Cousin Hepzibah," he said, "it is my fixed purpose to see Clifford before I leave this house. I will give you my reason. Of my uncle's estate, which I inherited, not one-third was apparent when he died. Clifford can give me a clue to the recovery of the remainder. It is as certain as that I stand here!"

"And what if he refuse?"

"My dear cousin," smiled the judge, blandly, "the alternative is his confinement for the remainder of his life in a public asylum for the insane."

"You cannot mean it!" cried Hester; but the judge only shrugged his shoulders and said: "Time flies. Bid Clifford come to me." And Hester turned and went slowly up the stair and knocked at her brother's door, and called. None answered. After a long waiting, she knocked again; then she undid the door and entered—the chamber was empty.

Back she ran down the stair, calling frantically:

"Clifford is gone! Help, Jaffrey Pyncheon! Some harm will come to him!" She ran through the hall, calling and searching for him. When she approached the parlor door again Clifford stood in the door, coming from within. He pointed his finger back into the room.

"Come, Hepzibah!" he cried, with a wild gesture. "The weight is gone from us! We can sing and laugh now. Aye, we can be as light-hearted as little Phœbe herself."

Horror-stricken at his looks and motions, Hepzibah slipped past him into the parlor. Almost immediately she returned, a cry choking in her throat.

"My God!" she cried, "What will become of us!"

"Come with me!" cried Clifford, still with that wild gaiety. "Put on your cloak and hood, take your purse with money in it, and come!"

Still with that wild gaiety so foreign to him, Clifford led the way, first to the depot, where he made her take the train. When they left it at an out-of-the way station, still leading, he drifted away with her into the cold, sullen Mist.

With the day came many people to the cent-shop, but none gained admittance; but when Phœbe came the garden door opened for her. A hand clasped hers and she was led to the disused reception-room.

The sun streamed in through the uncurtained windows and she saw her companion was Holgrave.

He told her the judge was dead—in the same manner as his ancestor, "To whom God had given blood to drink!" He convinced her that the uncle, for whose supposed murder Clifford had suffered for thirty years, had died in the same fashion.

"We must not hide it a moment longer!" cried Phœbe. "Clifford is innocent! God will make it manifest! Let us throw the door wide and call the neighbors to see the truth!"

"Wait!" begged Holgrave. "Phœbe, in all our lives there can never be another moment like this. Is it all terror? Are you conscious of no joy, as I am, that has made this the only point of life worth living for?"

"It seems a sin," faltered Phœbe, "to speak of joy at such a time."

"Phœbe," cried Holgrave, "before you came my past was lonely and dreary, my future seemed a shapeless gloom. With you came hope, warmth, and joy. I love you, Phœbe. Do you love me?"

"Look into my heart," said Phœbe, dropping her eyes. "You know I love you."

At that moment, the mingled voices of Hepzibah and Clifford came to them. Phœbe and her lover went to meet them. Hepzibah, when she saw them, burst into tears; Clifford smiled and murmured that the rose of Eden had bloomed in the old house at last.

By the death of Judge Pyncheon, Hepzibah, Clifford, and Phœbe became rich. They decided to live at the judge's country-place. At the very moment of departure, through Clifford's troubled mind drifted a recollection of the time when, a mere boy, he had discovered the secret spring which caused the portrait of the colonel (before which they stood) to swing forward, disclosing a recess wherein were important papers. But he had forgotten the secret of the spring.

"Perhaps I can recall it," said Holgrave, and touched the spring.

It was much rusted, and, therefore, when released, the portrait tumbled to the floor. There was the recess, and there the title-deeds to vast Indian lands—old Jaffrey Pyncheon's missing property.

"But how came you to know the secret of the spring?" Phœbe asked of Holgrave, apart.

"My dearest Phœbe," smiled Holgrave, "how will it please you to take the name of Maule? This secret is the only inheritance that has come down to me from that ancestor. When Thomas, son of Wizard Maule, built this house he took the opportunity to construct this recess and hide away those title-deeds. I would have told you all this before, but I feared to frighten you."

Phœbe's smile forgave him, and as their carriage rolled away, the old House of the Seven Gables, freed from its burden of secret and curse, smiled after them brightly as the Mist lifted and fled away.

HUCKLEBERRY FINN

by

MARK TWAIN

CONDENSATION BY MARGARET GILLETT

"I am sorry to know you are smoking so much, Mr. Clemens," remarked a lady in Mark Twain's early days. "This is the second time within the week I have seen you with a box of cigars under your arm."

"Don't be disturbed, dear madam," replied Mark, in a confidential tone, "I'm just moving again."

With characteristic humor SAMUEL LANGHORNE CLEMENS indicated the vicissitudes of his early days. He was born in Florida, Missouri, November 30, 1835. The common schools gave him all the formal education he got. He became an expert compositor, wherein he resembled William Dean Howells, with whom he later became linked in a lifelong friendship of deep attachment. In 1851 he became a Mississippi pilot, where he picked up his pen-name from the soundings of the river. He started in to fight for the Confederacy, later drifted to reporting, turned to mining in California, when he made Calaveras County famous by the well-known "Jumping Frog," moved on to the Sandwich Islands, and then made the trip to Europe which resulted in "Innocents Abroad (1869). In 1871 he married

Olivia L. Langdon, and made Hartford his home for many years afterward. "Roughing It," "The Gilded Age" (in conjunction with Charles Dudley Warner), "Tom Sawyer," "A Tramp Abroad," "The Prince and the Pauper," "Huckleberry Finn," "The Tragedy of Pudd'nhead Wilson," were some of the various books which kept Americans and Europeans laughing for many years. The failure of the publishing venture in which he had engaged led him to repeat the chivalric deed of Sir Walter Scott in repaying debts for which he held his honor responsible; a splendid failure!

Despite the picturesque and never-failing humor of Mark Twain, he had a deep vein of seriousness. In "Tom Sawyer" and "Huckleberry Finn" he has described a phase of American life which will become a permanent part of American literature.

He died April 21, 1910.

You don't know me, without you have read a book by the name of *The Adventures of Tom Sawyer* by Mr. Mark Twain, where he told the truth mainly. Now the way that book winds up, Tom and me found the money the robbers hid in the cave and we each got $6000. Judge Thatcher invested it for us so that we got one dollar a day each. After that the Widow Douglas took me for her son, and allowed she would civilize me which was a very uncomfortable thing from my point of view. Right from the beginning, her sister, Miss Watson, took a set at me with a spelling book until I was all tuckered out. I ran away onct but then I went back cause Tom Sawyer wanted me to.

But by and by, one night after everybody was off to bed I heard the "me-yow! me-yow!" down in the trees so I scrambled out of my window quick and slipped to the ground. Sure enough Tom was there waiting for me. We went down the hill near the house and met some of the boys that hid in the old tanyard. Then we unhitched a skiff and pulled down the river a couple of miles to the cave where we took the oath and elected Tom the first captain of the Robber Gang after we all signed our names in blood. I got home just before day-break dog-tired.

Well, three or four months run along like this, and it was well into the winter, now. Pap had not been seen for more than a year except for the drownded man they found in the river and thought was him. But I figured he was too smart to drown, even though he was drunk, and he'd be turning up one of these days, especially if he heard about the money I'd found. Anyway he'd want to whale me for something or other just on principle. And my hunch was right because that very night he was home when I got there. He'd clumb in my window. How he done it at his age I don't know. He was fifty and looked it, besides being generally ragged and dirty and mean as sin.

Pap began by being sarcastic because I was going to school. "*Ain't* you a sweet-scented dandy, though? A bed; and bedclothes; and a look'n glass; and a piece of carpet on the floor—and your own father got to sleep with the hogs in the tanyard. Why, there ain't no end to your airs—they say you're rich. Hey?—how's that?"

"They lie—that's how."

"Don't gimme no sass. And looky here—you drop that school, you hear? Your mother couldn't read, and she couldn't write, nuther, before she died. And I can't so you needn't nuther. I'll lay for you, my smarty and if I catch you about that school I'll tan you good. First thing you know you'll get religion, too. I never see such a son." He made me shell out the dollar the Judge have give me that day, and said he was gonna get some whisky cause he hadn't had a drink all day.

Later, after he'd been jailed a number of times and let out, he made me go with him up the river a way to the Illinois shore and live with him in an old log hut. He had a gun which he had stole, I reckon, and we fished and hunted for our food. He said he would show who was Huck Finn's boss. It was kind of fun, campin' out like that, and after a while I didn't want to go back to the Widow's place.

But by and by, pap got too handy with his hick'ry and I was all over welts. I watched for a chance and made my getaway in a canoe that came floatin' down the river empty at high tide. I took some pains before I left to make it look as though I'd been murdered, then I went to Jackson's Island about two and a half miles downstream. The fourth day I found there was somebody else campin' there, too, and I was scared stiff until I found out it was black Jim, who had run away from Miss Watson. We made a fine camp together in a cave where it was dry and comfortable even though it poured rain outside.

One night when things got sorta dull on the island, I dressed up in some girl's clothes I had found before and rowed over to the other side of the river to see what was going on. I found out that the folks back home had posted a three hundred dollar reward for Jim. They thought he had killed me and they were just about ready to begin a search of Jackson's Island, so we took off down the river for Cairo on a raft we catched one night as it was floating by. If we could get to one of them free states, where the Ohio River goes up Northeast, Jim would be all right and nobody could sell him down to Orleans, which was why he ran away from Miss Watson in the first place. Jim put our wigwam up on the raft, over all the stuff I had brought along from pap's camp, and we set out together for the long trip.

We had some queer adventures on the way and once, after a big thunder storm, we saw a house floating right down the river on the flood and just a little tilted on one side. Jim and I went in to scrounge around and there was a dead man upstairs with a lot of empty whisky bottles. He had been dead sometime and was awful gruelsome looking, Jim said. I didn't really see his face cause Jim had him all covered over and tole me it was too bad to look at.

When we was almost to Cairo a big steamboat hit us and we both dived over the side in opposite directions. Jim must of come up on the other shore cause I didn't see him no more that night. I made my way to dry land by hanging onto a plank that floated by just as I came up. Later we found the raft again and Jim fixed her up so we could go on down the Mississippi like before. We run nights and laid up and hid day-times; soon as nights was most gone, we stopped and tied up. Then we set out the lines for fish. A little smoke wouldn't be noticed in the early daylight so we cooked a hot meal for breakfast. We was always naked on our travels—when the mosquitoes would let us—cause the clothes we had wasn't comfortable, and besides I didn't go much on clothes nohow.

One morning I paddled about a mile up a crick in a borrowed canoe to see if I couldn't get some berries, and a couple of men came tearing toward me. I thought I was a goner, but it turned out they was running away too. They was both dressed like bums and one was about seventy and the other about thirty. They begged me to save them so I let them come with me back to the raft. Pretty soon the younger one figured out a way we could travel by day. He said we could tie Jim up and make believe he was a runaway slave we was taking back South to the owners. But Jim got tired being tied up all day, lying on his back in the wigwam, so he was mighty glad when the two fakers got in trouble a few days later and we had to all go back to moving only by night.

We dasn't stop again at any town for a long time until we had gone a good way. Then these frauds reckoned they was out of danger and could begin working their tricks in the villages again. First they done a lecture on temperance. Then in another place they started a dancing school. Another time they had a go at yellocution. They tackled missionarying, and mesmerizing, doctoring and telling fortunes, but they didn't have no luck makin' much money at any of 'em.

Finally one day the older one of the two turned Jim in as a runaway nigger for the reward. I didn't know about it until I came back looking for him so we could make a getaway and leave the fakers behind. When I found out where-to they had taken poor Jim, I went there to claim him. Well, it was the Phelps' place and it seems they was expecting a visit just then from their nephew, Tom Sawyer so they took me for him and I just let them and made believe I was Tom. Then when Tom came I managed to head him off and explain everything. He was sure surprised to see me since he thought I was dead. He said he would be Sid, Tom's brother, and the Phelps would never know the difference.

It worked out that way and, for some reason, Tom agreed to help me free Jim. After a lot of trouble we got him to the raft but, in the fracas that followed, Tom got a bullet in the leg and we couldn't leave right away like we'd planned. I had to go for a doctor so Jim was recaptured, but not for long. Tom finally told the news that Miss Watson had died and set Jim free in her will. To top the whole thing off, the Phelps found out I was Huck Finn and Sid was Tom Sawyer from Tom's Aunt Polly who just then arrived on an unexpected visit.

We had Jim out of his chains in no time and he was so tickled to hear he was free he was practically speechless. Tom told me some good news too. He said the $6000 and more interest was waiting for me and that pap hadn't got it. Then Jim spoke up and confessed that pap would never be able to drink it up like he planned since it was him he found dead in the house floating down the river.

Tom's most well, now, and got his bullet around his neck on a little chain and so there ain't nothing more to write about, and I am rotten glad of it, because if I'd a knowed what a trouble it was to make a book I wouldn't a tackled it and ain't a-going to no more.

But I reckon I got to light out for the Territory ahead of the rest, because Aunt Sally she's going to adopt me and civilize me, and I can't stand it. I been there before.

THE END

Yours truly

Huck Finn

HOMER'S ILIAD

CONDENSATION BY PROF. WILLIAM FENWICK HARRIS

The Greeks were princes of story-telling, and HOMER was their king. Who he was and where he lived is one of the unanswered questions of history. Seven cities and more claimed him as their greatest source of pride. The most we can be sure of is that to us have come down two of the many poems that bear his name, the "Iliad" and the "Odyssey."

Like the Hebrew Bible, they have become part of the heritage of universal humanity. We call them epic poems; they are rather great historical romances.

Each has a story of its own; in the "Iliad" it is the wrath of Achilles against King Agamemnon; in the "Odyssey" it is the wanderings of Odysseus on his way back from the wars at Troy. Back of them both as remoter cause is the tale of the fatal beauty of Helen. In each are innumerable short stories, which have been storehouses of romance for writers ever since first they became known.

It is one of the marvels of the Greeks that they step out of the mist of unrecorded history with a highly developed civilization, portrayed in two of the world's masterpieces of literature. The Greeks in later years wrote "lives" of Homer with great exactness and minute detail. They knew no more about the "blind bard" than do we. Indeed they were not even sure that one poet wrote both tales. But that the stories were the work of supreme genius they were as sure as have been all men since their day who have read them.

Homer was the Greeks' "best seller"; they thronged in thousands to hear him recited; their religion, their thought, their education were all based on him under whose name is told the great story of their heroes.

It is the charm of the stories of the "Iliad" and the "Odyssey" that has allured readers in all ages. As the "Iliad" is the first great romance of high adventure, of deeds of perfect chivalry and wild fighting, of brave men and noble women, so the "Odyssey" is the first great novel of adventure in strange parts, of miscreants thwarted and brought to justice by the hero, who in the end comes to his own and rescues the true wife who bides at home and waits the triumphant return of him who shall free her from the trials that beset her.

The Greeks started the modern world going. As with Icarus they thought of the flying-man, with Agamemnon of wireless telegraphy in the message he sent leaping across the sea from Troy to Argos in the flames upon the hilltops, and with Odysseus of the motion-picture in the vision of all past men and women who flitted before his eyes on his trip to the lower world, so, too, they introduced us to practically every form of human expression. The prose-romance came late in their development. The novel and the short story as they knew them for centuries were embodied in the "Iliad" and "Odyssey."

The elders of the Trojans from their seats upon the Scæan gate looked down upon the hosts of Greeks and Trojans marshaled in the plain. For nine long years the armies had contended. Why had Agamemnon brought the men of many cities to fight around the walls of Priam's Troy? What was it all about?

Homer sings of the wrath of Achilles, but the beginning of all the trouble goes far back of that, to the tale of a princely shepherd on a night surprised as he watched his flocks upon Mount Ida. The goddesses Hera, Athene, and Aphrodite make him choose one of the world-old wishes; the judgment of Paris is for a fair face and love. To fulfil her promise Aphrodite leads him to King Menelaus's court in Sparta. Back to Troy Paris brings Queen Helen and great treasure. A hue and cry follow throughout Greece; Menelaus calls to his help the great overlord, his brother Agamemnon, Achilles the sacker of cities, wily Odysseus, venerable and genial Nestor, and all the chivalry of the land with men and ships to make war on Troy.

Others must pay for the wrong-doing of Paris—old King Priam of the Ashen Spear, his venerable Queen Hecuba, Hector and his noble wife Andromache, his little son Astyanax, Cassandra, and all the rest whom the toil of war involves. Other stories of the many Greek epics, now lost, bring the tale of warring years up to the tenth, where the "Iliad" begins. Hector is the leader of the Trojans; Achilles has been the great fighting force of the Greeks, though now he has withdrawn in anger to his tent because of a slight put upon his honor by King Agamemnon.

The hostile hosts are advancing to the battle; a dramatic moment brings Menelaus and Paris in sight of one another. The wrath of Hector blazes out against Paris for all the evil and shame his theft of woman and wealth have brought. The gay and debonair Paris, however, can show splendid moments. "Hector, thy taunt is just. But throw not at me the lovely gifts of golden Aphrodite. The glorious gifts that the gods give are not to be flung away; no man could take them by mere willingness. But if thou dost wish me to battle and fight, make all the rest of the Trojans and Achaians sit down, and put me in the midst with warlike Menelaus to fight for Helen and all her goods, to see which shall conquer and prove the better man; let the rest conclude a friendship of trusty oaths; may ye dwell in fertile Troyland, and the others go back to Argos, nurse of steeds, and Achaia of fair women."

So it was that the hosts sat in high expectation in the plain, and Priam and the Trojan elders were gathered on the Scæan gate. And Priam, who bore no grudge against Helen for all the misery her fair face had brought to him and Troy—for he saw the hands of the gods in it all—called her to his side to tell him of the chiefs among whom she had once lived. Then those elders, who had long since seen their fighting days, paid the finest compliment a woman's beauty has ever received—how many thousand years ago?—as they saw Helen advancing. "No cause for anger that Trojans and well-greaved Achaians for such a woman long time should suffer sorrow." Not another word! But those old men upon the wall have drawn for you and me a picture of The World's Desire. "But even so," they continued, "let her go home upon the ships and stay not as a source of sorrow to us and to our children after us."

The high hopes raised of settling all the troubles by the duel of the champions were in vain. The contest was inconclusive and the truce was broken.

The scene changes to Troy itself. In an interval of the battle great Hector of the Glancing Helm had gone to the citadel. And there he said farewell to Andromache, his wife, and to his little boy, a picture that has never been surpassed for true tenderness, although it was so many hundred years ago. He smiled and looked upon the little boy in silence. "Ah, Hector," she cried, "stay here upon the wall! Thou art to me father and mother and brother, too, as well as lord. The foe will attack thee alone!"

"I know the day shall come," he answered, "when holy Ilios shall perish, and Priam and the folk of Priam of the goodly Ashen Spear. But thought of him, of my mother, of my brothers, does not trouble me so much as that some warrior of the Achaians shall rob thee of the day of freedom." He stretched out his hand to the little boy, who shrunk back to his nurse's breast in fear of the bronze and the horsehair crest that nodded dreadfully from the top of the helm. Straightway Hector took off the helm and placed it on the ground. And when he had kissed his son and tossed him in his arms, he spoke in prayer to Zeus and the rest of the gods. "Grant, ye gods, that this son of mine prove foremost among the Trojans, a good and mighty king. And as he comes back from battle may many a man say of him, 'A far better man than his father,' and may his mother rejoice in heart." And then he handed him back to his mother, who received him smiling through her tears, and so departed to the battle with words of high cheer.

There follow many scenes of varied action—the "Iliad" is one of the great collections of short stories in the world's literature—in which is given a perfect picture of the life of that lordly society of so long ago. The plain people play little part, although their champion, Thersites, is the first democrat mentioned in literature. Mighty deeds of derring-do, high adventure, love of lords and ladies, the pranks of merry children—are all preserved as it were in amber, and the sentiment for the most part is so modern that it is almost impossible to believe that we are reading of people who lived many hundreds of years before Christ was born.

But over all impends one dreadful fate. It is a Greek tale—yet Hector, prince and leader of the foe, is the hero of the story. Of course he is not quite so strong, not quite so great a fighter as

Achilles, the Greek champion, and all know that in the end Achilles will win. The great scenes are worked up to with consummate artistry. Achilles is still sulking in his tent; Hector is pressing the Greeks hard; Patroclus, Achilles's dearest friend, begs his chief to let him don his lord's armor and save his people; he has his way and Hector slays him. Achilles's anger blazes forth in all its passion. What now a petty slight? The great scene of the battle between the two inspires the poet to all his noblest power. They fight; Achilles pursues Hector thrice around the walls of Troy; Zeus weighs in golden scales the fates of the two; Hector is doomed to die; inexorable destiny may not be stayed. Achilles slays Hector and every heart but that of the victor is wrung with the pity of it all. And in the end, even Achilles's heart is moved. For old King Priam can neither sleep nor eat while his son's body lies dead in the camp of the foe. Against the will of all that was dearest to him he gathered great store of ransom and made his way by night under the kindly guidance of the gods to Achilles's tent and sought for the body of his dear son. It is a scene of love and pity, of chivalry and greatness of heart that all the years since then have never seen surpassed. "Be not angry with me, Patroclus," prayed Achilles, "if thou shalt learn in Hades's house that I have given back noble Hector to his dear father." And Patroclus, one may be sure, shared the pity of all brave men and all true women ever since.

IVANHOE

by

SIR WALTER SCOTT*

CONDENSATION BY PROF. WILLIAM FENWICK HARRIS

"And I must lie here like a bedridden monk!" exclaimed Ivanhoe, "while the game that gives me freedom or death is played out by the hands of others! Look from the window once again, kind maiden,

* For biographical information see page 138.

but beware that you are not marked by the archers beneath. Look once more, and tell me if they yet advance to the storm."

With patient courage Rebecca again took post at the lattice.

"What dost thou see, Rebecca?" again demanded the wounded knight.

"Nothing but the cloud of arrows flying so thick as to daze mine eyes and to hide the bowmen who shoot them."

"That cannot endure," said Ivanhoe; "if they press not right on to carry the castle by pure force of arms, the archery may avail but little against stone walls and bulwarks. Look for the Knight of the Fetterlock, fair Rebecca, and see how he bears himself; for as the leader is, so will his followers be."

"I see him not," said Rebecca.

"Foul craven!" exclaimed Ivanhoe; "does he blench from the helm when the wind blows highest?"

"He blenches not! He blenches not!" said Rebecca. "I see him now; he leads a body of men close under the outer barrier of the barbican. They pull down the piles and palisades; they hew down the barriers with axes. His high black plume floats abroad over the throng, like a raven over the field of the slain. They have made a breach in the barriers—they rush in—they are thrust back! Front-de-Bœuf heads the defenders; I see his gigantic form above the press. They throng again to the breach, and the pass is disputed hand to hand and man to man. God of Jacob! It is the meeting of two fierce tides—the conflict of two oceans moved by adverse winds!"

She turned her head from the lattice, as if unable longer to endure a sight so terrible.

"Look forth again, Rebecca," said Ivanhoe, mistaking the cause of her retiring; "the archery must in some degree have ceased, since they are now fighting hand to hand. Look again; there is now less danger."

Rebecca again looked forth, and almost immediately exclaimed: "Holy prophets of the law! Front-de-Bœuf and the Black Knight fight hand to hand on the breach, amid the roar of their followers, who watch the progress of the strife. Heaven strike with the cause of the oppressed and the captive!" She then uttered a loud shriek and exclaimed, "He is down—he is down!"

"Who is down?" cried Ivanhoe; "for our dear lady's sake, tell me which has fallen?"

"The Black Knight," answered Rebecca, faintly; then instantly again shouted with eagerness: "But no—but no! The name of the Lord of Hosts be blessed! He is on foot again and fights as if there were twenty men's strength in his single arm! His sword is broken; he snatches an ax from a yeoman; he pushes Front-de-Bœuf with blow on blow—the giant stoops and totters like an oak under the steel of the woodman. He falls—he falls! . . . The Black Knight approaches the postern with his huge ax—the thundering blows which he deals—you may hear them above all the din and shouts of the battle. Stones and beams are hailed down on the bold champion; he regards them no more than if they were thistle-down or feathers!"

"By Saint John of Acre!" said Ivanhoe, raising himself joyfully on his couch, "methought there was but one man in England that might do such a deed!"

Ivanhoe was right; the Black Knight of the Fetterlock was Richard Plantaganet of the Lion Heart, King of England, only just returned to his kingdom from the Holy Land, though but few knew of his arrival as yet. In his absence England had been under the selfish rule of the king's younger brother John, who was planning to usurp the kingdom.

The great story-teller gathers his characters together at the tournament of Ashby. There come for the sports of chivalry Rowena, heiress of Saxon rulers now dispossessed by the Normans, accompanied by her sturdy uncle Cedric; Rebecca, beautiful Jewish maiden, whose fate is constantly joined with that of Ivanhoe, disinherited son of Cedric, a father who will have naught to do with a Saxon son who is willing to accept the Normans and their ways, and even to be a devout follower of Richard the king; Isaac of York, Rebecca's father, wandering Jew of vast wealth, who is constantly the prey of the ruthless Norman nobles who would wring his riches from him by torture and imprisonment; Robin Hood and his merry men of the forest glades, not forgetting the redoubtable Friar Tuck, equally adept in the ways of the clerk, the yeoman, or the roisterer. To them are added of Norman stock the redoubtable Front-de-Bœuf, Brian de Bois-Guilbert, the prior of Jorvaulx, and Prince John; Athelstane, Saxon lord, destined by Cedric for the hand of Rowena; Gurth the swineherd and Wamba the jester; and the mysterious Black Prince, who, like Ivanhoe, makes his appearance incognito till he shall discover how things have gone in his absence.

Sir Walter prided himself on his mastery of what he called "the big bow-wow" style; no other of the Waverley Novels illustrates this power better than *Ivanhoe*. One stately and stirring event follows another, all holding the reader rapt in thrills, but none quite so much as the siege of the castle of Front-de-Bœuf by Richard and his Saxon friends. Rebecca, from the lattice recounting to the wounded Ivanhoe the fortunes of the battle, stands out in the memory of many a reader as Sir Walter's greatest success in the grand style. And despite the heroic mold in which the characters are cast, they yet surpass in the hold they gain upon the reader.

> The knights are dust,
>   And their good swords are rust,
> Their souls are with the saints, we trust.

In the passage at arms at Ashby appears the Mysterious Knight, whom the reader knows to be Ivanhoe, fresh from the Crusade in the Holy Land; in the contests of chivalry he valiantly defeats the Norman champions and bestows the prize of Queen of Beauty upon the youthful love, Rowena; the reader gets but a glimpse of a still more mysterious knight, whom he can only suspect to be the king. From the jousts all journey on their several ways, but in the forest the Normans plan a lawless ambuscade and carry off to the castle of Front-de-Bœuf, for motives of revenge, or passion, or greed, Ivanhoe, who had been wounded at Ashby, Rebecca, Rowena, and Isaac of York. The mysterious Knight of the Fetterlock appears as the timely leader of the merry men of the greenwood, who besiege the castle, to the great disaster of the lordly brigands. After the rescue of the prisoners, all save Rebecca, there follows the joyous celebration of the forest outlaws, a happy interlude between the scenes of derring-do.

The strenuous king departed for still more strenuous struggles in wining back his kingdom; Rowena and Cedric sought their home; Ivanhoe followed his chief; Brian de Bois-Guilbert, Templar though he was and pledged to holy practices, bore off his uphappy prisoner, Rebecca. But he was discovered in his wicked designs by the austere head of his order. In an assembly of the Templars, however, Rebecca was condemned to death as a sorceress who has seduced from the paths of virtue an unwilling knight! Her only chance for life lies in the ordeal of battle. Her one champion is Ivanhoe, far away though he is, whom she has cured of the wound received at Ashby.

Brian de Bois-Guilbert, by the irony of chivalry, is the champion of his order and of virtue in distress. At the last possible moment Ivanhoe comes spurring into the lists, to a victory which all the laws of fiction foreordain. Hot after him comes clattering Richard and his train, to unfurl the royal standard as undisputed King of England. And all live happy ever after? Save only Rebecca! If Ivanhoe must wed Rowena, every masculine reader feels that he would gladly offer himself to her rival. For as Prince John cried when first he saw her, "By the bald scalp of Abraham, yonder Jewess must be the very model of perfection whose charms drove frantic the wisest king that ever lived!"

JANE EYRE
by
CHARLOTTE BRONTË

CONDENSATION BY THURMAN L. HOOD

CHARLOTTE BRONTË, sister of Emily and Anne Brontë, was born April 21, 1816, and died March 31, 1855.

Their father was an Irishman of poor health and eccentric ways. Their mother died when the children were young, and they were left to bring themselves up in a bleak and solitary house, close to the churchyard, their only solace an intense enjoyment of the world of make-believe. Deaths in the family, sorrow and tribulations of all kinds, the struggle to make a way in the world by teaching and serving as governess, the necessity of acting as mother to the family, all were a part of the intense life of Charlotte.

In 1846 the three sisters issued a small volume of poems under the names of Currer, Ellis, and Acton Bell. The book was hardly noticed at the time. The three sisters each began a novel. Emily's "Wuthering Heights" and Anne's "Agnes Grey" found publishers, but "The Professor" of Charlotte remained unaccepted until she had made her name famous with other work. She threw herself into the composition of "Jane Eyre," which was published in 1847. It took the reading public by storm; the literary sensation of the day was "Who is Currer Bell?" The answer did not come till "Shirley" had been published in 1849, when the author became a part of the great world of letters. "Villette," her last book, came in 1853. The next year she was married to the Rev. Mr. Nicholls; she died the year after, when success and happiness should have crowned her life.

Beginning with the life by Charlotte's friend, Mrs. Gaskell, the three sisters have been the subject of innumerable books and articles.

At her very birth Jane Eyre was left in the cold lap of Charity. Her aunt-in-law, Mrs. Reed of Gateshead Hall, kept the orphan ten years, during which she was subjected to such hard, fixed hatred that she was glad enough to be packed off to Lowood School, a semi-charitable institution for girls.

Her career there was very honorable: from a pupil she became a teacher. She left it to become governess of Adela Varens, the ward of Mr. Edward Rochester, at Thornfield Manor. There she thoroughly liked her situation: the grand old house; the quiet library; her little chamber; the garden with its huge chestnut-tree; and the great meadow with its array of knotty thorn-trees, strong as oaks.

If Mr. Rochester had been a handsome, heroic-looking young gentleman, Jane could never have felt at ease with him. But he was a somber, moody man, with broad and jetty eyebrows, decisive nose, and grim, square mouth and jaw; and in his presence the plain little governess felt somehow happy. Yet his character was beyond her penetration; she felt a vague sense of insecurity.

He confided to her that Adela Varens was not his child, but the daughter of a Parisian dancer who had deceived him and deserted the little girl. So much he told her; but of the strange shadows that passed over his happiest moments, of his apparent affection for Jane Eyre along with his withholding from her some secret grief, she could make nothing.

Then came most mysterious happenings to Thornfield. One night Jane Eyre found the door of Mr. Rochester's room open, and his bed on fire. She managed with great difficulty to quench the flames and rouse him from the stupor into which the smoke had plunged him. He advised her to remain silent as to the affair.

Later a Mr. Mason, from Spanish Town, in Jamaica, arrived at Thornfield while Mr. Rochester was entertaining a large party. That night Jane was awakened by a cry for help. When she reached the hall the guests were aroused.

Mr. Rochester, candle in hand, was descending the stairs from the third floor. "A servant has had a nightmare," he said.

Thus he persuaded the guests back into their rooms. But all night Jane was obliged to attend Mr. Mason, who lay in a bed on the third floor, badly wounded in the arm and shoulder. From scattered hints Jane gathered that a woman had inflicted the wounds. A doctor was summoned, and before morning Mr. Rochester had spirited the wounded man away in a coach, with the doctor to watch over him.

Then Jane was suddenly summoned to Gateshead, to her aunt, Mrs. Reed, who lay dying. Mrs. Reed gave her a letter. It was from John Eyre, in Madeira, asking that his niece Jane Eyre come to him, that he might adopt her, as he was unmarried and childless. It was dated three years back. Mrs. Reed had never attempted to deliver it to Jane Eyre, because she disliked her too thoroughly to lend a hand in lifting her to prosperity.

When Jane returned to Thornfield, Mr. Rochester proposed to her; and because she loved him and believed in him, she accepted.

A month later, at the wedding, when the clergyman's lips were unclosed to ask, "Wilt thou have this woman for thy wedded wife?" in the gray old house of God, a distinct and near voice spoke in the silence of the empty church:

"The marriage cannot go on. I declare the existence of an impediment."

Asked by the clergyman for the facts, the speaker showed a document to prove that Mr. Rochester had married Bertha Mason, fifteen years before, in Spanish Town, Jamaica, and produced Mr. Mason to witness that the woman was alive and at Thornfield.

Edward Rochester confessed hardily and recklessly that he had married, as the lawyer asserted; that his wife was still living; and that he had kept her secretly at Thornfield for years. She was mad; and she came of a mad family, idiots and maniacs for three generations. He had been inveigled into the marriage by her family, with the connivance of his father and brother, who had desired him to marry a fortune. He invited the clergyman, the lawyer, and Mr. Mason to come up to Thornfield and see what sort of a being he had been cheated into espousing, and judge whether or not he had a right to break the compact.

At Thornfield he took them to the third story. In a room without a window there burnt a fire, guarded by a high and strong fender, and a lamp suspended from the ceiling by a chain. A trusty maid-servant bent over the fire, apparently cooking something. In the deep shade, at the farther end of the room, a figure ran backward and forward. What it was, at first sight, one could not tell; it groveled, seemingly, on all-fours; it snatched and growled like some strange wild animal; but it was covered with clothing; and a quantity of dark, grizzled hair, wild as a mane, hid its head and face.

"That is *my wife*," said Mr. Rochester.

Then all withdrew.

That night Jane stole away from Thornfield. The few shillings that she possessed she gave to the driver of the first coach she saw, to take her as far as he would for the money. Thirty-six hours later he let her off at a crossroads in the moorlands. Into the heather she walked. That night she ate bilberries, and slept under a crag.

Two days later, famished and drenched, she was taken into Marsh End, the house of the Reverend St. John Rivers, a young and ambitious clergyman in the neighboring village of Morton. His two sisters, Mary and Diana, were more than kind to Jane. They were soon to return to their work as governesses in a large south-of-England city.

St. John secured employment for Jane as mistress of the new girls' school in Morton. His plan was to become a missionary in India. He asked Jane to become his wife and go with him. But something kept her from consenting—he did not really love her; he felt the call to missionary work, but she did not.

Then he discovered for her that her uncle had died, leaving her twenty thousand pounds. This was confirmed by Mr. Briggs, the solicitor in London. She discovered, too, that the mother of St. John and Mary and Diana had been her father's sister, so that they, too, should have been heirs to her uncle in Madeira. She insisted on a division of the legacy with them.

One night St. John was pressing her for her final decision. The one candle was dying out; the room was full of moonlight. She heard a voice from somewhere cry—

"Jane! Jane! Jane!"

Next day she was on her way to Thornfield. In thirty-six hours she arrived at "The Rochester Arms," two miles away. With much misgiving she walked up to Thornfield—to find only a blackened ruin.

Back at the inn she learned that Thornfield Hall had burned down about harvest-time in the previous year. The fire had broken out in the dead of night. Mr. Rochester had tried to rescue his wife. She had climbed on to the roof, where she had stood, waving her arms, and shouting out till they could hear her a mile off. Mr. Rochester had ascended through the skylight. The crowd had heard him call "Bertha!" They had seen him approach her; and then she had yelled, and given a spring, and the next minute she had lain dead on the pavement.

Mr. Rochester had been taken from the ruins alive but sadly hurt; one eye had been knocked out, and one hand so crushed that the surgeon had had to amputate it directly. The other eye inflamed; he lost the sight of that also.

He was now at Ferndean, a manor-house on a farm he had, about thirty miles off; quite a desolate spot. There Jane found him, sad, helpless, and crippled. She married him. Eventually the sight returned to his eye, so that when his first-born was put into his arms he could see that the boy had inherited his own eyes, as they once were—large, brilliant and black. On that occasion, with a full heart, he acknowledged that God had tempered judgment with mercy.

Diana and Mary Rivers were both married soon after, and alternately, once a year, came to visit Jane and Mr. Rochester. St. John Rivers left for India, to labor until called at length into the joy of his Lord.

~✦~

JEROME
A POOR MAN*

by

MARY E. WILKINS-FREEMAN

CONDENSATION WRITTEN BY SPECIAL REQUEST
BY MARY E. WILKINS-FREEMAN

MRS. MARY ELEANOR WILKINS-FREEMAN was a direct descendant of the Puritans. In her was born an understanding of old New England, its quaint and lovable people and their ways. She spent her childhood and youth in Randolph, the place of her birth (January 7, 1862), and in Brattleboro, Vermont. So she knew her New England characters through intimate contact during many years.

Wide reading and keen observation were most important factors in Mary Wilkins's early education, although she took a course at Mt. Holyoke Seminary. Nevertheless, her first manuscript was so ungrammatical and involved that it was rejected.

The girl writer, however, knew in her heart that she was destined to tell the stories that filled her imagination. Quite undaunted by rejections, she toiled at writing until "The Humble Romance" and "The Revolt of Mother" established her fame. "But," says the first publisher who read her work, "the hard work, the reading, and the study that the little sensitive-faced woman put in must have been stupendous."

These stories, with "A New England Nun and Other Stories" and "Silence and Other Stories," won her distinction as a skilful writer of short stories, rich in suggestiveness and charm. She excelled in sympathetic interpretation and

* Printed by permission of, and arrangement with, Harper & Bros., authorized publishers.

*analysis of the wonderful patient life about her. This is true
in her novels as well as in her short stories.*

*"Jerome: A Poor Man," "The Jamesons," and "The Por-
tion of Labor" are among those which have been widely
read.*

Mary E. Wilkins-Freeman died March 15, 1930.

For a poor New England boy, Jerome Edwards, the tragedy of
life began at the age of ten. His father, Abel Edwards, had gone,
that morning, with his wagon and old nodding white horse, to his
wood-lot to cut wood for Doctor Prescott.

Doctor Prescott had an obsession for owning land. When there
was a lack of ready money to pay his exorbitant bills, he seized with
avidity upon a mortgage, and he foreclosed without grace or mercy.

Doctor Prescott had held a thousand-dollar mortgage upon the
Edwards house for years. Jerome had always a fancy of it as a
huge black bird with hissing beak perched upon the ridge-pole.

The old white horse coming home, turning out at the beck of a
phantom driver for the bad places in the country road, was met upon
his arrival at the Edwards cottage with wild shrieks in a woman's
voice, a child's frightened sob, and a boy's sober answer to the eager
questions of a small mob of men and boys following after.

There was an immediate rush to the wood-lot, but Jerome had
reached the spot the first of all. On the shore of a black pool of
water, reputed among the boys to be bottomless, he found his father's
hat. Jerome weighted it with stones and flung it in. Then he bolted
for home by another route. "Let 'em say father drowned himself
now," he gasped out as he ran.

Abel Edwards had been missing two years when Jerome, studying the situation day and night knew the truth: They could never,
although they half starved themselves, meet the interest of the mortgage. He made a plan.

He went to consult Squire Eben Merritt. The squire was a notable
hunter and fisher and had been bent that morning upon a fishing
excursion. He was the kindest man in the place, not rich as had
been his ancestors, but lived as a rich man, being possessed of generosity which is the real Horn of Plenty.

Jerome looked straight at the squire and made his little speech.

He had rehearsed it often. When he had finished, the squire burst into a great roar of laughter and caught the boy by the shoulder. "You don't mean you planned this all yourself?"

"Yes, sir. I've been layin' awake nights, plannin'."

"How old are you?"

"Twelve, sir."

"By Jove!"

Then a lovely, gentle little girl stole into the room. Her dimpled arms and neck were bare and her shower of gold curls fell to her waist. She wore a frock of soft blue below which showed the finest starched pantalets and little blue Morocco shoes. The squire turned and caught her up, and she sat on one shoulder, with his golden beard spreading over her blue skirt.

The squire told Jerome to call on Doctor Prescott and show his plan.

A small, dark, very kind, and quick lady, who was the squire's wife and Lucina's mother, showed Jerome the door, and he went down the street in a daze. Jerome almost forgot the important paper he carried. He had never seen a little girl like Lucina Merritt.

Jerome called on Doctor Prescott, who deigned to read his paper and then summarily dismissed him. He hated him in a strange way for a man to hate a boy. On his way home Jerome encountered Squire Merritt coming out of a woodland road with a great string of fish. "What luck, son?" he called out.

"He turned me out. I'd like to kill him."

The squire laughed and made Jerome walk along with him to his sister Camilla's, who kept elderly maiden state in the old Merritt house.

Jerome always remembered that hour of tea-drinking and cake-eating in the arbor with Squire Merritt and his sister and little Lucina, as he would have an especially beautiful turn of his kaleidoscope of life.

Until he was much older Jerome did not fully comprehend in that way Eben Merritt had solved his financial difficulties. Then he discovered that the squire had made great sacrifices of his none too large competency to buy from Doctor Prescott, and take the Edwards mortgage into his own hands.

Now life began to look brighter for Jerome. He could not go to school in the ordinary sense, so he went direct to Nature. He, in his scanty free time, roamed fields and woods. Jake Noyes, a queer character who ostensibly was Doctor Prescott's coachman, but who had been permitted to assimilate, and some said had even been taught, much of the doctor's medical lore, taught Jerome much about simples.

Jerome attained a local under-celebrity, since he gave aid for nothing and with success.

Gradually Jerome's business ideas developed and strengthened. There was an exceptional chance for a sawmill in the village. He went one evening to Lawyer Means with a request that he should sell two hundred and sixty-five dollars' worth of his land on Graystone Brook, and came away with the deed. He then began to save for the mill.

In those days he worked like a tiger, for he was in love. That meant he had become a conqueror of all foes in his path and achiever of the impossible.

Lucina Merritt had come home from school and he had seen her in church. Lucina Merritt was a very great beauty and her father contrived to deck her out like one. He bought a little white horse for her. Then Lawrence Prescott came home, and was often seen cantering about with Lucina, on a blooded horse his father owned.

Jerome worked harder. Occasions multiplied during which he and Lucina met. At first she wondered at him obviously with dilating blue eyes; then she began to blush softly.

Jerome's looks at her could have but one meaning.

In the meantime Elmira Edwards had her own little romance with Lawrence Prescott, but it promised to be an unhappy one. Lawrence was threatened with disinheritance, and Elmira dismissed him. Then she fell ill, and that night was in a high fever. Lawrence came and she did not know him. Lawrence went home and had a scene with his father.

As under the circumstances Prescott could not be employed, a doctor from Westbrook was sent for. Elmira was ill several weeks. Lawrence and his mother were assiduous in care and attention.

Her illness cost so much that Jerome had not been able to make good the deficit caused by a loan to Ozias Lamb, to prevent a foreclosure of a mortgage on his little home. The loan had postponed his mill. Sometimes Jerome reflected with bitter amusement upon the bet made in the village store a few years ago. Egged on by some village wags, Doctor Prescott and Simon Basset had signed before Lawyer Means a document whereby they promised to pay, for the benefit of the poor, ten thousand apiece, if Jerome Edwards should ever have twenty-five thousand and give it all away.

Jerome thought it the safest business deal in all creation. Meanwhile he worked so hard he seldom saw Lucina. He had not the time to call upon her. He was sure that they understood each other, although no formal engagement had been made. He was sure that Lucina understood that he could not call because he was working so hard for her sake. But Lucina did not understand. She grew thin and pale, and her parents, fearing a decline, sent her West for a change.

But he was not sure when she returned from the West, looking blooming, and sent him a little note informing him sweetly but firmly that they would be friends but nothing more.

Even then Jerome did not believe. His faith in the girl was almost sublime. However, he made no attempt to see her and did not answer the letter. He worked harder and harder.

The mill was built and work began. Jerome set himself a certain sum to be earned before he went to see Lucina.

One day the village was startled by the news that Col. Jack Lamson had come into a fortune of sixty-five thousand dollars from some old mining stock, and had gone to Boston with Lawyer Means upon business connected with it.

Shortly after that the village had another shock. Abel Edwards came home. He had been all the time on a farm fifty miles away, and had brought home all his earnings in a tin box.

But nobody in the village knew that the box had been robbed in a country tavern where Abel had stayed overnight, and Jerome had replaced the stolen gold with some from a secret hoard of his own.

Jerome was prospering, when one night there came a rain that was almost a cloudburst, the brook ran in flood, and the next morning the mill was carried away.

Jerome for the first time had given up hope, when Colonel Lamson suddenly died and left twenty-five thousand dollars to him, twenty thousand to Lucina, five thousand to Eben Merritt, ten thousand to John Jennings, five thousand to Lawyer Means.

People at once remembered the old bet in the store. Would Jerome give away the money? He soon set doubts at rest. He gave the money to the poor of the village, and a factory was to be set up, using the money as capital stock.

The bet was not binding legally. Prescott knew, but did not fail to abide by his word. Simon Basset hung himself before he knew **he** need not pay a dollar unless he chose.

Squire Merritt's wife took a hand. She offered Jerome the five thousand dollars which her husband had inherited, to build a new mill, but Jerome refused, although he knew that it meant giving up Lucina.

Mrs. Merritt said that she inferred that he did not wish to marry Lucina. Jerome burst out with mad vows of his love for Lucina.

Mrs. Merritt returned that he loved his pride more. Finally Jerome yielded. They were standing outside under a tree, talking, and in the parlor were Elmira and Lawrence Prescott, talking. Everything was settled happily for them. Doctor Prescott had given his consent.

When Jerome met Lucina in the parlor she clung to him **and** wept at first, then she drew him to a little damask sofa and took **a** letter from her pocket. They read it together. It was from Col. Jack Lamson, dated just before his death. In it he begged that the sum of twenty thousand dollars be regarded by Lucina as a dowry,

to be employed by you both when you wed Jerome Edwards, for your mutual good and profit during your married life.

I am, dear Miss Lucina, your obedient servant to command and your affectionate foster-father,

JOHN LAMSON.

P.S.—I meant Jerome's twenty-five thousand to be used as he used it.—J. L.

KENILWORTH

by

SIR WALTER SCOTT*

CONDENSATION BY REV. R. PERRY BUSH, D.D.

There could be no fitter setting for a story of love and tragedy than that afforded by the court of England during the reign of Elizabeth.

* For biographical information see page 138.

It was the heyday of gorgeous costuming and an age saturated with the occult. Every one patronized the astrologers and the alchemists. The queen coupled with the dignity and strength of the monarch the foibles of the weak. It was her policy to play one favorite against another and thereby secure the working of her own strong will, but she often gave way to furious temper and she was most susceptible to flattery. She was forever undecided between her duty to her subjects and her attachment to Robert Dudley, the Earl of Leicester, whom it was commonly reported that she really intended to marry, for he was a courtier *par excellence,* and his ambition to share the throne overpowered every other purpose of his life. He had, however, been secretly wedded to Amy Robsart, and so, to further his chances to be king, he consorted with one Richard Varney, and plotted the murder of his wife, which was accomplished at Abingdon Manor.

These threads of fact, with many others of fancy, Scott wove into the fabric of *Kenilworth.* To him who would listen to those who make fulsome compliment and laudation a fine art, to one who would understand the subtle poisoning of the mind by insinuation, to such as are interested in the machinations of men and women anxious to mingle in high society, to all who would be regaled by the conversations of lords and ladies and have unfolded for their edification a phase of history which never appears in the text-books of our schools, at the same time that they are reading a romance of wonderful interest and plot, *Kenilworth* offers a rare and wholesome treat.

The story opens at an inn kept by one Gosling, whose nephew, Michael Lambourne, a swaggering drunkard, returns after years of absence and finds that Tony Foster, an old crony, who lighted the fires when Latimer and Ridley were burned, is keeping guard over a beautiful woman at Cumnor Mansion. Lambourne gains admission there, accompanied by Tressilian, a knight of peerless character, who is in search of her to whom he has been betrothed and who has been lured away from her father's house. Lambourne becomes an accomplice in crime with Foster, and Tressilian meets the mysterious lady, who proves to be none other than Amy Robsart, for it was she who was his promised bride.

He tries to persuade her to return to her father, but in vain, and in attempting to escape from the premises he meets Richard Varney, master of horse to Leicester, a shrewd, calculating villain, who is a constant spur to the earl's ambition to be king.

Tressilian naturally concludes that Amy is this fellow's mistress, and, drawing his sword, overcomes and would have slain him but for the timely arrival of Lambourne, when he was obliged to flee, and, knowing the queen's interest in such affairs, he resolves to obtain her intervention in Amy's behalf.

And here Scott makes use of a superstitious bent of the age. Tressilian's horse loses a shoe and a blacksmith cannot be found until an imp of a boy leads the way to a mysterious farrier, named Wayland Smith, who is thought by those who know him to be an emissary of Satan, and who turns out to be an alchemist with a laboratory underground, and who is persuaded to enter the employ of Tressilian, and with him visits Sir Hugh Robsart, who signs a warrant of attorney to help to secure Leicester's powerful influence in persuading the queen to free Amy from Varney.

Tressilian and Wayland soon after this make a visit to Lord Sussex, and when he, for a seeming discourtesy to the queen's physician, is called to court for explanation, they accompany him.

The depicting of this trip to Greenwich is fascinating. The obeisance to royalty; the first step in Sir Walter Raleigh's career when he submits his elegant cloak for Elizabeth to walk upon; the boat; the river; the discussion of Shakespeare and a hundred touches of genius—it must be read in full to be appreciated.

Sussex, upon examination, is fully exonerated, and thereupon calls the queen's attention to the fact that Amy Robsart is cruelly held prisoner, and forthwith Varney and Leicester are summoned into the royal presence. And before the latter has opportunity to speak, Varney affirms that Amy is his wife; and, as every one is cognizant of Leicester's confusion, Varney assures Elizabeth that it is due to the earl's transcendent love for her gracious self. The case is apparently settled, and Varney is ordered to appear at the coming festivities at Kenilworth, and to bring with him the woman who has been the occasion of so much trouble.

Here is a problem! Amy will never consent to be received as Varney's wife. She must somehow be detained at Cumnor!

It resolves into a battle of the alchemists.

Demetrius, in Varney's employ, prepares a drug for Amy, but Wayland, as Tressilian's servant, enters her apartments as a peddler and provides an antidote for the poison. He also apprises her of the enemies by whom she is surrounded and with him she flees from Cumnor.

The time of the great carnival at Kenilworth is near at hand. Multitudes are on their way thither. Every avenue of approach is crowded. Wayland and Amy attach themselves to a group of strolling players, and after many interesting experiences reach the castle, where she is by chance lodged in a room in Mervyn's Tower, which has been assigned to Tressilian.

Here she writes a letter to Leicester, beseeching him to come to her, and, after tying it with a true-love knot of her hair, intrusts it to Wayland to deliver, but it is stolen from him.

Meanwhile Tressilian has occasion to return to his room, and is dumfounded to find Amy there; but as she expected Leicester would come in answer to her letter, she bound Tressilian not to speak or act in her behalf for the next twenty-four hours, and he departed to witness the coming of the queen. According to history it was a wonderful preparation that Leicester made for the reception of Elizabeth at Kenilworth. Money was lavished without stint, and the details of pomp and pageantry gleam vividly before us when touched by the descriptive genius of Scott. At Warwick there is music, a salvo of smaller arms, a round of artillery, and a roaring welcome by the multitude. The cavalcade is illuminated by two hundred waxen tapers borne by men on horseback.

The queen is adorned with countless jewels and attended by the ladies of the court and valiant knights magnificently attired, among whom Leicester glitters like a golden image. The procession advances over a bridge built for the occasion, and here the courtiers dismount; a floating island reaches the shore and the "Lady of the Lake" announces that this is the first time she has ever risen to pay homage, but she could not refrain from obeisance to her gracious Majesty. Then, as the queen enters the castle, there is a discharge of fireworks, new and wonderful in that age, and she moves on through pageants of heathen gods and heroes of antiquity to the great hall, which is hung with gorgeous silken tapestry, where she is seated by Leicester upon a royal throne, who after kissing her hand and eulogizing her most profusely, retires and shortly reappears appareled from head to foot in dazzling white.

The queen very shortly after sends for Varney, and asks why

his wife presumes to disobey the mandate of her sovereign and absent herself from the festivities, and he replies that she is indisposed and presents certificates to that purpose. These Tressilian madly asserts are false, but, remembering his promise to Amy to keep silent for twenty-four hours, he halts and stammers and the queen orders Raleigh to place him under restraint.

Then follows the banquet, served upon a most magnificent scale, and at its close Varney seeks Leicester and assures him that the stars promise that he shall marry the queen, and he also notifies him that Tressilian has a mistress in Mervyn's Tower.

From here events hurry to a climax. The next morning Amy escapes from her room and is in hiding near the plaisance, when close at hand Leicester avows his love to Elizabeth and is given great encouragement; but, as they separate, the queen discovers Amy, who declares that she is not the wife of Varney, and that "Leicester knows all."

Accordingly she is hurried to the presence of the earl, where Elizabeth rages violently, but Leicester's marriage remains still unrevealed, and Amy is thought to be insane and she is placed in custody. Moreover, Leicester is angry with Amy for coming to Kenilworth and exposing him to the resentment of the queen, and he resolves to see her and insist that for the present she must consent to be known as Varney's wife.

This proposition is scornfully refused. Amy, no longer a child, but with the strength of injured womanhood, calls upon the earl as a man and as her lawful husband to take her to Elizabeth and acknowledge that she is his wife.

Leicester yields to this masterly plea to his honor and prepares for the ordeal; but Varney, clearly perceiving that this involves his own personal ruin, concludes that "either he or Amy must die," and is not slow in deciding which it shall be. He persuades Leicester that Amy is conniving with Tressilian, and so convinces him of her perfidy that the earl finally consents to her doom.

That evening Leicester and Tressilian meet. The latter still believes that Varney holds Amy in his power, and he begins to plead for her; but his words and motives are misinterpreted. Swords are drawn and they do battle, but are interrupted and meet again on the morrow in a secluded spot, when, just as Leicester is about to prevail, his sword is seized by the young rascal, Dicky Smudge, who delivers to him Amy's letter, which he had stolen from Wayland. The tangle of affairs is unraveled and Amy is proclaimed as the Countess of Leicester.

At this revelation, Elizabeth is beside herself with rage, declaring that "Leicester's stolen marriage has cost her a husband and England a king."

In the violence of her chagrin and anger she forgets for a while her royal dignity, and recovers command of herself only when Lord Burleigh warns her that "such weakness little becomes a queen." Meanwhile Varney fatally shoots the drunken Lambourne and conducts Amy to Cumnor, where she is confined in Foster's bedchamber, a mysterious room reached by a drawbridge, which she is admonished never to attempt to cross; but when Tressilian and Raleigh come to take her to Kenilworth, and she hears the sound of their horses' hoofs, she thinks it is the earl and rushes from her room, and Varney has so manipulated the drawbridge that she falls to her death. When, however, this villain learns how matters have developed, he commits suicide. His alchemist is found dead in his laboratory and Tony Foster disappears and his skeleton is found long afterward in a secret chamber where he hid his gold. Leicester retires from court for a season, but later is again a favorite in waiting upon the queen, and dies at last by taking poison he had designed for another.

KIDNAPPED

by

ROBERT LOUIS STEVENSON*

CONDENSATION BY JAMES B. CONNOLLY

It was dawn; the blackbirds were whistling in the lilacs, the mists of the valley arising and melting, when I set out for the house of Shaw. On the forenoon of the second day, coming to the top of a

* For biographical information see page 90.

hill, I saw the city of Edinburgh smoking like a kiln below me. There was a flag upon the castle and ships anchored to the blue floor of the Firth, a sight which thrilled me.

I walked on toward Cramond, making inquiries as I went of my uncle, who seemed to be in no favor thereabout, some giving me a half-civil word, some a scowl or a curse for an answer. It was night, and his house barred and dark when I came to it; and it was a long while before my shouts and knocks brought him to the window from where, with a blunderbuss by way of welcome, he screamed to inquire my business.

It was a mean, stooping, clay-faced creature; and a big muckle house and an ill-kept one I saw when at last he let me in, with dirt, mice, and spiders having their play of it. Here I stayed some days, the while he sparingly fed me with porridge and a rare half-cup of ale.

One night he gave me forty pounds, saying it was a debt he owed my father, and with it gave me also a rusty key to the high stair tower, telling me to bring him down the chest at the top of it. I went, poor fool, into the dark to bring it; and only a blink of summer lightning saved me from stepping into space and being dashed sheer down from the top of the tower.

Of the estate that he had defrauded my father in life I had then no suspicion; but that happening of the tower gave me a glimpse of his villainy. In the morning my body would be discovered at the foot of the tower, his forty pounds in my pockets, as one trying to escape after robbing his host. What a tale he would make of it!

Next day my uncle spoke of a friend, Captain Elias Hoseason, of the brig *Covenant*, then lying off Queensferry on the Firth, proposing that I go to call there with him. I agreed, being eager to get away from that evil house; also I had knowledge that residing in Queensferry was Mr. Rankiellor, the counselor and agent, a friendly person and one who knew more than any other of my father's business in life.

We arrived at Queensferry, but I did not see Mr. Rankiellor, foreby I first allowed myself to be led into looking over the brig with Captain Hoseason and my uncle. It was so that I came to be knocked on the head and kidnapped to sea on the agreement between my uncle and Captain Hoseason that I was to be sold into slavery in the Carolines.

It was a fair wind the first day to sea, but following days were all head winds, the ship making so little way on her course to the north that Captain Hoseason made a fair wind of a foul one by heading her south back the way we had come. During this time of bad weather the cabin-boy was killed by the first officer in a drunken passion, his body cast overboard, and I pressed into his berth.

It was night, with a swell and a thick white fog, the men listening for breakers, when the brig ran over a boat; and sent all but one man to the bottom. That one, with a leap and a clutch which showed his rare agility and strength, boarded us by way of the brig's bowsprit.

He entered the cabin, or roundhouse, looking cool as you please, and called for something to eat and the drink to wash it down. He was a well-set, rather small man with a dark face and dancing bright eyes. Under his greatcoat were two silver-mounted pistols, a dirk, and a great-sword. He made his name known, Alan Stewart Breck, and without fear announced himself as on a mission for Prince Charlie. From a money-belt about him he offered the captain sixty guineas to be set ashore on Linnhe Loch.

The captain shook hands on the bargain, but at once went on deck to plot with his first officer as how best to come at the money-belt. I had no love for the captain, and also it was scurvy hospitality to a man we had all but drowned; so I warned the stranger of the plot. Surprised he was, but not put out, asking me would I stand with him. Jacobite though he was, I said I would.

Two doors and a skylight furnished entrance to the roundhouse. Alan placed me with loaded pistols where I could see to shoot through at whoever might come at one closed door or through the glass skylight. The other door he left open, standing before it with dirk and sword. They came with a rush of feet and many loud cries toward Alan. I heard a shout from him and a cry as of some one hurt. Then came five men with a spare yard for a battering-ram to drive my door in. For the first time in my life I fired a pistol; and hit one of them, which drove them back. By then Alan's sword was running blood; and the first mate, he who had murdered the cabin-boy, lay dying on the floor. Another lay beside him.

They came next to my side, some to the barred door and one dropping through the skylight to the floor, where, after first closing my eyes, I shot him. He dropped with a horrible groan. Another one's legs dangled through the skylight, and him I shot, too, he dropping dead atop of his companion. Alan was then dirking one who clung to his legs, and putting the cutlass to another who was coming head on at him. A third held a cutlass over him and yet more were crowding at him through the door. He seemed lost; but he broke clear and, taking his distance, clove one, clove another, and then, his sword flashing like quicksilver, drove the others like sheep along the deck.

We were masters of the brig. Alan embraced and kissed me, saying: "David, I love you like a brother. But oh, man, am I no the bonny fighter!" and sitting down by the table, sword in hand, he burst into a Gaelic song.

The very next night we struck on a reef. I was thrown into the sea, thinking I would drown, but found a spar and with it kicked myself along till my feet found quiet water and dry land. Of the ship or her company I could see nothing. Later I learned that all but the wounded were safe. The ship herself was a total loss to Captain Hoseason, which I did not grieve to hear.

After days of wandering and secret inquiry, for he was one with a price on his head, I found Alan. It was in the same hour that I witnessed the killing of Campbell of Glenure, the man who had been doing the King's will against the Jacobites. The shot came in such fashion that I seemed to be an accomplice. I had to flee or be hanged. It was Alan who secured my immediate escape. For two months thereafter, with redcoats guarding every road and glen, I followed Alan through the country of the Campbells.

It was wet and cold and slim food for us both, with now and then a little something not much better in the hut of a Jacobite. Weary I grew and full of pain, crawling the wet heather and climbing the ragged crags and hills. Posted bills promised great rewards for our capture—I saw them everywhere—and many there were who knew us for what we were; but never one, poor and miserable though they might be, to speak the word of betrayal. "Such," cried Alan, proudly, "is the loyalty of the Hielander!"

We came safe at last to Queensferry and the home of Mr. Rankiellor, who proved a shrewd, kindly friend and who at once set about retrieving my rights in the Shaw estate. "Your father," he explained, "was a good man, but weak. He loved your mother. To win your mother he let your uncle steal the estates. But he will have them back soon."

Alan aided us greatly in our plans. Half by quick wit and half by sheer boldness, he had my uncle admit his plan to have me kidnapped and sold into slavery in the Carolines, Mr. Rankiellor and his clerk all the while listening in the shadows. And so I came into my own.

And Alan, who made a man of me? All he asked was to be put on the road of his mission. As to that, let me say if I say no more, that he went safe on his way and all went well with him thereafter.

~◊~

THE LAST DAYS OF POMPEII

by

EDWARD BULWER-LYTTON

CONDENSATION BY PROF. WILLIAM FENWICK HARRIS

EDWARD GEORGE EARLE LYTTON BULWER, more often known to novel readers as Bulwer-Lytton, was born in London, May 25, 1803. He was more of a prodigy in his youth and had a much more public career than most men who have achieved fame as novelists. At the age of fifteen he distinguished himself by publishing a volume of poems and by falling so violently in love that he became highly morbid when his proposal of marriage was not taken seriously by the father of the girl he loved. She died a few years later and Bulwer said that the disappointment embittered his whole life. At Cambridge, he won a medal for the excellence of a poem and published another book of verse.

In 1827 he had sufficiently recovered from his premature love-affair to marry, against his mother's wishes, a brilliant beauty of society. The marriage was doomed from the outset to be unhappy, for both Bulwer and his wife were too

*unrestrained to live together. They quarreled, were legally
separated, and continued to quarrel in print for years.*

*Bulwer was rapidly winning renown. His first novels were
successes, but it was not until "The Last Days of Pompeii"
(1834) that his fame was assured. Nine years later appeared
"The Last of the Barons," which many good judges have
considered his best work. He wrote numerous other stories,
novels of society, of crime, of mysteries, of family life. He
was the most successful dramatist of his time. He dabbled
in journalism. For ten years he was a member of Parliament,
was later secretary for the colonies, and in 1866 was raised
to the peerage as Baron Lytton. He died on January 18,
1873.*

" 'Glaucus the Athenian, thy time has come,' said a loud and clear
voice; 'the lion awaits thee.'

" 'I am ready,' said the Athenian. He had bent his limbs so as
to give himself the firmest posture at the expected rush of the lion,
with his small and shining weapon raised on high, in the faint hope
that one well-directed thrust might penetrate through the eye to the
brain of his grim foe.

"But to the unutterable astonishment of all, the beast seemed
not even aware of the presence of the criminal. At the first moment
of its release it halted abruptly in the arena, raised itself half on
end, snuffing the upward air with impatient sighs; then suddenly
it sprang forward, but not on the Athenian. At half speed it circled
round and round the space, turning its vast head from side to side
with an anxious and perturbed gaze, as if seeking only some avenue
of escape; once or twice it endeavored to leap up the parapet that
divided it from the audience, and, on failing, uttered rather a baffled
howl than its deep-toned and kingly roar. It evinced no sign either
of wrath or of hunger; its tail drooped along the sand, instead of
lashing its gaunt sides; and its eye, though it wandered at times to
Glaucus, rolled again listlessly from him. At length, as if tired of
attempting to escape, it crept with a moan into its cage, and once
more laid itself down to rest.

"The first surprise of the assembly at the apathy of the lion soon
grew into resentment at its cowardice; and the populace already
merged their pity for the fate of Glaucus into angry compassion for
their own disappointment. The manager called to the keeper:

" 'How is this? Take a goad, prick him forth, and then close the door of the den.'

"As the keeper, with some fear, but more astonishment, was preparing to obey, a loud cry was heard at one of the entrances of the arena; there were a confusion, a bustle, voices of remonstrance suddenly breaking forth, and suddenly silenced at the reply. All eyes turned in wonder toward the quarter of the disturbance; the crowd gave way, and suddenly Sallust appeared on the senatorial benches, his hair disheveled, breathless, heated, half exhausted. He cast his eyes hastily around the ring. 'Remove the Athenian,' he cried; 'haste, he is innocent! Arrest Arbaces the Egyptian: *he* is the murderer of Apæcides!'

" 'Art thou mad, O Sallust!' said the prætor, rising from his seat. 'What means this raving?'

" 'Remove the Athenian! Quick! or his blood be on your head. Prætor, delay, and you answer with your own life to the emperor! I bring with me the eye-witness to the death of the priest Apæcides. Room there! Stand back! Give way! People of Pompeii, fix every eye upon Arbaces. There he sits! Room there for the priest Calenus!'

"Pale, haggard, fresh from the jaws of famine and of death, his face fallen, his eyes dull as a vulture's, his broad frame gaunt as a skeleton, Calenus was supported into the very row in which Arbaces sat. His releasers had given him sparingly of food; but the chief sustenance that nerved his feeble limbs was revenge!

" 'The priest Calenus! Calenus!' cried the mob. '*Is* it he? No, it is a dead man!'

" 'It *is* the priest Calenus,' said the prætor, gravely. 'What hast thou to say?'

" 'Arbaces of Egypt is the murderer of Apæcides, the priest of Isis; these eyes saw him deal the blow. It is from the dungeon into which he plunged me, it is from the darkness and horror of a death by famine, that the gods have raised me to proclaim his crime! Release the Athenian—*he* is innocent!'

" 'It is for this, then, that the lion spared him. A miracle! a miracle!' cried Pansa.

" 'A miracle! a miracle!' shouted the people. 'Remove the Athenian. *Arbaces to the lion!*'

"The power of the prætor was as a reed beneath the whirlwind; still, at his word the guards had drawn themselves along the lower benches, on which the upper classes sat separate from the vulgar. They made a feeble barrier; the waves of the human sea halted for a moment, to enable Arbaces to count the exact moment of his doom! In despair, and in a terror which beat down even pride, he glanced his eyes over the rolling and rushing crowd, when, right above them, through the wide chasm which had been left in the velaria, he beheld a strange and awful apparition; he beheld, and his craft restored his courage!

"He stretched his hand on high; over his lofty brow and royal features there came an expression of unutterable solemnity and command.

" 'Behold!' he shouted with a voice of thunder which stilled the roar of the crowd; 'behold how the gods protect the guiltless! The fires of the avenging Orcus burst forth against the false witness of my accusers!' "

The fires of the "avenging Orcus" were those of the great eruption of Vesuvius in A.D. 79. Toward such a melodramatic climax, furnished him by nature, the author had been spinning the lives of his characters in the little city which nestled under the shadow of the volcano.

The converging threads of the story are many, giving in the final weaving a complete picture of the life of Pompeii—its shops, tiny palaces, baths, forum, theater, circus, and all that daily took place in the energetic life of this toy copy of Rome at the beginning of the Christian era. The story centers around Glaucus the Athenian, brilliant, gay, witty descendant of a nobler race frivoling himself away amid the coarser pleasures of the Romans, until finally all that was fine in him was brought forth by his love for Ione of Naples, who, like himself, was a child of Greece. And alongside this tale of love runs the pathetic story of Nydia, the blind slave girl, who centers all her hopes of happiness in winning the affection of Glaucus. To this end she gains possession of a love potion which the opulent Julia has had prepared in the belief that it will bring to her the much-desired Glaucus. In reality the potion is a poison which will drive the unfortunate drinker mad. It is designed by the sinister Egyptian Arbaces to clear his path to Ione from his rival Glaucus. In his raving, Glaucus comes upon Arbaces just as the latter has killed Ione's brother Apæcides, a young priest of Isis, who, much to the annoyance of Arbaces, has embraced the new Christian faith. Arbaces throws the guilt upon poor Glaucus with apparent success.

But the priest Calenus was a hidden witness, with the final result shown in the great episode of the book. As the crowd in the circus turned their eyes toward Vesuvius they beheld "a fire that shifted and wavered in its hues with every moment, now fiercely luminous, now of a dull and dying red, that again blazed terrifically forth with intolerable glare. Then there arose on high the universal shrieks of women; the men stared at one another, but were dumb. At that moment they felt the earth shake beneath their feet; the walls of the theater trembled, and beyond in the distance they heard the crash of falling roofs; an instant more and the mountain-cloud seemed to roll toward them, dark and rapid, like a torrent; at the same time it cast forth from its bosom a shower of ashes mixed with vast fragments of burning stone! Over the crushing vines, over the desolate streets, over the amphitheater itself, far and wide, with many a mighty splash in the agitated sea, fell that awful shower! No longer thought the crowd of justice or of Arbaces; safety for themselves was their sole thought. Each turned to fly—each dashing, pressing, crushing, against the other."

It was save himself who could in that night of horrors. Of the many episodes seen in the flashes of light was that of blind Nydia guiding Glaucus to Ione, and then leading both to safety, she the only one at home in the darkness in which she had always lived. And then, when they had gained a ship and put to sea and all but Nydia had fallen into exhausted slumber, "May the gods bless you, Athenian!" she murmured. "May you be happy with your beloved one; may you sometimes remember Nydia!"

A sailor, half dozing on the deck, heard a slight splash on the waters. Drowsily he looked up, and believed, as the vessel merrily bounded on, he fancied he saw something white above the waves.

THE LAST
OF
THE MOHICANS
by
JAMES FENIMORE COOPER*

CONDENSATION BY THOMAS D. CONNOLLY

In the third year of the war between France and England in
North America news came to Ford Edward, where lay General
Webb with five thousand men, that Montcalm was advancing on
Fort William Henry, held by the veteran Scotchman, Munro. Webb,
instead of going to the assistance of Munro, sent him a scant handful
of men.

Munro's daughters, Cora and Alice, determined to visit their
father, despite the danger. Captain Duncan Heyward, deeply in
love with Alice, offered to serve as their escort. The party set out
by little-frequented paths, guided by an Indian, Le Renard Subtil,
or Magua, as he was known to his tribe. An eccentric singing-master,
David Gamut, attached himself to the party, despite Heyward's
protests.

As the unsuspecting travelers pressed through the thick forests,
a savage face glared at them from a thicket. Magua was leading
the party into a trap.

Two men sat by the banks of a small stream about an hour's
journey from Fort Edward. One, a magnificent specimen of Indian manhood, had a terrifying emblem of death painted upon his
naked breast. The other, tall, with the lithe muscles of the woodsman, was white.

"Listen, Hawkeye," said the Indian, "we Mohicans came and
made this land ours. Then came the Dutch, and gave my people
the fire-water. Then they parted with their land. Now I, a chief
and a sagamore, have never seen the sun shine except through the

* For biographical information see page 86.

195

trees, and have never visited the graves of my fathers. And my son, Uncas, the last of the tribe, is the last of the Mohicans."

As his name was mentioned, Uncas slipped into view and seated himself gravely by the side of his father, Chingachgook.

Almost immediately the little cavalcade from Fort Edward came into view. Heyward, addressing Hawkeye, inquired as to their whereabouts, explaining that their Indian guide had lost his way.

"An Indian lost in the woods?" said the scout in perplexity. "I should like to look at the creature."

He crept stealthily into the thicket, to return after a moment, his suspicions fully confirmed. Explaining to Heyward that the Indian had tried to trap the party, he outlined a plan for the capture of the traitor. But, as they stole upon him, Magua divined their plan and vanished in the thick woods.

Hawkeye realized the serious plight of the little party and volunteered to help them. They set off up the river in a canoe, bound for a cave where none but the scout and his Indian companions had ever set foot. This haven they reached in safety, although pursued by a band of Indians as they crossed the lake.

They had barely reached their island fortress when Magua's band appeared on their trail. The scout and his companions valiantly defended their cave against a horde of Indians, inflicting heavy losses until their ammunition gave out. Then Cora, seeing that resistance was useless, begged the scout and two Indians to slip down the river and attempt to secure reinforcements at Fort William Henry. But a short while after the scouts set off Magua and his warriors appeared and made captive the whites who remained in the cave.

Magua divided his band, and set off with his captives, attended by a handful of braves. He offered to send Alice to her father if Cora would go with him to his wigwam. Alice indignantly refused, and Magua, enraged, prepared to torture his captives.

Just as a brave rushed at Alice, with tomahawk raised, a rifle cracked, and the Indian dropped. Hawkeye, followed by Uncas and Chingachgook, rushed upon the bewildered Indians; only Magua escaped the fury of their attack. The captives were freed, and in a short time the party entered Fort William Henry, despite the fact that Montcalm was attacking it.

Their stay in the fort was brief, however, for Munro, his forces heavily outnumbered by those of Montcalm, was forced to capitulate.

Montcalm promised that the defenders of the fort should be permitted to depart for Fort Edward, and guaranteed that they should not be molested. Munro agreed, and the English abandoned the stronghold.

As the women and children were filing across the plain before the fort, an Indian reached out for a trinket on the breast of a woman who bore a child in her arms. Affrighted, the woman drew back, whereupon the Indian seized the child and dashed it to the ground, then buried his tomahawk in the head of the woman. In an instant the Indians of Montcalm's army fell upon the helpless women and children. Death was everywhere and in horrible forms.

Suddenly Magua caught sight of Cora and Alice, who stood helpless by a pile of slain. He seized the terrified girls and hurried them off into the woods. Gamut, whom the Indians venerated as one insane, was permitted to accompany them.

A few days later Hawkeye and his Indian companions, with Heyward and Munro, stood on the bloody plain. They had searched carefully for the bodies of the girls, but without success. Hawkeye, certain that Magua had carried them off, searched diligently for the trail. Suddenly they found it, and the little party set off after the wily Magua.

The trail led to an Indian village, where they came upon Gamut, ludicrously attired as an Indian warrior. Heyward, disguised as a medicine-man, entered the camp with Gamut. He had been in the encampment but a short while when an old chief requested him to drive the evil spirit from the wife of one of his young men. As Heyward was preparing for the unwelcome task, an Indian was brought into the camp, and all thought of the woman vanished at the news that the prisoner was Uncas, deadly foe of the tribe.

Soon, as the excitement over the captive subsided, the old chief remembered the sick woman, and escorted Heyward to her chamber, in a cave of the neighboring mountain. As Heyward, alone in the chamber, save for the dying woman, looked around him, he was startled by a great, shaggy bear which padded noiselessly in. Suddenly its head slipped off and, Heyward, astounded, was gazing at Hawkeye, who, thus attired, had made his way into the Indian village.

As the scout rearranged his disguise, Heyward, hearing a slight noise in another chamber, investigated, and found Alice there. With Hawkeye's assistance he managed to bring the girl from the chamber and stole out of the village. Hawkeye, still in the character of a bear, fearlessly entered the cabin where Uncas was imprisoned, and succeeded in liberating him. Together they made their way into the forest.

Magua, although keeping Alice with his own tribe, had intrusted the care of Cora to a friendly tribe of Delawares. Immediately after the escape of Alice he hurried to the encampment of the Delawares to claim Cora. By Indian law, the girl was his captive, and he bore her away, despite the intervention of Uncas, a hereditary chief of the tribe.

As soon as he had vanished in the forest, the tribe, under the leadership of Uncas, prepared to follow him and war against his people. In their hideous war panoply they hurried on Magua's trail.

A bloody battle was fought between the two Indian tribes, and the forces of Le Renard Subtil crushingly defeated. Seeing that the day was lost, the wily savage seized Cora in his arms and hurried toward the mountains, Uncas, Heyward, and Hawkeye in hot pursuit.

Cora, knowing the fate that lay before her, suddenly refused to move from the ledge on which she stood.

"Woman!" cried Magua, raising his knife, "choose—the wigwam or the knife of Le Subtil?"

As he spoke, Uncas thudded down beside him, having jumped from a fearful height to the ledge. Magua, a ferocious smile on his dusky face, plunged his knife into the body of his prostrate enemy. While Magua gloated over the dying Uncas one of his companions sheathed his knife in Cora's bosom.

With a wild cry of triumph, Magua, after leaping a wide fissure, made for the summit of the mountain. A single bound would carry him to the brink of the precipice and assure his safety.

He shouted, defiantly: "The palefaces are dogs! The Delawares, women! Magua leaves them on the rocks for the crows!"

He turned and leaped for the height, but fell short, and only saved himself by grasping a bush that grew from the side of the mountain. As he slowly pulled himself up, Hawkeye's rifle cracked from below. Magua, shaking his hand in defiance of his enemy, shot downward to destruction.

THE LEGEND OF
SLEEPY HOLLOW

by

WASHINGTON IRVING

CONDENSATION BY MABEL HERBERT URNER

*WASHINGTON IRVING was born in New York in 1783
and died at his home "Sunnyside" on the Hudson in 1859.*

*Intended for the law, in which he had no interest, im-
poverished by the failure of business ventures, Irving turned
to literature as a profession, and made a success which won
for him a position at home and abroad as the most important
American man of letters of his time. "Salmagundi" and
"Diedrich Knickerbocker's History of New York from the
Beginning of the World to the End of the Dutch Dynasty"
gained him a reputation by their satire and comic power.
When he went to England he found Sir Walter Scott ready
to welcome him as a friend and to start him on a literary
career there. "The Sketch-Book of Geoffrey Crayon" shows
the charm he found in English life, as well as introduces the
world to Rip Van Winkle. "Bracebridge Hall" and "Tales of
a Traveler" established his fortunes. A long stay in Spain
led to his "Columbus," "The Conquest of Granada," and
"The Alhambra." On his return to America his reception
was that of a great personage. The traditions of men of
letters in our diplomatic profession had already begun, and
Irving was sent as ambassador to Spain.*

*His later years produced his lives of Goldsmith, Moham-
med, and Washington. The days of painstaking investigation of sources had not yet arrived; it was as a man of
letters rather than as a scholar that Irving wrote his historical books; the charm of his personality and the power to
visualize people and circumstances helped him greatly. But
his really creative and original work, such as "The Sketch-*

*Book" and "Knickerbocker," will always find the most de-
voted readers of the earliest American man of letters.*

In a sequestered cove of the Hudson lies the drowsy valley of
Sleepy Hollow—once a remote, enchanted region, abounding in
haunted spots and twilight superstitions.

The dreamy, visionary Dutch folk, descendants of the early
settlers, were given to marvelous beliefs. Many were their fireside
tales of ghosts and evil spirits.

The most awesome wraith of this bewitched neighborhood was a
headless figure on a powerful black charger, which at midnight
rode forth from the church graveyard.

At every country fireside were told blood-curdling stories of
the weird and ghoulish pranks of this headless horseman of Sleepy
Hollow.

Perhaps the most superstitious soul throughout the valley, in
the days just following the Revolution, was the country schoolmaster, Ichabod Crane. Tall, lank, long-limbed, he was a grotesque
figure, yet not lacking in conceit.

As was the custom he led an itinerant life, boarding with the
farmers whose children he taught. Since he brought the local gossip
and helped with the chores, his periodical visitations were welcomed
by the housewives.

He also enlivened the long wintry evening with direful stories of
witchcraft. In a snug chimney corner before a crackling wood fire
there was a fearsome pleasure in these blood-chilling tales.

But for this gruesome enjoyment, how dearly he paid when out
alone at night! What menacing shadows beset his path! Every snow-
covered bush stood a sheeted specter in his way.

However, it was not only these phantoms of the night that disturbed his peace, for his days were haunted by the most bewitching
of all witches—a woman.

In his weekly singing class was Katrina Van Tassel, only child
of a substantial farmer, famed for her beauty and vast expectations.
The enraptured Ichabod became her ardent suitor.

Gloatingly he surveyed her father's rich meadowlands, the over-
flowing barns, and the great, sloping-roofed farm-house filled with
treasure of old mahogany, pewter, and silver. All these rich possessions made Ichabod covet the peerless Katrina.

The most formidable of his many rivals was the roistering Brom

Van Brunt, nicknamed, from his Herculean frame, Brom Bones.

He was the hero of all the country round, which rang with his feats of strength and hardihood. A reckless horseman and foremost in all rural sports, he was always ready for a fight or a frolic.

Yet even the old dames, startled out of their sleep as he clattered by at midnight, looked upon his wild pranks with more goodwill than disfavor.

This rantipole hero had chosen to lay siege to the blooming Katrina. And when on a Sunday night his horse was tied to Van Tassel's palings all the suitors passed on in despair.

Ichabod, however, in his rôle of singing-master, made frequent visits at the farm. Neither old Van Tassel, an easy, indulgent soul, nor his busy housewife interfered with the pedagogue's suit; yet his wooing was beset with difficulties.

Brom Bones had declared a deadly feud, and as Ichabod shrewdly avoided a physical combat, he became the object of whimsical persecutions by Brom and his boon companions.

They smoked out his singing school, broke into and turned topsy-turvy his schoolhouse, and, still worse, taught a scoundrel dog to whine as a rival instructor in psalmody to the fair Katrina.

One fine autumnal afternoon Ichabod, in a pensive mood, sat enthroned on the lofty stool from which he ruled his laggard pupils.

The buzzing stillness of the schoolroom was broken by a galloping messenger, who brought an invitation to a "quilting frolic" that evening at Van Tassel's.

Promptly dismissing school, Ichabod furbished up his only suit of rusty black, and soon rode forth—a gallant cavalier to this bidding of his lady fair.

Gunpowder, the bony old plow-horse, borrowed from the farmer with whom Ichabod was domiciled, was a suitable steed for his long, gaunt frame.

Jogging slowly along, it was after sundown when he reached Van Tassel's, where were gathered the farmer folk of the surrounding country.

However, it was not the buxom lasses that held Ichabod enthralled; it was the sumptuous abundance of the supper-table. Such luscious ham and chicken, and heaping platters of doughnuts, crullers, and ginger cakes!

Ichabod's rapacious appetite did ample justice to this repast, while he gloated over the opulence of which some day he might be master.

Soon the sound of fiddling bade all to the dance. With Katrina as his partner, smiling graciously at his amorous oglings, the lank but agile Ichabod clattered triumphantly about, while Brom Bones, sorely smitten with jealousy, kept brooding aloof.

Later, Ichabod joined the sager folk, who sat smoking and spinning tales of ghosts and apparitions, and of the headless horseman that nightly tethered his steed among the churchyard graves.

Most terrifying were the adventures of those who, on dark nights, had met that gruesome specter. Even Brom Bones testified that once, overtaken by the midnight trooper, he had raced with him to the church bridge, where the horseman had vanished in a flash of fire.

When at a late hour the revel broke up Ichabod lingered for the customary lovers' talk. What passed at that interview with the heiress was never known, but when he finally sallied forth it was with a dejected, chopfallen air.

Had Katrina's encouragement been only a coquettish trick to secure her conquest of his rival?

It was near the witching midnight hour that the crestfallen Ichabod pursued his solitary travel homeward. All the stories of ghosts and goblins told that evening now crowded hauntingly upon him.

The night grew deeper and darker as he approached the lonely churchyard—sombrous scene of many of the tales. Suddenly through the leaf-stirred stillness came the clatter of hoofs! Something huge and misshapen loomed above the crouching shadows.

In quaking terror Ichabod dashed ahead, but the unknown followed close. Then the moonlight, through a rifting cloud, revealed the headless horseman! More ghastly still, his head rested on the pommel of his saddle!

Away they flew, Ichabod madly spurring Gunpowder, while the sinister horseman came galloping after.

As they reached the haunted road, turning off to Sleepy Hollow, the girth of Ichabod's saddle broke. Gripping his steed around the neck, as the saddle slipped from beneath him, he still plunged on, with the ghostly rider pursuing him.

The church bridge, where in Brom Bones' tale the specter had vanished, was just ahead. Another moment and old Gunpowder was thundering over the resounding planks.

Here Ichabod, casting a backward glance, saw the goblin rising in his stirrups and in the very act of hurling his head.

The horrible missile crashed against Ichabod's cranium and he plunged headlong into the road—while Gunpowder and the ghostly horseman swept on.

The next morning the old horse was found, saddleless, grazing at his master's gate. But no Ichabod!

In the road by the church was found the saddle. Farther on was the trampled hat of the unfortunate pedagogue—and close beside it a shattered pumpkin!

The whole neighborhood was aroused. Brom Bones's story and all the other weird tales were called to mind, and the good folk sagely concluded that Ichabod had been carried off by the headless horseman.

Soon the school was removed to a less haunted section. Another pedagogue reigned, and Ichabod became only a legand.

It is true that several years later an old farmer, returning from New York, brought news that Ichabod was still alive; that fear of the goblin, and chagrin at his dismissal by the heiress had caused his flight; that in another part of the country he had taught school, studied law, and become justice of the Ten-pound Court.

Brom Bones, who, shortly after his rival's disappearance, had led the blooming Katrina to the altar, was observed to look exceedingly knowing whenever the story of Ichabod was related. At the mention of the pumpkin he never failed to laugh heartily, which led some to suspect that he knew more about the matter than he chose to disclose.

The old country wives, however, maintain to this day that Ichabod was spirited away by the headless horseman. And many gruesome tales of the pedagogue's fate are still told round the wintry firesides of Sleepy Hollow.

~⦿~

THE LITTLE MINISTER
by
JAMES M. BARRIE

CONDENSATION BY MARGUERITE E. ALLEY

JAMES MATTHEW BARRIE, one of that great army of Scotchmen who take general charge of England, was born at Kirriemuir, May 9, 1860 and died in London on June 19, 1937. He was educated at Dumfries Academy and Edinburgh University. He was created first baronet in 1913, but long before that date by universal suffrage he had acquired the title of Prince of Whimsies and First Lord of All Hearts. Unlike other British titles, these latter are perfectly valid in the United States as well as in Great Britain and the dominions beyond the seas.

After the usual skirmishes of a penman to find himself by way of the newspapers, Barrie published "Better Dead," in 1887. Then at intervals of a year or less came "Auld Licht Idylls," "When a Man's Single," "A Window in Thrums," "My Lady Nicotine," "The Little Minister," followed by "Sentimental Tommy," "Margaret Ogilvy" (the infinitely tender story of his own mother), and the immortal "Peter Pan." He soon found his way to the stage (a way all his own) with "The Professor's Love Story," "The Little Minister," "Quality Street," "The Admirable Crichton," "Peter Pan," "What Every Woman Knows," "A Kiss for Cinderella," and "Dear Brutus," and was most successful with plays, or rather playlets, of the war, such as "The Old Lady Shows Her Medals."

His appeal to public imagination was almost instantaneous, and he has continuously held a warm place in the hearts of the whole English-speaking race wherever a tender fancy appeals to loving imagination.

Gavin Dishart was barely twenty-one when he and his mother came to Thrums. All Thrums was out in its wyndes and closes—a few of the weavers still in knee-breeches, to look at the new Auld Licht minister. I was there, the dominie of Glen Quharity, four miles from Thrums, and heavy was my heart as I stood afar off so that Gavin's mother might not have the pain of seeing me. I alone of the crowd looked more at her than at her son.

Eighteen years had passed since we parted, and already her hair had lost its brightness, and Margaret was an old woman at only forty-three, and I, who have loved her since I was a hobbledehoy and shall till I die, am the man who made her old.

Many scenes in the little minister's life come back to me. The first time I ever thought of writing his love-story as an old man's gift to a little maid since grown tall, was one night in the old school-house, when my gate creaked in the wind, and my mind drifted back to another gate creaking, the first time I ever saw Gavin and the Egyptian together.

Gavin was brought up to be a minister from his earliest days, and took to the idea enthusiastically. It had been the dream of the two of a manse, of which Margaret was mistress, and Gavin the minister, and now it was fulfilled.

Gavin became at once popular in Thrums, and, though short of stature, he cast a great shadow. He converted a drunkard, Rob Dow, who adored him and would do anything in the world for him.

On the fateful evening of October 17th Gavin was returning from Rob Dow's, and going home through Caddam Woods, when he heard singing.

The singer came dancing up Windyghoul. Only when she passed him did Gavin see her as a gipsy elf, her bare feet flashing beneath a short green skirt, a twig of rowan berries in her black hair. She was pale with an angel's loveliness. A diamond on her finger shot a thread of fire over a pool as she danced by.

Undoubtedly she was the devil. Gavin leaped after her, but as she saw him she beckoned mockingly, then kissed her hand, and was gone.

A moment later came the sound of a horn. The minister was on the alert at once, and hurried to the Square. That horn was a signal that soldiers were marching on the village folk to arrest some malefactors among the weavers, who would resent it.

In the Square was an uproar. It was the gipsy who had given the warning. Gavin tried to persuade the people to disperse to save bloodshed, but the Egyptian cried:

"Do not heed this little man! Save yourselves," and they obeyed her. The soldiers came, but caught only a few, the real culprits escaping. The Egyptian was even caught, but escaped the officers first through a clever ruse, and again through impudently pretending she was Gavin's wife!

He was furious, and yet he felt his anger die as he looked at the beautiful girl with the appealing eyes and coaxing, laughing mouth. He even told her to hide in the manse garden in the summer seat, till the soldiers had gone.

Gavin was in two minds after that, angry at himself because of the Egyptian, and yet he constantly thought of her, and wondered. He preached sermons against women, those days—their witching ways were the devil.

One winter day, the Egyptian's timely appearance saved old Nanny Webster from the poorhouse. The gipsy impulsively offered five pounds to support Nanny till her brother came back from jail. Then it was that Gavin first believed in her and said he'd trust her word.

The happy Nanny persuaded the minister to stay for tea. That tea-drinking bewitched the little minister, for the fascinating Babbie teased him—and he liked it.

Babbie brought him the money to Caddam Woods next day, and gave Gavin a holly spray that he secretly treasured. Again and again he was drawn to Nanny's cottage, where Babbie frequently came, and he didn't understand at first that he was in love with the mysterious girl with her many caprices—all of which charmed him. He little knew that Rob Dow had discovered him with Babbie in their trysts, and wondered why Rob avoided him and was drinking again. Rob's greatest fear was that the kirk elders should learn of the Egyptian and the minister and stone him out of Thrums.

One night Babbie flashed a lantern in at the manse window to attract Gavin's attention. He waited breathlessly till the manse was quiet in slumber, then stole out to meet Babbie at the summer seat. There in the darkness Gavin kissed her, and Babbie realized for the first time his love for her. She had been playing with him, and felt ashamed. She wanted to run away, and she wanted to stay and have him put his kiss into words. But it was late, and it was that night as Gavin took her back to Nanny's that I saw them together for the first time.

Love dawned in Babbie's heart that night, and all the world looked new to her, and she longed for Gavin to come. Then she met Rob Dow's little son weeping bitterly, who told her of what sorrow the "wooman who'd bewitched the meenister" would bring every one, and Babbie, touched to the heart, went away. Months passed, and the little minister looked in vain for her.

Then came the 4th of August, the eve of Lord Rintoul's marriage, an old earl staying at the Spittal, whose bride was reported as young and bonny.

But nearly all of Thrums were concerned over the long drought that had become a calamity, and that night there was to be a special prayer-meeting for rain.

Then suddenly Babbie came to me in the school-house, saying that Gavin had been killed by a drunken Highland piper. It was not true —a rumor, but I found Gavin, and told him where he would find Babbie, though I felt I was doing wrong.

Babbie told Gavin her story then—that she was to be Lord Rintoul's bride on the morrow. He had found her when a mite, fallen from a gipsy wagon, and for her beauty had reared and educated her. Babbie and Gavin tried to give each other up; then Babbie heard Lord Rintoul's voice, and in terror clung to Gavin, and the two ran off in the darkness to the gipsy camp on the hill to be married over the tongs by the gipsy king.

That terrible night, when the storm coming, the earl seeking his lost bride, the dour elders relentlessly following their errant minister —and drunken Rob madly bound to save his friend.

Then came the flood, when the heavens opened and lochs seemed to fall. Babbie, separated from Gavin after the gipsy marriage, fell into Rob's hands, but mercifully escaped and reached the manse. Gavin wandered all night through the storm after Babbie, and I found him exhausted near my house next morning. He told me all that had passed, and my anxiety for Margaret at the consequences of his rash act led me to attempt to reach Thrums. But before I left it was necessary to tell Gavin my story, that he was my son and Margaret was my wife. Margaret had married Adam Dishart first, and he had gone to sea, and after two years all thought him lost, and she married me. Then when Gavin was three years old Adam suddenly returned, and I passed out of Margaret's life forever.

Gavin sought to learn if Babbie had been carried off by Lord Rintoul, and found the earl on an island in the midst of floods. Gavin jumped to his aid, but nothing could be done, and it was

thought both must perish. His congregation, gathered by the precipice, forgot they had meant to expel him, and listening with dim eyes
to his brave last words, knew only that they loved him. Then Rob
Dow threw his life away to save his friend, and the rope with which
he sprang into the flood withdrew minister and earl to safety.

So Gavin and Babbie were married, and no one seeing Babbie going
demurely to church on Gavin's arm would guess her history. Yet
sometimes at night Babbie slips into her gipsy's frock, with rowan
berries in her hair, and Gavin always kisses her. My little maid
knows this story as well as I do. She was named for Margaret, and
has been my dearest comfort since my Margaret died; but I have
lived to rejoice in the happiness of Gavin and Babbie and their
children.

LITTLE WOMEN*
by
LOUISA MAY ALCOTT

CONDENSATION BY CAROLYN WELLS

*LOUISA MAY ALCOTT was born in 1832 and died in
1888. Her father was A. Bronson Alcott, the "Sage of Concord." Her early surroundings were of a highly intellectual
and literary character, and she naturally took to writing
while still very young.*

*In her sketch "Transcendental Oats" she describes in an
amusing way the experience of a year at Fruitlands, where
an attempt was made to establish an ideal community.*

*Miss Alcott was obliged to be a wage-earner to help out
the family income, and so taught school, served as a governess and at times worked as a seamstress. Wearying of
this, she wrote for the papers stories of a sensational nature,*

* Printed by permission of, and arrangement with, Little, Brown & Co.,
authorized publishers.

which were remunerative financially, but unsatisfactory to her as a literary pursuit, and she abandoned this style of writing.

In a Washington hospital she served as a nurse for a time, but the work was so hard that she failed in health, and when she recovered she had to find new fields of work; then she traveled as attendant to an invalid, and with her visited Europe.

After several attempts at literature, Miss Alcott wrote "Little Women," which was an immediate success, reaching a sale of 87,000 copies in three years. She wrote from the heart, and wove into the story incidents from the lives of herself and her three sisters at Concord. She afterward wrote "An Old-Fashioned Girl," "Little Men," "Aunt Jo's Scrap Bag," "The Eight Cousins," and "Rose in Bloom," besides other stories and sketches.

In their old-fashioned New England home the little women lived with Mrs. March, their brisk and cheery mother, who always had a "can-I-help-you" look about her, and whom her four girls lovingly called "Marmee."

Pretty Meg, the oldest, was sixteen, and already showed domestic tastes and talents, though she detested the drudgery of household work; and, a little vain of her white hands, longed at heart to be a fine lady. Jo, fifteen, was tall, thin, and coltish, and gloried in an unconcealed scorn of polite conventions. Beth, thirteen, was a loveable little thing, shy, fond of her dolls and devoted to music, which she tried hopefully to produce from the old, jingling tin pan of a piano. Amy, twelve, considered herself the flower of the family. An adorable blonde, she admitted that the trial of her life was her nose. For, when she was a baby Jo had accidentally dropped her into the coal-hod and permanently flattened that feature, and though poor Amy slept with a patent clothes-pin pinching it, she couldn't attain the Grecian effect she so much desired.

Father March was an army chaplain in the Civil War, and in his absence Jo declared herself to be the man of the family. To add to their slender income, she went every day to read to Aunt March, a peppery old lady; and Meg, too, earned a small salary as daily nursery governess to a neighbor's children.

In the big house next door to the Marches lived a rich old gentleman, Mr. Laurence, and his grandson, a jolly, chummy boy called Laurie. Though awe-inspiring at first, Mr. Laurence proved both kindly and generous, and even timid Beth mustered up courage to go over to the "Palace Beautiful" at twilight and play softly on the grand piano there. But, as she confessed to her mother, when she began she was so frightened her feet chattered on the floor!

The night Laurie took the two older girls to the theater, Amy, though not invited, insisted on going too. Jo crossly declared she wouldn't go if Amy did, and, furiously scolding her little sister, she slammed the door and went off, as Amy called out: "You'll be sorry for this, Jo March! See if you ain't!" The child made good her threat by burning up the manuscript of a precious book which Jo had written and on which she had spent three years of hard work. There was a terrible fracas, and, though at her mother's bidding Amy made contrite apology, Jo refused to be pacified. It was only when poor little Amy was nearly drowned by falling through the ice that conscience-stricken Jo forgave her sister and learned a much-needed lesson of self-control.

Meg, too, learned a salutary lesson when she went to visit some fashionable friends and had her first taste of "Vanity Fair." Her sisters gladly lent her all their best things, and, as she said to Jo: "You're a dear to lend me your gloves! I feel *so* rich and elegant with two new pairs and the old ones cleaned up for common!" Yet she soon saw that her wardrobe was sadly inadequate to the environment in which she found herself. Whereupon the rich friends lent her some of their own finery; and, after laughingly applying paint and powder, they laced her into a sky-blue silk dress, so low that modest Meg blushed at herself in the mirror, and Laurie, who was at the party, openly expressed his surprised disapproval. Chagrin and remorse followed, and it was not until after full confession to Marmee that Meg realized the trumpery value of fashionable rivalry and the real worth of simplicity and contentment.

All four of the girls had leanings toward a life of luxury and ease, and when Mrs. March smilingly proposed that they try a whole week of "all play and no work," they agreed eagerly. But the experiment was a miserable failure; and after mortifying scenes at a company luncheon, a canary-bird dead from neglect, several slight illnesses and lost tempers, the girls decided that lounging and larking didn't pay.

Now John Brooke, the tutor of Laurie, was a secret admirer of pretty Meg. Discovering this, the mischievous boy wrote Meg a passionate love-letter, purporting to be from Brooke. This prank caused a terrible upset in both houses, but later on Brooke put the momentous question, and Meg meekly whispered, "Yes, John," and hid her face on his waistcoat. Jo, blundering in, was transfixed with astonishment and dismay, and exclaimed, "Oh, *do* somebody come quick! John Brooke is acting dreadfully, and Meg *likes* it!"

At Christmas, Father March came home from the war, and great celebration was made. The neighbors from the Laurence house were invited, and there never *was* such a Christmas dinner as they had that day!

Later came the first break in their restored home circle. The Dovecote was the name of the little brown house that John Brooke had prepared for his bride, and it *was* a tiny affair with a lawn in front about as a big as a pocket handkerchief! The wedding, beneath the June roses, was a simple, homey one, and the bridal journey was only the walk from the March home to the dear little new house. "I'm too happy to care what any one says—I'm going to have my wedding just as I want it!" Meg had declared; and so, leaning on her husband's arm, her hands full of flowers, she went away, saying: "Thank you all for my happy wedding-day. Good-by, good-by!"

Jo developed into a writer of sensational stories. This, however, was because she found a profitable market for such work and she wanted the money for herself and the others. For little Beth was ailing, and a summer stay at the seashore might, they all hoped, bring back the roses to her cheeks. But it didn't, and after a time the dark days came when gentle Beth, like a tired but trustful child, clung to the hands that had led her all through life, as her father and mother guided her tenderly through the Valley of the Shadow and gave her up to God.

Then came a day when Laurie was invited to the Dovecote to see Meg's new baby. Jo appeared, a proud aunt, bearing a bundle on a pillow. "Shut your eyes and hold out your arms," she ordered, and Laurie, obeying, opened his eyes again, to see—two babies! "Twins, by Jupiter!" he cried; "take 'em, quick, somebody! I'm going to laugh, and I shall drop 'em!"

Laurie had loved Jo for years, but Jo, though truly sorry, couldn't respond. As she said, "It's impossible for people to make themselves love other people if they don't!" And so, after a time, Laurie decided that Amy was the only woman in the world who could fill Jo's place and make him happy. And the two *were* very happy together, Amy taking great pride in her handsome husband.

"Don't laugh," she said to him, "but your nose is *such* a comfort to me!" and she caressed the well-cut feature with artistic satisfaction.

Jo found her fate in an elderly professor, wise and kind, but too poor to think of marriage. For a year the pair worked and waited and hoped and loved, and then Aunt March died and left Jo her fine old country place. Here Jo and her professor set up their home, and established a boys' school which became a great success. Jo lived a very happy life, and, as the years went on, two little lads of her own came to increase her happiness. Amy, too, had a dear child named Beth, but she was a frail little creature and the dread of losing her was the shadow over Amy's sunshine.

But the little women and all their dear ones formed a happy, united family, of whom Jo truly wrote:

> Lives whose brave music long shall ring
> Like a spirit-stirring strain.

LORD JIM

by

JOSEPH CONRAD

CONDENSATION BY MARGARET GILLETT

JOSEPH CONRAD (1857–1924), great English writer of the sea, was a Pole whose family name was originally Korzeniowski. Orphaned as a child, he was brought up at Cracow by an uncle and was fluent in French at an early age, although he did not learn English until he was an adult. When he was seventeen, he went to sea and later became an officer in the British merchant service, sailing to Australia, in the Indian Ocean, to China, and finally around the world. In 1886 he became a master mariner and a British subject. Four years later he commanded a Belgian steamer in the Congo, where he was stricken with fever. It was while convalescing from the attack that he started to write.

Conrad's first novel, "Almayer's Folly," appeared in 1895. He married soon after and settled down in Kent to write "An Outcast of the Islands," which was published the next year. This was followed by his great sea stories, "The Nigger of the Narcissus" (1897) and "Lord Jim" (1900). Although he achieved a modest fame late in life, his place as a great English novelist was not fully recognized until after his death.

His other works include: "Nostromo" (1904), "The Mirror of the Sea" (1906), "The Secret Agent" (1907), "Under Western Eyes" (1911), "Chance" (1913), "Victory" (1915), "The Shadow Line" (1917), "The Arrow of Gold" (1919), "The Rescue" (1920), "The Rover" (1923), and "Suspense" (1925). He also wrote tales: "Youth" (1902), "Typhoon" (1903) and "Within the Tides" (1915).

Conrad has been called a tragic novelist whose deeper themes are concerned with codes of behavior. "Lord Jim" is an example of his concern with ethical questions. It has been criticized as an elongated short story that has become mixed-up in its process of elongation, but it has also been highly praised for its method of narration in which the author involves the reader so completely.

Water clerk to a ship-chandler is not a big job, as jobs go around a seaport, but it requires some ability in the abstract. And Jim had it—it was part of his vocation for the sea. Or so Captain Marlow explained as he told the story of the boy from the English parsonage and his strange adventures in the Eastern Archipelago.

"The first time I saw him was at the inquiry," Marlow began, "but it was later I learned his story . . .

"From the time of his training course for the merchant marine, Jim had made many voyages until, disabled by a falling spar, he found himself in a hospital in a distant Eastern port. When he recovered he went back to sea again as chief mate on the *Patna*, a local steamer as old as the hills but not nearly so solid. It had been chartered by an Arab to carry a pilgrimage of eight hundred members of a religious sect through the Red Sea. And because it was so old, with a rotten bulkhead, it threatened to sink at once when it struck something mysteriously submerged in the opaque water.

"Immediately after the dull thud of the impact, Jim had been ordered by the captain, a drunken reprobate, to investigate the damage, and he found great chips of rust, as big as his hand, crackling off the battered bulkhead. The ship was apparently doomed with only minutes to stay afloat and there were only seven lifeboats for eight hundred passengers who, fortunately, had not been alarmed or even awakened by the accident.

"The captain, the two engineers, and the chief mate, the only Europeans aboard, were awake and aware of the imminent danger. All the rest, the dark-skinned people—the sleeping pilgrims and the crew—had no idea of the terrible fate in store for them. Except, perhaps, the two stolid Malays at the helm who never took their hands from the brass wheel during all the excitement.

"With no possibility of saving so many, the officers—all except Jim—under cover of darkness took stealthily to one of the boats and prepared to abandon ship. At the last moment and almost automatically, Jim jumped in with them in the midst of a heavy and mantling squall that made disaster even more certain for the foundering *Patna*. Thus the officers committed the unforgivable sin of deserting their sinking ship—a crime which, in the event of their rescue, they planned to conceal with the greatest of care in their report.

"Rescue came just before sunset the next day. Meanwhile, the *Patna*, by some miracle, had not sunk and was discovered by a French gunboat which towed it to the nearest port flying the English flag.

"In the ensuing inquiry, Jim, filled with remorse, lost his certificate and was downgraded now to this water clerk job, a dull, unglamorous post, indeed.

"Yet when I offered him a chance to escape the legal prosecution —it was only a small loan, he could have repaid it at his convenience—he would not accept. After all, as I pointed out, no passengers had been drowned and his staying for a lengthy and painful trial would only make more of a scandal to blacken British nautical history. But he was firm.

"'You don't seem to understand,' he said, 'I can't run away fr-from this.' All the pathos of his twenty-three years was in his final stammer.

"But, somehow, I *did* understand and, for reasons unknown even to me, I felt a kind of responsibility for this unlucky lad in such grave difficulty so far from home. His case haunted me and three years later, after he had gone through his period of probation amongst the ship-chandlers, I had come almost to the point of giving him up. I had written a few letters to friends in distant ports and found him several situations which he left one after the other as the story of the *Patna* caught up with him. In each of these places he had been well-liked by his employers, who were entirely satisfied with his work and were puzzled and upset to see him go.

"Finally, as I say, when there seemed to be nothing left for me to do for him, and I was almost convinced he was bent on his own destruction in his excessive sensitivity to the reputation for cowardice that he felt pursued him wherever he went, I remembered Stein and his various widespread commercial enterprises in outlying stations of the Malay Archipelago. Surely Jim's crime couldn't follow him to Stein's trading post at Patusan, a spot as remote as a distant star. I talked to Stein, told him Jim's story, or as much as I knew of it. It did not take Stein, a man of large human experience, long to recognize Jim's failing which he summed up briefly. 'He's a romantic,' was the way he put it, and he ended up by sending him to romantic Patusan with a silver ring which Doramin, one of the elders in that country, had given Stein as a parting gift. This would be Jim's credential to insure his acceptance in that strange land where he was to become 'Tuan Jim,' Lord Jim, and where, at last, he was to be able to bury the disgrace of his past.

"By the time I finally got around to visiting Jim in his faraway sanctuary, two years later, he had made a place for himself, as the name the natives gave him indicates. He had fallen in love with, and taken as his wife, a curious waif of a girl, stepdaughter of the Portuguese clerk Cornelius, his predecessor in Patusan, an ineffectual abject man who naturally resented Jim's intrusion into his domain. 'Jewel,' for that was what Jim called her, loved him completely and his devotion to her seemed equally unbounded. But her aging stepfather felt that Jim had divested him not only of his job and his daughter but of his distinction as *the* white man of Patusan. He hated Jim with a consuming hate that drove him to the brink of madness.

"When a band of pirates attacked the village during Jim's absence in the bush, Cornelius found his chance to get his revenge. Posing as an interpreter, he showed the leader a secret way to ambush the stockade and, in the fighting which followed, Doramin's son was killed. Distraught with grief, the father blamed Jim for the tragedy, as did the villagers, who felt the white man had lost his magic. Although Jim had been warned of all the hostility toward him, and knew of the old man's determination to avenge his son's death, he walked calmly through the village toward Doramin and his fate, displaying a courage beyond his wildest dreams. A shot rang out, and he fell beside the corpse of Doramin's son, a smile of triumph on his still young face."

LORNA DOONE

by

R. D. BLACKMORE

CONDENSATION BY KATHERINE R. MARKWARD

RICHARD DODDRIDGE BLACKMORE was born at Longworth, Berkshire, England, June 7, 1825. He was educated at Blundell's School, Tiverton, and Exeter College, Oxford, where he obtained a scholarship. His first publication was a volume of poems which showed no particular promise, nor did a later volume; but he was, nevertheless, ambitious to succeed, and enthusiastic in his pursuit of literature. A complete breadown in health rendered it necessary for him to leave city life in London, and he determined to combine a literary life in the country with a business career as a market-gardener.

He settled down in Teddington, and set earnestly to work. Several publications followed, the first novel being "Clara Vaughan," the merits of which were promptly recognized. But it was in 1869 that he suddenly sprang into fame with "Lorna Doone." This story was one of the first in the revival of the romantic novel, and appearing, as it did, at a time,

*when the reading public was waiting and ready for a work
of this type, it was a great success, and pronounced a novel
of "singular charm, vigor, and imagination."*

*Thcugh Blackmore wrote many other stories, none has
reached the popular heart like "Lorna Doone"; and he will
be remembered chiefly as the author of this charming story,
which is a classic of the west country. Many pilgrimages
are made annually to the Doone Valley, although the actual
characteristics of the scene of the story differ greatly from
the descriptions inspired by the lively imagination of the
author.*

*"Lorna Doone" is a truly outdoor story; at times it is very
dramatic and picturesque and threaded with adventure.*

*Blackmore kept to his quiet country life to the last, and
passed away at Teddington on January 20, 1900.*

In Exmoor, in the county of Somerset, in the year of grace 1661,
dwelt the outlawed Doones, who, huge and brutal, defied king and
commons, committed brazen robberies with impunity, and took
refuge after every outrage in the well-nigh impregnable Glen Doone.
On the near-by farm of Plover's Barrows dwelt John Ridd, a great-
limbed lad who had been summoned home from boarding-school in
his teens to learn that his father, a wealthy farmer, had been slain in
a night raid by the Doones. John, blunt and honest, was kind to his
mother and his two sisters, did his share of the farm-work, and, as he
grew to manhood, learned to ride a horse and shoot a blunderbuss
with unfailing skill.

One day, while yet a boy, his fishing excursions in Bagworthy
Water led him to discover an entrance to Glen Doone, so secret, so
remote that the robber band stationed no guard there, never dreaming that living soul would discover it. Following a little cascade, John
emerged at last into a dell blooming with primroses, and beheld with
amazement a beautiful child of eight with hair like a black shower
and eyes full of pity and wonder. Her name (pretty, like herself)
was Lorna Doone, and John often had her in his thoughts through
the six years which followed. He was twenty then and Lorna fourteen, and already John Ridd knew that he loved her, that fate had
decreed it so and that all the world was naught when weighed against
this girl.

To be found in Doone Valley spelled death for any man, but the thought of Lorna, "light and white, nimble, smooth, and elegant," filled John with yearning and lured him to the hazard. Again and again he sought the maid in the primrose bower above the cascade, and then one afternoon in the splendor of an April sunset John once more threw down the gauntlet which love ever casts at danger. To Lorna's tremulous, "You are mad to come; they will kill you if they find you here," John smiled and thought her fairer than the primroses amid which she stood. She lived in constant fear, she confessed, for the gigantic and passionate Carver Doone openly paid her homage and glowered with jealous eyes at any man who durst cast a glance at her.

"I care naught for him or his jealousy," cried John Ridd. "I have loved you long, as child, as comely girl, and now as full-grown maiden. I love you more than tongue can tell or heart can hold in silence." Lorna raised her glorious eyes and, flinging her arms about his neck, cried, with her heart on his: "Darling, I shall never be my own again. I am yours forever and forever." But before he went she was in tears. "How dare I dream of love? Something in my heart tells me it can never be."

That fear of his beloved's spurred John to penetrate into Glen Doone one night at the risk of his life for word of Lorna. Once a guard leveled his gun at him, but went off cringing at the thought that, after all, so huge a form could be only that of Carver Doone.

It was a real danger which threatened Lorna, for old Sir Ensor Doone, head of the robber crew, lay dying, and he alone had been her protector against the brutal Carver. For John to play a desperate game and carry Lorna off would but incite the Doones to wreak vengeance upon the countryside with fire and sword. At times he swore to smoke out this nest of rascals, but the timid farmers, overawed by their savagery, would promise no support.

Meanwhile an unparalleled winter had set in. Day after day the snow fell steadily and, blown by the wind, almost smothered the low-eaved cottages. Desperate for some word of Lorna, John made his way on snowshoes into the very heart of Glen Doone, unobserved in that feathery fog. John found Lorna's hamlet, stifled her exclamations of surprise with kisses, and felt his heart swell with anger on learning that she and her maid, Gwenny Carfax, were kept in confinement and deprived of food by order of Carver Doone until Lorna should consent to be his wife. Not for naught was John Ridd a giant —and in love. Throwing discretion to the winds, he carried Lorna and Gwenny away upon his sledge that very night to the warm refuge of his mother's fireside.

The Doones, though so openly set at defiance, bided their time. With spring the roads were open, and one moonlight night, with an arrogance worthy of Carver, they attacked Plover's Barrows in force. John Ridd, nothing daunted, defended his fireside and loved ones with spirit, meeting the attackers squarely with a handful of men and putting them to speedy flight. A murderous attack by the Doones was bad business enough, but to John's honest soul a worse trouble followed.

His Lorna was discovered to be no true Doone, but the niece of the great Lord Dugal, kidnapped as a child. To London and the protection of her noble uncle she was summoned, her heart as well as her lover's torn by the separation. The thought that he might never again behold his Lorna plunged him into misery.

"After all," he asked himself, "who am I but a simple farmer who dares lift his eyes to the niece of an earl?"

But this was no time for repining, for the ill-starred rebellion of Monmouth flamed out, catching John Ridd, innocent though he was, in its toils. But all came to a happy issue when John, summoned to London, frustrated the intended murder of Lord Dugal, captured the attackers, and turned them over for punishment to the terrible Lord Jeffreys. Events moved swiftly: his exploit made London ring, he was knighted by King James and when the Earl of Dugal died soon after, a well-directed bribe secured Jeffrey's permission to let Lorna, his ward in Chancery, wed the redoubtable Sir John Ridd.

Back to Exmoor and Plover's Barrows went John Ridd, knight, to lead the farmers of the countryside, who, infuriated by a new outrage committed by the Doones, took the law into their own hands and swept the robber stronghold clean with fire and sword. Only the scheming old "Counselor" and his son, the brutal Carver, escaped a bloody death.

Now at last the great day dawned for John and Lorna, and they made their way to the little country church to be wed, while all the neighboring farmers came to applaud the event. Scarcely were the sacred words pronounced when a shot rang through the church and Lorna, her dark eyes drooping, her wedding-gown stained with blood, sank into her husband's arms. John Ridd never forgot the agony of that moment and yet he seemed strangely calm. Only Carver Doone could have done this dastardly deed, and as John dashed off in hot pursuit he swore that the world was too narrow a place to harbor him and his enemy another day. For Carver on his jaded horse there was no escape. His pistol missed fire, and at last in a narrow defile flanked by a wood and a stretch of bog the two men came to grips. They spoke little and that grim duel was fought with neither knife nor pistol, but body to body as became two giants.

John felt a lower rib crack beneath Carver's terrible embrace, but his iron hand ripped the muscles of his assailant's arm from the bone like an orange pulp and he flung him, crushed and bleeding, upon the ground. In an instant the black lips of the bog fastened upon Carver's huge limbs, swiftly, silently, and John Ridd had scarce time to get his own feet upon firm soil before his enemy was sucked down into those grim depths, his face distorted with agony, but his quivering lips uttering no sound.

Love's true course does not always run awry and both John and Lorna recovered, he to worship her and she to assure him through the serene years with eyes and lips all eloquent, "I love you, John Ridd."

MADAME BOVARY

by

GUSTAVE FLAUBERT

CONDENSATION BY LAWRENCE FALCONER

GUSTAVE FLAUBERT (1821–1880) whose father was a surgeon in Rouen, was a handsome, morbid, and precocious child. Before reaching his teens he had written two serious essays, one on Corneille and one on Constipation. At eighteen he took a trip to Corsica, including a sightseeing tour of southern France. Although his father wanted him to take up medicine as a career, Gustave refused, and in 1842 he was sent to Paris to study law, but he developed a nervous malady and soon returned home.

After his father died in 1846, leaving his son a substantial annuity, Flaubert lived with his mother near Rouen until 1849 when he took another trip, this time to the Near East. Although he never married, he had a mistress, Louise Colet, herself a poet, whom he had met in Paris and who became a great inspiration to him. In 1851 he began writing "Madame Bovary," but in spite of the affection of his mother and Louise, he frequently succumbed to fits of depression and developed a thoroughly misanthropic view of human nature.

With the serial publication of "Madame Bovary" in 1856, Flaubert was arrested on the charge of "foisting pornographic literature on the public." As a result he became more embittered and withdrawn, avoiding even his close friends, Turgenev and George Sand. After his mother's death in 1872 he became almost a recluse until apoplexy ended his dejected existence as he was writing his last novel, "Bouvard and Pécuchet" (1881).

"Salambo" (1862), "A Sentimental Education" (1869) and "The Temptation of Saint Anthony" (1874), followed by "Three Tales" (1877), are perhaps the best-known of his other works. Flaubert spent years on each production in order to develop his faultless style. His cult of perfection became a major influence on later novelists who tried to imitate his exact realism.

Charles Bovary, a dull student, flunked the examination that would have qualified him to practice medicine. For the sake of his fond mother he tried again and after a great deal of cramming passed with a good grade. His mother set him up in practice at Tostes and found him a wife, a wealthy widow. The poor woman, who was forty-five, thin, pimpled, and bucktoothed, was suspicious of her youthful husband, domineered over him, and became a nagging shrew.

Mme. Bovary complained a great deal—of her nerves, her chest, and her liver, besides her husband's imagined unfaithfulness. In the spring a blow fell which put an end to her miseries. A notary absconded with most of her money. It was found that the house in which the Bovarys lived was eaten up with mortgages. The widow had lied about her wealth! Charles' parents made a scene. A week later his wife began to spit blood. The next day she suddenly sighed "Oh God!" and died.

At first Charles was sorrowful—after all, she had loved him—but soon he was enjoying the freedom of his solitary state.

One morning M. Rouault, a prosperous farmer, came to pay Charles for the treatment of a broken leg and invited the bereaved young man to his farm for a visit. "My daughter," he said, "thinks about you now and then, you know; she says you've forgotten her." But Charles had not forgotten beautiful Emma Rouault, on whose account he had made more trips than were necessary to treat her father's leg. Now, a free man, he visited the Rouaults frequently. In a few months he and Emma were betrothed.

The following spring, a year after his first wife's death, Charles and Emma were married. As Emma entered the conjugal chamber she saw, in a carafe, a dried bouquet of orange blossoms, tied with white ribbons—the other bride's bouquet! Without a word, Charles picked it up and took it to the garret. Emma wondered what would happen to *her* bouquet.

Charles, who adored his charming wife, was now supremely happy. But Emma, a romantic girl, did not find the happiness in marriage that she had expected. She found her husband dull. His conversation was flat as a sidewalk; his commonplace ideas aroused neither emotion nor laughter nor thought. He was very busy and preoccupied with his work; he had no other interests. Lovemaking became a habit like the habit of having dessert after dinner. One day Emma asked herself: "Good heavens! why did I marry this man?" She occupied herself with her house and garden, she drew, she played the piano, she walked in the country, but boredom, like a spider, was weaving its web in all the corners of her heart.

Toward the end of September this boredom was momentarily relieved when the Bovarys were invited to a party by the Marquis d'Andervilliers, for whom Charles had lanced an abscess—and who had noticed that Emma had a pretty figure and did not have the manners of a peasant. The elegance and gaiety of the ball were a revelation to Emma. She treasured the memories of it for weeks and months. The occasion was like a crevasse dividing her past life from her future.

Emma dreamed of Paris; she bought a map of the city and took imaginary walks about it. She subscribed to a lady's magazine and a fashion journal. She read Balzac and George Sand. Absorbed in fantasies of high Parisian society, of travel to foreign countries, of exquisite love affairs, she found her immediate surroundings insufferable. Charles was getting fat and his manners were deteriorating; he ate noisily. He would go to sleep shortly after dinner with his medical journal in his lap.

Emma was waiting for something to happen, but nothing happened. She gave up her music, her drawing, her sewing, her reading; she even became careless about her dress. At length, from sheer ennui, she grew pale and developed asthma and heart palpitations. A consulting physician advised a change of air. So, after four years at Tostes, Charles abandoned his practice there and took Emma to the market town of Yonville-l'Abbaye, near Rouen.

When the Bovarys arrived at Yonville, Emma was pregnant. Charles' happiness knew no bounds. Emma longed for a son and when she was told that she had borne a daughter, she fainted. The infant was put to nurse with a carpenter's wife, and Emma lost interest in her.

There was one person in Yonville with whom Emma could converse with pleasure, a handsome young clerk, Léon Dupuis. This young man sang well, painted, was interested in literature and the theater, and like Emma was suffocating with boredom. Though they had few occasions to enjoy each other's company, Léon and Emma each began to imagine a love for the other. Léon cultivated Charles' friendship; he ventured to bring Emma some cactuses from Rouen. She bought him a rug for his room.

Emma, eaten up with desire for Léon and with hatred for Charles, the obstacle to her happiness, grew thin and pale. But she maintained a formal relationship with Léon and took pride in the virtuous suppression of her love for him. He concluded that she did not love him. He found it unbearable to remain in the village and departed for Paris.

Now Emma's life seemed black indeed. She cursed herself for not having dared to love and to be loved. In time love was quelled by absence, and pure boredom took its place. She often fainted, and one day even spat blood. Charles was alarmed, but she only said, "Bah! What does it matter?"

One day a young gentleman, M. Rodolphe Boulanger, brought a plowman to the doctor's house to be bled. He had just bought a château nearby; he was a wealthy bachelor of thirty-four. When he saw Emma he said to himself: "She is very pretty, this doctor's wife. Wherever did this fat fellow pick her up? . . . She is tired of him, no doubt. With three words of gallantry she'd adore you. . . But how get rid of her afterwards?" He thought of his mistress who was growing fat and tiresome. "I must have her!" he cried.

Not long after this a fair was held at Yonville. On this occasion Rodolphe and Emma met again. Rodolphe lost no time. He spoke of himself as a lonely, unhappy man who had vainly sought happiness in dissipation and folly. Emma was entranced with the young roué's romantic talk and bold admiration for her. She was not so shy as she had been with Léon.

Some weeks later Rodolphe came again to the doctor's house on the pretext that his plowman was having dizzy spells and needed another bleeding. When Emma met him he said that the thought of her was driving him to despair. He begged her for one word—but the doctor entered. Charles spoke of his wife's poor health, and Rodolphe asked if riding would not be good for her. "Just the thing!" exclaimed the doctor. And so it was arranged that Emma and her lover could have daily excursions together into the country. On the first of these excursions she gave herself up to him.

All Emma's romantic dreams had now come true. "I have a lover!" she repeated to herself in ecstasy. She was transfigured with joy and pride. But with time Rodolphe's love for her began to cool; she was, in her passion and adoration, like other mistresses he had had.

Emma found Charles more and more odious. At last she began to plead with Rodolphe to take her and her little girl to Paris, or abroad. In a moment of tenderness he agreed to go away with her. A date was set. Emma made all her preparations.

But when the time came, Rodolphe said to himself: "I can't exile myself, have a child on my hands. The trouble, the expense! No, no, a thousand times no! It would be too stupid!" He wrote Emma a letter that began: "Courage, Emma, courage! I do not wish to ruin your life." He said he was going away, to avoid the temptation of seeing her. He would never cease to love her. He had the letter sent to Emma in a basket of apricots.

Charles enjoyed the apricots. But as he was munching them, Emma fainted. She fell ill of a brain fever. Never suspecting the cause of her condition, Charles neglected his patients to give her all his attention.

Meanwhile he was having financial difficulties. In the course of her love affair, Emma had become a spendthrift, buying luxuries for herself and gifts for her lover. The draper and notary, Lheureux, who was aware of what was going on, had encouraged her to go into debt to him. He now demanded payment; but Charles, devoting all his time to his wife, had no income and found it necessary, instead of paying his debts, to borrow from Lheureux at a high rate of interest.

In her convalescence Emma turned to religion. She became as extravagant in her piety as she had been in her passion; she addressed to God the words of love she had formerly whispered to her lover. She aspired to be a saint.

It occurred to Charles to divert his melancholy wife by taking her to the opera in Rouen. At the intermission Charles came upon Léon, now a law clerk in that city, and invited him to his box. After the opera the three went to a café. Emma seemed in such good spirits that Charles urged her to stay in Rouen an extra day to attend another performance. When Charles returned to Yonville, Emma and Léon consummated their interrupted love affair.

When Mme. Bovary arrived in Yonville she learned that her father-in-law had died of apoplexy. He left Charles a substantial inheritance. Lheureux persuaded Emma that the doctor should not have to trouble himself about financial matters and that he should let Emma handle his affairs. She learned enough from Lheureux to impress her husband with her financial acumen, and when she suggested it he was glad to give her the power of attorney.

Emma convinced Charles that she should take music lessons once a week in Rouen. In this way she and Léon managed to spend every Thursday together. They always engaged the same hotel room, which they called "our room." Léon adored her as his "angel." She called him "child."

The days between their meetings were almost unbearable to Emma, who had become the slave of her unbridled lust. In her depravity she became a skilled deceiver, inventive in her lying and resourceful in fraud. She forged receipts for the music lessons she was supposed to be taking. Without the knowledge of her husband she sold a property he had inherited, to pay her debts to Lheureux, who encouraged her to spend recklessly.

Emma was more ardent, more fearless, more resolute than Léon, and she furnished most of the money for their pleasures. It was as if Léon were her mistress. He resented her dominance and feared her extravagant whims. She scorned what she considered Léon's weakness. Their love became mere sensuality and habit and they wearied of each other like any married couple.

At last the inevitable blow fell. Lheureux had sold Emma's notes to another notary, and this man had obtained a judgment for the entire eight thousand francs. If this sum were not paid within twenty-four hours, her household goods and other effects would be seized.

The next day the bailiff, with two assistants, turned up to make an inventory of the contents of the house. When Charles returned in the evening he knew nothing of what was happening. The following day Emma went to Rouen to appeal to Léon. "You are mad!" he exclaimed when she told him she must have eight thousand francs. When they found that no one would lend them money, Emma tried to persuade Léon to steal money from his office. The young man, frightened, offered instead to try to borrow from a wealthy friend, but Emma knew that he was deceiving her.

The next morning bills were posted announcing the sale of the furniture. In desperation Emma went to Rodolphe, who had returned to his château. He coldly informed her that he did not have the money.

As Emma left the château, her memories and ideas were like fireworks exploding in her head. She felt the approach of madness. She ran to the chemist's shop and asked the young assistant for some rat poison. She poured the white powder into her hand and began eating it as she walked home.

Charles was out searching for her. When he returned she gave him a letter. "You are to read it tomorrow," she said; "till then, I beg you, do not ask me a single question, not one!"

She lay down. Soon she became very ill. She died that night, screaming, in convulsions.

After the death of his beloved wife Charles Bovary was sunk in an abyss of grief and tormented by creditors demanding payment for debts Emma had incurred.

One day Charles opened a secret drawer of Emma's desk and found there her love letters from Léon and Rodolphe.

Now Charles ceased to see his patients, allowed himself to grow shabby.

One day he met Rodolphe. "I do not blame you," he said. "It is the fault of fatality." The phrase struck Rodolphe as absurd.

The next day his little daughter found Charles Bovary sitting in the garden with his head thrown back. She thought he was asleep, but he was dead. No cause of death was discovered.

THE MARBLE FAUN

by

NATHANIEL HAWTHORNE*

CONDENSATION BY REV. PAUL REVERE FROTHINGHAM, D.D.

Four individuals were standing in the Sculpture Gallery of the Capitol of Rome. Three of them were artists, and they had been simultaneously struck by a resemblance between one of the antique statues, and a young Italian, the fourth member of their party.

"You must confess, Kenyon," said a dark-eyed young woman whom her friends called Miriam, "that you never chiseled out of the marble a more vivid likeness than this. Our friend Donatello is the very Faun of Praxiteles. Is it not true, Hilda?"

"Not quite—almost—yes, I really think so," replied Hilda, a slender New England girl whose perception of form was singularly clear.

"Donatello," said Miriam, "you are a veritable Faun. Shake aside those brown curls and let us see whether this resemblance includes furry ears."

"No, no! dearest Signorina," answered Donatello, "you must take my ears for granted," and he lightly tripped beyond the reach of her extended hand, only a moment later to come close to her and look into her face with appealing affection.

"You have bewitched the poor lad," said the sculptor, laughing. "That is a way of yours. I see another of your followers behind yon pillar, and his presence has aroused Donatello's wrath."

They had emerged from the palace, and there, partly concealed by a pillar in the portico, stood the wild figure of a bearded man.

"Miriam," whispered Hilda, "it is your model."

Miriam's model, as Hilda called him, had suddenly appeared a few weeks previously when the four friends were visiting one of the Catacombs. In the dark depths of the earth, amid the labyrinth of passageways, Miriam had been lost. Guided by the shouts of the others, she had finally reappeared, accompanied by this strange and

---

* For biographical information see page 153.

uncouth creature. And from that time on he continued constantly to haunt her footsteps, disappearing perhaps for days, only to return and glide like a shadow into her life. What hold he had on her or she on him remained unknown, enhancing the mystery, already deep, which hung about this beautiful woman.

One of Miriam's friends took the matter sadly to heart. This was the light-hearted faun-like Italian count, who seemed such a child of nature. He cherished against the mysterious stranger one of those instinctive antipathies which the lower animals sometimes display.

In the Medici Gardens the unwelcome creature had appeared among the trees just as Donatello was declaring his love for Miriam.

"I hate him," muttered Donatello as he caught sight of the sinister figure.

"Be satisfied; I hate him, too," said Miriam.

Whereupon Donatello had offered to clutch him by the throat, that they might be rid of him forever; and the woman had difficulty in restraining the gentle youth, whose hitherto light-hearted nature seemed suddenly suffused with rage.

But it was otherwise a few nights later on a moonlight ramble that a company of artists were enjoying among the ruins of old Rome. The four friends were of the party, which, after visiting many places, climbed the Capitoline Hill and stood on the Tarpeian Rock. It was bordered by a low parapet. They all bent over the railing and looked down. Miriam and Donatello stood together gazing into the moonlit depths. They were so absorbed with the scene and with each other that they did not notice the departure of their friends. Hilda had gone off with Kenyon, who had drawn her quietly away, and the others had departed in twos and threes, leaving Miriam behind alone with the Italian. But not entirely alone. Hilda had gone but a short way with the sculptor when she missed her friend and turned back. She reached the paved courtyard with the parapet just in time to witness unnoticed a tragic scene. Out of the shadows the familiar figure of Miriam's persecutor had appeared and approached her. There was a struggle beginning and ending in one breathless instant. Along with it was a loud, fearful cry which quivered upward through the air and sank quivering down to the earth. Then silence! Poor Hilda saw the whole quick passage of a deed which took but that little time to grave itself in the eternal adamant. She turned and fled unseen, and the lovers were indeed alone.

"What have you done?" said Miriam in a horror-stricken whisper.

"I did what ought to be done to a traitor," Donatello replied; "what your eyes bade me do as I held the wretch over the precipice."

The last words struck Miriam like a bullet. Had her eyes indeed provoked, or assented to this deed? She had not known it. But, alas! thinking back, she could not deny that a wild joy had flamed up in her heart when she saw her persecutor in mortal peril. Yes, Donatello's had been the hand; but hers had been the look, except for which the hand had not been lifted.

She turned to her fellow-criminal, the youth so lately innocent, whom she had drawn into her doom, and pressed him close, close to her bosom, with a clinging embrace that brought their hearts together. "Yes, Donatello, you speak the truth," said she. "My heart consented. The deed knots us together like the coil of a serpent." They threw one glance at the heap of death below to assure themselves that it was not all a dream—then turned from the fatal precipice and made their way back into the city arm in arm and heart in heart.

An agreement had been entered into before the moonlight tragedy had taken place that the four friends should meet next morning in the Church of the Capuchins to study together Guido's famous picture of St. Michael and Satan. Thither at the hour agreed upon Miriam and Donatello turned their steps. Conscious of secret guilt, they were the more anxious to keep a casual engagement. But when they drew near the church Kenyon alone was waiting for them. Hilda had promised to be of the party, but she was not there. The three pushed back the heavy curtain and entered the nave, only to have their gaze arrested at once by a conspicuous object. On a slightly elevated bier lay the body of a dead monk, tall candles burning at his head and feet. The rigid figure was clad in the brown woolen frock of the Capuchins, with the hood drawn over the head, but so as to leave the features uncovered. Something seemed to act like a magnet upon Miriam. She passed between two of the lighted candles and looked down. "My God!" she murmured, "what is this?" She grasped Donatello's hand and felt it give a convulsive shudder. No wonder that their blood curdled. The dead face of the monk gazing at them beneath its half-closed eyelids was the same visage that had glared upon their naked souls the night before as Donatello had flung him over the precipice. What did it mean? Kenyon drew nearer, perceived their agitation, and started to say something. But Miriam laid her finger to her lips and quietly said, "Hush!" From the shadowy church the three emerged into the Roman sunlight, Kenyon to go in search of Hilda, but leaving a darker shadow still to settle down upon the lovers. The young Italian was petrified with horror. Miriam tried to cheer him, assuring him of her undying love. But she met with no response. They parted, almost as strangers, it being agreed that Donatello should seek his castle in the mountains.

Thither, in the summer, Kenyon went to pay a long-planned visit. He found the poor faun sadly changed. The idea of a life-long penance had taken firm possession of Donatello. He was intent on finding some method of self-torture. Kenyon, knowing now something of what had happened, arranged with Miriam that she should be in the public square of Perugia on a specified day, near the statue of Pope Julius. There the lovers met again. The sense of their mutual crime had stunned, but not destroyed the youth's affection. They needed one another. Kenyon cheered and encouraged them. Their two lives flowed together and the great bronze statue of the Pope, his hand outreached in a papal benediction, beneath which they had met, appeared to impart a blessing on their marriage.

So Kenyon went back to Rome to woo the gentle Hilda, whose sensitive soul was burdened by the knowledge of the awful guilt of her friends. The secret weighed upon her heavily. She sought the seclusion of great churches, and at last, Protestant though she was, she found relief by pouring out in the confessional at St. Peter's the story of the crime that she had witnessed.

But for Miriam and Donatello the end was not yet reached. The sense of sin had awakened in the faun-like youth what human love could not assuage. Miriam could not rid him of the idea that he must surrender himself to justice. Kenyon had glimpses of the pair now taking part in revelries, but again concealed behind habiliments of woe. In a desolate spot in the Campagna, Miriam at last disclosed the mystery surrounding her own past. It was the story of a marriage to be forced upon her from which her soul revolted. She escaped, though not without unjust suspicions of a crime. Concealing her identity, she gave herself to art. Then, in the Catacombs, the man whom she loathed, half brute and half religious maniac, had reappeared, dogging her steps and threatening to disclose her to the world—with what catastrophe the sculptor knew.

As for Hilda and Kenyon, they went forward into happiness, their

pure love consecrating all they did. But even as they plighted their
troth to one another in the Pantheon before the tomb of Raphael,
upon turning around they saw a kneeling figure on a pavement. It
was Miriam, who reached out her hands in a blessing, but a blessing
which seemed also to repel. As for Donatello, remorse eventually
worked its way, and when heard of last he was in a dungeon as deep
as that beneath the Castle of St. Angelo.

THE MASTER
OF
BALLANTRAE
by
ROBERT LOUIS STEVENSON*

CONDENSATION BY JAMES B. CONNOLLY

The Duries of Ballantrae were a strong family in Scotland from
the days of David I. Their ups and downs I pass over, to come to
that year 1745 when the foundations of this tragedy were laid.

There was my lord, studious, tactful, and retired from the world.
There was The Master (James in baptism) with his father's love of
study; but what was tact in the father changed to black dissimula-
tion in him. Though ever in broils, invariably he left his partners in
mischief to pay the piper. The second son, Mr. Henry, was neither
able nor bad; an out-of-doors, solid sort, who had had an active hand
from a boy in the management of the estate. In the house also was
Miss Alison Graeme, an orphan, comely and self-willed, heiress to a
fortune and, because of my lord's necessities, pledged in marriage
to The Master.

Then came the uprising for Prince Charlie. Against the wishes
of the other three The Master elected to ride with the Prince; which

* For biographical information see page 90.

left Mr. Henry to take King George's side, this being a common policy of great houses in that day. So The Master rode to the north. Then came the word of Culloden and The Master's death. After a decent time Mr. Henry, to preserve the estate, married Miss Alison, although he no more than any other doubted her love for The Master's memory.

But The Master was not dead. He had escaped to sea, his escape being not to his credit. At sea he was captured by a pirate ship. By the most ingenious deviltry he secured the treasure of the pirate ship as she was about to fall into the hands of a King's cruiser, and escaped with it to the swamps on the American shore. One man he took to guide him out of the swamp, and dirked him to death after they were safely clear of it. Thence he continued his march to French Canada, although forced on the way to hide his treasure in the wilderness. This we learned from a Colonel Burke, an Irish soldier of fortune, who came in the night to plead money for the support of The Master, who was then in France.

There was a letter from The Master which threw Mr. Henry in a passion. "He calls me a niggardly dog!" he cried. "But if I ruin the estate I shall stuff him, the blood-sucker! And all this I foresaw when he elected himself and not me to go with Prince Charlie."

The gap made in our accounts by The Master's demands became a sore embarrassment. As steward of the estate I must needs ride to Edinburgh and there raise new loans on hard terms to keep old ones afloat; and this held for seven years, Mr. Henry shaving everything to the last farthing to raise more money, and yet more money, winning for himself thereby no better title than miser with the countryside as well as at home; for never a word of this business did he even tell to the old Lord or Mrs. Henry, it being the devilish malice of The Master to require this secrecy and the loyal nature of his brother to comply.

The odium attaching to Mr. Henry, and the knowledge, which came to me, that The Master all this time had also a pension from the Scotch fund in Paris, became too great a burden for me. I took it on myself to tell Mrs. Henry how her husband had already sent seven thousand to The Master. Thereafter no further moneys were sent abroad, and the telling did much to check a widening restraint between Mr. Henry and my lady, a great joy to me.

This action resulted in The Master's return to us, a great curse to the household; for in all matters of contention, though Mr. Henry might be right, The Master had the trick of setting him in the wrong. He still demanded money, and to satisfy him, the entail was broken and a great piece of land sold; and all the while he ceased not to lay siege to the heart of Mrs. Henry, carrying it on so deftly that I scarce knew if she was aware of it herself, she that I doubt not still loved him.

This brings me to the night when he laid the most unbearable of insults on Mr. Henry. "I never knew a woman," said The Master, "who did not prefer me, nor—I think—who did not continue to prefer me to you." At which Mr. Henry coldly struck him on the mouth.

"A blow!" cried The Master. "I will not take a blow from God Almighty! I must have blood for this!"

They fought beyond the shrubbery, I bringing the candles for them. From the first Mr. Henry showed himself the stronger, which so surprised and confused The Master that he tried foul play, but got only the length of Mr. Henry's sword through the body. He fell, apparently lifeless.

Mr. Henry shook with sobs. I led him into the house and told the old lord and my lady; but, going back to bring in the body, I found it gone. A good riddance, I thought, whether dead or alive, but the night's work threw Mr. Henry into a fever, and his mind was never again the same clear mind as of old.

The old lord died, and to my lady and Mr. Henry, now my lord, was born a boy, and to that boy my lord became a slave, which had not been so with his first child, Katherine. He would pass by his wife as though she were a dog before the hearth to come at the boy. Without doubt this was in the nature of a judgment on my lady, she who had been so cold so many years to every mark of his tenderness; but to me it was monstrous, and I was emboldened, much as I loved him, to say so; but my saying so only served to send my lord sick to bed and to earn for me from my lady the word that I was no better than an old maid.

This brings me to that morning in April, 1764, that The Master returned to us again, this time with an Indian servant. With his return my lord and lady, I urging them on, took ship for New York, where my lady had property through her father. This voyage, so I thought, will at one stroke rid them of The Master and weave them closer together.

Twenty days it took The Master to learn where they had gone;

whereupon he also sailed for New York, and I on the same ship, praying that she would go down, even with myself with her, if it would but take The Master also. I looked forward with woe to the day he should set foot in New York; but our ship was a slow sailer, and other ships which sailed later arrived before us; so it happened that my lord had word of The Master's coming and prepared for him. There was suspicion of more than one murder, it seems, to The Master's hand during the earlier stay he made in America, and so now he found it a better business to leave New York and hunt in the wilderness for that treasure which he had buried so many years before.

At this time all the evil The Master had done seemed borne in a flood upon my lord's brain. He became moody and took to drink. There had been talk that he connived with the crew which The Master had hired for his expedition into the wilderness, bribing the leaders to make way with his brother. There is no evidence of that, but it is true that The Master's Indian servant, to save his life, as he said, did bury him alive, with the intent to resurrect and restore him later by the agency of some secret Oriental trick.

My lord and a party, I being of it, followed The Master, and it was when the East Indian was lifting his body from the grave that we came upon them. I thought for a moment that the eyelids fluttered. Others say that the lips strove to speak, that his teeth showed through his beard, which may have been, as I was busy elsewhere, for at the first disclosure of the dead man's eyes my lord had fallen to the ground. When I raised him he was a corpse.

I buried him there; my lady laid an equal stone to each; and there where they died, side by side, they lie to this day.

LES MISÉRABLES
by
VICTOR HUGO

CONDENSATION BY NATHAN HASKELL DOLE

VICTOR MARIE HUGO was born at Besançon, France, February 25, 1802, so puny an infant that it was not believed he could live. He was the third son of a distinguished soldier under Napoleon. He came from sturdy but not noble stock, his ancestors on his father's side having been simple peasants.

He was well educated in France and in Spain, where his father held high rank under Napoleon's brother. He was a precocious lad, writing long plays in verse and prose while hardly more than a child. Before his twenty-first year he had won several high prizes for his verse. But, thrown on his own resources by the death of his mother, he found it difficult to live by his pen. He moved into an attic, where he had his only experience of actual poverty. His writings, however, soon became popular and he was able to marry, at the age of twenty-one, Adele Foucher, his playmate of childhood days. It was a happy marriage for ten years. Then Hugo became infatuated with an actress, to whom he was devoted fifty years.

From his youth until his death, on May 22, 1885, Hugo wrote rapidly—poems, plays, and novels. No other man of his time had such an international reputation. Swinburne hailed him as "the greatest man born since the death of Shakespeare."

His most famous novel, "Les Misérables," was published in 1862, but he had been working on it for fifteen years. Thirty years before had appeared his first great prose romance, "Notre Dame," and the third, "Toilers of the Sea," came out in 1865.

Hugo was an exile from his native land when these novels

were published. When Napoleon III mounted the throne, the novelist, a fiery republican, found it wise to turn his back upon Paris. He fled to Brussels, disguised as a laborer, and then settled in the Channel Islands. There he lived for nearly twenty years, although each summer he traveled on the Continent. He did not re-enter France until the downfall of Napoleon following the disaster at Sedan.

What France thought of him was evidenced at his funeral. More than one million people lined the streets of Paris as the procession moved to the Pantheon, where he was buried in that last resting-place of the great men of France.

About the time of the French Revolution, Jean Valjean of La Brie, a day-laborer, earned a scanty living for his sister and her seven children. One time, when the family was starving, he stole a loaf of bread, was caught and condemned to the galleys for five years. Twice he attempted to escape and failed. He was a convict for nineteen years. When he was discharged in 1815 he was wicked, silent, chaste, ignorant, and ferocious; his affectionate nature had been poisoned against society. But he had taught himself how to read, and he had thought.

Refused shelter or food at tavern or private house, he came to Monsigneur Myriel, Bishop of D——, in the foot-hills of the Alps. He was treated like a prince; but in the night he stole some of the bishop's silver plate, was caught as he made off, and was brought back to the good bishop, who, with a smile, assured the gendarmes that the articles were not stolen, but given. Adding two silver candlestocks, the bishop said to him: "Take them and become an honest man. My brother, you no longer belong to evil, but to good. I have bought your soul of you. I give it to God."

As he fled he yielded to one last temptation to do wrong; he took from a hurdy-gurdy boy a two-franc piece, but almost immediately, filled with remorse, he tried in vain to find the boy. Two years later a stranger, dressed like a working-man, arrived at the little city of M—— sur M——. Just as he arrived a fire broke out in the Town Hall and he rescued two children belonging to the captain of the police. This saved him from having to show his passport. He made an invention and soon became prosperous. He built great workshops, endowed a hospital, founded schools, paid high wages, and was made mayor.

Employed in his factory was Fantine, a girl who had been deserted in Paris by an unworthy lover. She had left her baby, Cosette, with a crafty and hideous pair named Thenadier. When it was learned that she had an illegitimate child, she was discharged without the knowledge of M. Madeleine, the benevolent manufacturer, and was reduced to such poverty that she could not pay the Thenadiers, who took Cosette's clothes for their own girls and wrote Fantine for more. The girl sold her beautiful blond hair; then they informed her that Cosette was ill, which was a lie, and demanded one hundred francs. To obtain this she sold her front teeth to a traveling dentist; then she went on the town, and when a dissolute dandy, to annoy her, put snow down her back, she scratched his face and was arrested by Javert, inspector of police, a brutal and overofficious tyrant, who had been attached to the galleys when Jean Valjean was there and suspected the mayor of M—— of being the former convict. The mayor freed Fantine. She supposed he was the cause of her misfortunes and spat in his face. He took the affront meekly and investigated her complaint. She was ill of consumption and he provided for her and promised to look out for her child.

About the same time the police arrested another man who three former convicts swore was the missing Jean Valjean. Jean Valjean's conscience would not allow an innocent person to be punished in his place. Surmounting extraordinary difficulties, he went to Arras, where the trial took place, and just as the judge was condemning the wrong man, he confessed he was the missing convict that had robbed the bishop and the hurdy-gurdy boy.

The judge let him go; but Javert was implacable and apprehended him at Fantine's death-bed. He was lodged in jail, but, having enormous strength, he broke out and returned to his house to secure his great fortune. He had time to hide his money in the haunted forest of Montfermeil, but was captured once more and sent to the galleys for life.

Nine months later at Toulon he broke his chain and saved the life of a sailor who was hanging head down from the topmast of a ship, but he himself either fell or jumped off from the spar and was reported drowned. The battle of Waterloo had taken place and the Thenadiers, who had been guilty of robbing the dead on the fatal field, kept a wretched inn at Montfermeil. They treated Cosette, now eight years old, with great cruelty. Christmas, 1823, was the climax of her wretchedness; she was sent after dark to fetch water from a spring in the dreadful forest. A poorly dressed stranger, passing, carried her heavy bucket. At the tavern he protected her from her mistress's threatened punishment, and the next morning he paid Thenadier one thousand five hundred francs and took Cosette to Paris, where he occupied a tumble-down habitation just outside of the city, the gloomiest place in all the gloomy boulevard. By day ugly, at twilight lugubrious, and at night sinister. He thought himself secure there, but his benevolence made him conspicuous, and the old caretaker, being full of envy and uncharitableness, grew suspicious of her lodger.

One day he saw Javert. He took Cosette and again fled. But Javert was on his track. Only by unexampled adroitness and by his colossal strength did he escape by climbing over a high wall. He found himself in the garden of the convent of the Petit Picpus, where worked Père Fauchelevent, whose life M. Madeleine had saved when he was mayor of M——. The gardener, out of gratitude, got him appointed his assistant by representing him to be his brother. Cosette was taken into the convent school. She grew up into a charming girl; beauty suddenly came to her like the blossoms to a cherry-tree in April, and Jean Valjean, happy in loving her as his daughter, as his granddaughter, as the only woman he had ever loved, guarded her as a sacred treasure.

He had good reason to be wary, for the Thenadiers had come to Paris and joined a band of robbers, and Javert never forgot. He had several desperate encounters with them. On the one side outlaws; on the other undeviating law personified. He took part in the abortive revolution of 1830 and saved Javert's life, at last winning the admiration of that implacable and fatally honorable man.

But there was one danger from which he could not protect Cosette: the most beautiful thing in the world, which nevertheless seemed to him his worst enemy—love.

Baron Marius, the son of a man whom Thenadier had robbed at Waterloo and had incidentally saved from a terrible death, had been turned out of his house by his royalist grandfather and was earning a poor livelihood by literature. He saw her and they met. Their love went through more than the usual vicissitudes. During the insurrection Jean Valjean carried the youth through the mazes of the Paris sewers and brought him, desperately wounded, to his grandfather's house. The old man relented and consented to the marriage. Jean Valjean gave Cosette a dowry of about six hundred thousand francs.

In order to have a conscience perfectly clear he told his life story to Marius, who, not understanding the grandeur of the spirit that had never done anything but good, allowed him to go away with a broken heart. Thenadier, however, came to the baron to blackmail him and unconsciously revealed what a noble life Jean Valjean had led. Marius, taking Cosette, hastened to the old man's death-bed, and gave him one last taste from the cup of happiness. He died in their arms.

Victor Hugo calls *Les Misérables* "a drama in which the hero is the Infinite, the second character is Man." It is in reality a melodrama in which are mingled scenes of history, a host of characters from the highest to the lowest, improbabilities which strain one's credulity, a vast amount of rare and curious information on all sorts of subjects, dissertations on philosophy, science, politics and religion. Its treatment of social injustice had a powerful influence on public opinion, not only in France, but in many other countries. It has been an epoch-making book.

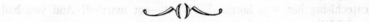

MR. MIDSHIPMAN EASY

by

FREDERICK MARRYAT

CONDENSATION BY JAMES B. CONNOLLY

FREDERICK MARRYAT was born in 1792 and died in 1848. His father was an Englishman of wealth, who sat in Parliament and was a writer of verse and political pamphlets. The son, however, had the sea in his veins, and even before he was allowed to enter the navy at fourteen he had made numerous attempts to run away to his favorite element. He served under Lord Cochrane in the famous "Imperieuse" and at once began to lay the foundation of that inexhaustible store of knowledge and experience which made him the prince of story-tellers of the sea.

The daring Lord Cochrane was an admirable master; during two and a half years he showed his young midshipman some fifty engagements and bold enterprises of every sort. And the latter was an apt pupil whenever there was anything strenuous doing. Honorable mention came his way frequently; in 1818 he received the medal of the Humane Society for "at least a dozen" gallant rescues; he invented a code of signals; he became a Fellow of the Royal Society.

He began his series of twenty-four books with "Frank Mildmay" in 1829, and kept them going for twenty years, to the delight of an expectant public.

"Mr. Midshipman Easy," "Snarley-yow," and all the rest of the two dozen tales hold a thrill for whoever loves the sea.

Mr. Easy was for natural equality and the rights of man, which Mrs. Easy did not mind, she being allowed to have her game of patience. Behold then a contented couple to whom, after eleven years of married life, was born our hero Jack. For nurse to the baby the family doctor introduced a strong, healthy young woman. Mrs. Easy, catechising her, was horrified. "What—not married! And you had a child!"

"If you please, ma'am, it was such a little one!"

The young woman joined the Easy household, where she aided every other member there to spoil young Jack; and so we have at five years of age a complete specimen of the headstrong young male. To save him from utter ruin the family doctor urged that he be sent to a school which he could highly recommend. The parents agreed, but with the proviso from Mr. Easy that he must not be flogged.

The benevolent-looking master of this school was against flogging also. Caning, in his judgment, was more efficacious; so without troubling to tell Mr. Easy of it, he caned our hero beautifully. Thus, when at fourteen Jack came home to live, all the bully was gone from him. In place thereof was a great disposition to argue things, with natural equality and the rights of man as his favorite themes.

Two disputatious people under one roof were too many. Jack's father packed him off to sea in H. M. sloop *Harpy,* where he very soon learned that the natural equalities were not in high favor. If he was not towed ashore on a grating by a court-martial order for some of his socially anarchistic opinions when his ship arrived at

Gibraltar, it was probably because the captain of H. M. S. *Harpy* was indebted to Jack's father for the loan of one thousand pounds.

Jack's radical opinions did not lessen his naval zeal. As midshipman in command of the ship's second cutter in a certain expedition, he ignored the recall signal and so lost sight of his own ship; but losing sight of her led to the capture of a fine big enemy ship; and among this ship's passengers was a lovely Italian girl whom Jack treated with great courtesy, even to seeing her safely ashore in a near-by port.

Being the only officer in his force, it was Jack's duty to navigate the prize back to Gibraltar. "Simple enough," he said. "The land was on our left hand coming out; it should be on our right hand going back"; and he was doing pretty well on that theory when a gale of wind came along and blew him out of sight of land.

In the cargo of their prize the crew had found some casks of wine, to which they helped themselves, and, coming to a group of islands where Jack put in to reconsider his navigation, they went ashore and got gloriously drunk. Their wine gave out. They hailed the ship for more. Jack said no. They set out to swim to the ship after it, but sharks caught three of them; the others returned aboard on Jack's terms.

Jack sailed his prize over pretty much the whole Mediterranean before he found his own ship again. He had been gone two months. But such a story as he had to tell! and fourteen thousand dollars he found in the cabin of the prize helped out the telling it. His captain commended him, but also advised him to give a little time to the study of navigation.

As Jack grew older he began to have his doubts of the natural equalities. For one thing the ship's boatswain, Mr. Biggs, was getting on his nerves; likewise Easthupp, the purser's steward, forever insisting that a gentleman should be treated as a gentleman. Having been a London pickpocket before entering his Majesty's Service, he was probably over-sensitive.

One day, after what Mr. Easthupp termed "hinvidious" remarks had been passed all around, Jack challenged Easthupp and Biggs to a duel, adding that he would fight them both or none, and at the same time. The arrangements were instrusted to Mr. Tallboys the gunner, a man of most exact mind. "Both or none, and at the same time—what did that mean exactly?"

"Ah, of course! Three combatants, three positions." Mr. Tallboys

got out his *Art of Gunnery,* and drawing an equilateral triangle of
twelve paces on a side, he said: "Each principal will take a corner.
By this method each party will get in his shot and be at the same
time shot at by another party. A fair proceeding all around, you
see."

The arrangement pleased Jack mightily. Mr. Biggs, after a while,
also agreed. "Shot for shot, I dare say it's all right," admitted Biggs.
Nobody cared what Easthupp thought—he was stood on his corner.
The question came up as to who was to fire at whom. "As sailors,"
explained Mr. Tallboys, "you should of course fire with the sun.
That is, Mr. Easy will fire at Mr. Biggs, who will fire at Mr. Easthupp, who will fire at Mr Easy. And now, if you please, take stations. Cock your locks! Take good aim! Fire! Stop your vents!
Very well done."

Where Easthupp's bullets went nobody could say, probably into
the ground. Jack's passed through both of Mr. Biggs's cheeks. "A
pretty business!" sputtered Mr. Biggs. "How am I to pipe to dinner
with my wind escaping through these holes in my cheeks?"

The boatswain's bullet had caught Mr. Easthupp in a tender rear
spot, which caused that gentleman to roar so loudly that every one
said he must be dead, or dying at least. Jack was scared, or pretended to be. He wrote a note to Captain Wilson, saying he feared
he had killed Mr. Easthupp, and so he would stay ashore for a time
to see what came of it.

This happened in Malta. With Midshipman Gascoigne, his second, carrying a pair of dueling pistols, Jack sailed on a speronare
with a crew of four men and a boy to Italy. During the night the
crew, having seen too many of Jack's doubloons, tried to kill the
lads; but the lads killed them instead—all but the boy, who providentially fell overboard and was drowned.

A storm overtook their little craft and threw her high up on the
shore of Sicily. While looking about them, they saw an elderly and
a young lady beset by two robbers with long swords. An old gentleman was lying unconscious on the ground. Jack and Gascoigne
drove off the villains. The old gentleman turned out to be a Don
Ribiera de Silva, the lady to be Donna Clara, his wife, and the bru-
nette young beauty, Donna Agnes, their daughter. On a second look
at Donna Agnes, Jack knew her for the young lady passenger of his
prize ship. At the home of Don Ribiera, where the lads were later
made welcome, he fell deeply in love with her.

Easthupp did not die; and the boys returned to their ship, where their captain read them a fine lecture on discipline and conduct, and the value of a regular study to develop their minds. Jack at once began the study of Italian.

His general conduct in the next two years was such as to promise an early promotion; but one day there came a letter from home informing him that his mother had died, and also that if his father was not mad he soon would be. Jack went home on leave, and there found his father working on a mechanical invention which was to rectify the mistakes of nature—to preserve to the human species the finer organs and destroy the baser. While demonstrating this invention the poor man had his neck broken.

A midshipman with eight thousand pounds a year was an anomaly in the service. Jack secured his discharge, the better to look after his estates. But as time went on he found himself thinking of Donna Agnes; so much so that one day he purchased a fast little armed brig, named her the *Ribiera,* procured letters of marque, and sailed for Italy. Here Agnes became his excellent and affectionate wife; eventually, in England, she became the mother of four children.

Having given up the sea and his early theories about the equalities, Jack stood for Parliament on the Conservative ticket and was elected; and all without too much expense, which was remarkable.

MOBY DICK*

by

HERMAN MELVILLE

CONDENSATION BY LAWRENCE FALCONER

HERMAN MELVILLE (1819–1891) shipped to Liverpool as a cabin boy when he was eighteen but returned after a year to teach school in New York and Massachusetts. But the spell of the sea was upon him and, in 1841, he boarded a whaler at New Bedford bound for the South Pacific. In less than two years he deserted ship in the Marquesas Islands, where he was captured by a native tribe but later released unharmed. The young New Yorker then served as a seaman on a United States man-of-war based in Honolulu. Discharged in 1844, he went back to Boston where, three years later, he married the daughter of the Chief Justice of Massachusetts. He was by this time something of a celebrity as a result of the publication of his two books: "Typee: A Peep at Polynesian Life" (1846) and "Omoo: A Narrative of Adventure in the South Seas" (1847). These were promptly followed by three more sea stories: "Mardi," "Redburne," and "White Jacket."

In 1850 Melville bought a farm near Pittsfield, Massachusetts, where he settled down to write and where he became friends with Hawthorne. "Moby Dick," published the next year, was dedicated to Hawthorne and with it the author reached the peak of his literary effort to portray the sweep and majesty of the sea. He worked hard on other books which did not have much success—"Pierre" (1852), a psychological study of a writer; "Israel Potter" (1855),

* *Moby Dick* is called a novel but it is also a compendium of information about whales and the whaling industry. It begins with the etymology of the word *whale,* followed by four score quotations about whales from literature. Of the 135 chapters of the book, 43 are devoted entirely to description of whales and whaling without a trace of narrative, and other chapters contain much factual material. It is, of course, only the narrative that is condensed here.

a story of the Revolution; and "Piazza Tales" (1856), a collection of short stories and sketches—until he left for a journey to the Near East. When he returned to America in 1857, he sold his farm and sailed to San Francisco on the clipper ship captained by his brother. Finally, in 1863 he moved to New York City, where he worked as a customs inspector for the next nineteen years. His last novel, "Billy Budd, Foretopman," was completed just a few months before his death.

Melville was never fully regarded as a writer until his rediscovery in the early twenties when his stature as a literary figure was greatly enhanced by numerous studies and appreciations. His complete works, including his poetry, were published in 1924.

Call me Ishmael. Some years ago, having little money in my purse and nothing much to interest me on shore, I thought I would see the watery part of the world, and I turned from schoolmaster to simple sailor. Whenever it is drizzly November in my soul and I am of a mind to knock people's hats off in the street, I take to the sea. True, I am ordered about and thumped about, but they pay me for my trouble, and I have not yet heard of a passenger being paid a single penny!

Now it was my fate that after having repeatedly smelt the sea as a merchant sailor, I took it into my head to go on a whaling voyage.

I stuffed a shirt or two in my old carpet-bag, and quitting the good city of old Manhatto, I arrived in New Bedford on a Saturday night in December and entered the Spouter Inn. The house was full, but the landlord offered to let me share a harpooner's blanket and rather than wander further on a bitter night, I accepted the offer.

At last I tumbled into bed and commended myself to the care of heaven. Just dozing off, I was awakened by the entry of my bed companion. His face was of a purplish yellow color, here and there stuck over with large blackish-looking squares. There was no hair on his head but a small scalp-knot twisted up on his forehead. Without noticing my presence, he undressed himself and, as I live, all parts of him were checkered over like his face. A tattooed cannibal!

The savage produced a small wooden idol, built a little fire of shavings before it, offered it a bit of ship's biscuit, and worshiped it with a series of guttural noises. Then, lighting a long pipe which had an axe-like blade and served as a tomahawk, he extinguished the light and sprang into bed. Giving a grunt of astonishment, he began feeling me. I sang out.

"Who-e debel you? You no speak-e, dam-me, I kill-e," he said. I shouted for the landlord, who, thank heaven, quickly appeared, grinning. He explained the situation to the savage—Queequeg—and we both settled down to a good night's sleep. I awoke to find my companion's arm lovingly thrown about me.

I spent two nights with Queequeg, who, for all his tattooings, was a clean and comely cannibal. What's all this fuss, thought I to myself—the man's a human being. Better sleep with a sober cannibal than a drunken Christian. We became friends. I—born and bred in the bosom of the infallible Presbyterian Church—united with him in worship of his idol Yojo. How could the God of heaven and earth be jealous of a bit of black wood?

On Monday morning my pointed-toothed friend and I made our way, by ship, to Nantucket, and from there we shipped on the Pequod. She was a rare old craft, seasoned and weather-stained in the typhoons and calms of all four oceans and appareled like any barbaric Ethiopian emperor with trophies of whale-bone.

We had been under weigh for several days before Captain Ahab showed himself upon deck. I had already learned from Captain Peleg, one of the owners who had signed me on, that Captain Ahab had lost a leg to a monstrous whale on his last voyage and had been out of his mind for a spell. "A grand ungodly, god-like man, Captain Ahab. Desperate moody and savage sometimes, but he has his humanities."

At last Captain Ahab stood upon his quarter-deck. His high, broad form seemed made of solid bronze. In place of his lost leg there was an ivory-white leg fashioned from the polished bone of the sperm whale's jaw. A lividly whitish scar threaded its way from among his grey hairs down to his collar; it resembled the seam made by lightning upon the trunk of a great tree.

The bitter cold of Northern Christmas slowly gave way to the eternal August of the Tropic. Captain Ahab had the entire ship's company assembled and addressed them:

"Whosoever of ye raises me a white-headed whale with a wrinkled brow and a crooked jaw, with three holes punched in his starboard fluke—look ye, whosoever of ye raises me that same white whale, he shall have this Spanish ounce of gold, my boys!" And he nailed a golden doubloon to the main mast.

Three harpooners—the Gay Head Indian Tashtego, the coal-black African Daggoo, and my cannibal friend Queequeg—spoke up. They had all seen Moby Dick, for so the white whale had been named.

"Captain Ahab," said Starbuck, our first mate, "was it not Moby Dick that took off thy leg?"

"Aye, my hearties, it was Moby Dick that dismasted me! Aye, aye! and I'll chase him round Good Hope, and round the Horn, and round perdition's flames before I give him up! And this is what ye have shipped for, men! to chase that White Whale till he spouts black blood and rolls fin out. What say ye, men, will ye splice hands on it, now?"

"Aye, aye!" shouted the harpooners and seamen. Captain Ahab's frenzy infected the crew, and my shouts went up with the rest. But Starbuck, a sober, careful, reasonable man, put on a long face. "I came to hunt whales, not my commander's vengeance," he said. "Vengeance on a dumb brute that simply smote thee from instinct! Madness! It seems blasphemous."

Ahab looked at him with his wild eyes. "Hark ye, all visible objects, man, are but as pasteboard masks. If man will strike, strike through the mask! How can a prisoner reach outside except by thrusting through the wall? To me, the white whale is that wall. He tasks me; I see in him outrageous strength, with an inscrutable malice sinewing it. That inscrutable thing is chiefly what I hate; and be the white whale agent or principal, I will wreak that hate upon him. Talk not to me of blasphemy, man; I'd strike the sun if it insulted me."

Stubb, the second mate, an easy-going, happy-go-lucky man, might have agreed with Starbuck, but no one knew his mind, if indeed he possessed one—he seemed indifferent to death and danger and was devoted only to his pipe. Flask, the third mate, was a young man who regarded all whales as his personal enemies, to be cruelly destroyed whenever encountered. Starbuck's reason had no other defender.

Ahab, though all his thoughts were of pursuing Moby Dick, was not unmindful of his obligations to his employers the ship-owners and to his crew, nor was he unmindful of the danger of being deprived of his command if he sacrificed the normal business of the voyage. So as we invaded the southern realm of Leviathan, the sudden wild cry of "There she blows!" would be heard and our four boats would take to the water in keen pursuit. The harpooner's iron would dart into the body of a whale. After the violence of the whale's mortal struggle, in which often boats were overturned and men flung into the sea, the dead body was made fast to the ship. The monster was then peeled like an orange of his blubber and decapitated, and the carcass was set adrift to feed sharks and sea birds. Then the precious spermaceti was removed by the bucketful from the head if the catch was a sperm whale. The head was also robbed of its teeth, its baleen, and its jawbone (sawn into slabs). Below decks, in the try-works, the blubber was turned into tons of oil.

Now and then we encountered another ship, and Captain Ahab always asked for news of Moby Dick. The Town-Ho had lost a mate to the white whale's teeth. The Jeroboam likewise had lost a mate, drowned when tossed from his boat by the whale. The Bouton de Rose, however, had never heard of a white whale. Captain Boomer, of the British ship Samuel Enderly, had lost an arm to Moby Dick and was resolved to avoid the monster thereafter, nor did he impute malice to the whale or feel any ill will toward him— a very sensible Englishman, and Ahab scorned him. The jolly commander of the Bachelor, a Yankee ship, had heard of Moby Dick but did not believe in his existence, and Ahab scorned him also, for a fool.

In the waters near Japan my pagan bosom-friend Queequeg was seized with a fever which brought him close to the very door of death. Having seen coffins in Nantucket, which reminded him of the canoes in which the dead warriors of his native isle were set adrift, Queequeg induced the carpenter to make him one. At his request, Queequeg was lifted into the coffin-canoe, with his little god, tomahawk-pipe, harpoon, and other possessions; but lying there calmly awaiting death he suddenly rallied and was in a short time good as new. He had recalled a duty unperformed, and had decided not to die.

When we came upon the Rachel we learned that only the day before she had encountered Moby Dick and that the whale, harpooned, had run away with one of the boats, as often happens. The captain, a Nantucket man known to Captain Ahab, begged him to join in search of the lost boat, which had held his own son, but twelve years old. But Ahab stood like an anvil, thinking only of the time lost from the pursuit of Moby Dick, now so near.

Days passed, and no whale was sighted. Ahab had himself hoisted to the main masthead, that he might scan the sea from that height.

The Pequod now met the miserably misnamed Delight, which had but yesterday lost five men to the wrath of the white whale. "Hast killed him?" cried Ahab.

"The harpoon is not yet forged that will ever do that," answered the captain of the Delight.

That night the old man, snuffing up the sea air, perceived that peculiar odor sometimes to a great distance given off by the sperm whale and ordered the ship's course to be altered in the direction from which the odor came.

At dawn, from his masthead, Ahab raised a gull-like cry: "There she blows! A hump like a snow-hill! It is Moby Dick!"

Quickly the boats were lowered. The sea was smooth as a meadow. The whale, alarmed, sounded. While Ahab in his boat scanned the sea, the whale rose beneath the boat and gently took it in his jaws; the gunwales bent in and snapped, as the jaws, like an enormous shears, bit the craft completely in twain. Moby Dick swam swiftly round and round the wrecked crew, churning the water. The Pequod turned and drove the whale away, and Ahab and his companions were dragged into Stubb's boat.

Moby Dick was sighted again the following morning as he hurled his entire bulk into the air, less than a mile ahead. Again boats were lowered and the whale rushed among them with open jaws and lashing tail. The skillful oarsmen eluded him and three irons were darted at him. But the whale in his evolutions entangled the lines, and Ahab was forced to cut his line. The other two boats were dashed together and overturned. The whale shot up from under Ahab's boat and threw it into the air.

As the whale went his way, the Pequod again came to the rescue of the floating mariners and picked up oars and whatever else could be saved. It was discovered that the only man missing was the Parsee, Fedallah. Ahab was shaken by his loss, for in some way Fedallah had intensified, like an evil spirit, Ahab's demoniac will to destroy the White Whale.

When Ahab swore "I'll slay him yet!" Starbuck once more sought to dissuade him. "Great God!" he cried, "never, never wilt thou capture him, old man. Shall we keep chasing this murderous fish till he swamps the last man? Shall we be dragged by him to the bottom of the sea? Impiety and blasphemy to hunt him more!"

But Ahab was not moved. "I am the Fates' lieutenant; I act under orders."

It was afternoon of the next day before Moby Dick was sighted. As the boats were lowered, Ahab solemnly asked Starbuck to shake hands with him. Their hands met; their eyes fastened, Starbuck's tears the glue.

"Oh, my Captain, my Captain!—go not—go not!"

"Lower away!" cried Ahab.

When, after sounding, the whale rose from the water, the torn body of Fedallah was seen entangled in the ropes that Moby Dick had in his turnings enwrapped about himself.

As Ahab's boat approached the whale, he darted his fierce iron, and his far fiercer curse into the hated whale. But as the monster suddenly turned, the line snapped. Moby Dick, catching sight of the black hull of the Pequod, and seemingly seeing in it the source of all his persecutions, bore down upon its advancing prow. The solid white buttress of his forehead smote the ship's starboard bow. Men and timbers reeled, and waters poured through the breach. The whale now turned from the ruined and settling ship and made for Ahab's boat.

Furiously Ahab flung his harpoon. The stricken whale flew forward. The line fouled and as Ahab stooped to clear it, it caught him round the neck and he was shot out of the boat. The rope was torn from the boat and disappeared in the depths of the sea. The tranced crew of the little boat watched their ship until it disappeared in a vortex, which drew them, spinning, out of sight.

It so chanced that I was not drawn down into that vortex and that Queequeg's coffin-canoe rose up from below and floated by my side. I clung to it for almost one whole day and night. On the second day, a sail drew near. It was the Rachel, that in her retracing search after her missing children, only found another orphan.

THE MOONSTONE

by

WILKIE COLLINS

CONDENSATION BY JESSIE A. PARSONS

WILLIAM WILKIE COLLINS, the son of a landscape and portrait painter, was born in London, January 8, 1824. He died September 23, 1889. After some private education at home he spent three years in Italy with his father. On his return he became a clerk with a firm of tea merchants in London, but tea was not to his taste; he studied law at the famous Lincoln's Inn and was called to the bar in 1851. But he was still drifting; he was not attracted to the law, though he found his studies of great use to him in later days.

The death of the elder Collins in 1847 put the son partly in the way of finding himself, for he published his father's life in two volumes the next year. He had been turning over his experiences of three years' life in Italy, and in 1850 appeared his first novel, "Antonia, or the Fall of Rome." "Basil" was published in 1852, and "Hide and Seek" in 1854. He had not attracted the attention of the public as yet. The great event of his life, however, came in 1851, when he made the acquaintance of Charles Dickens. The lives of the two were intimately connected thereafter. Dickens was conducting "Household Words," and for it Collins contributed, as he did for "All the Year Round," also in charge of Dickens, a large number of tales.

The close friendship and co-operation of Dickens not only found the direction for Collins to follow, but it seemed to lead him to the type of story on which rests his fame, that in which the skilful unwinding of an intricate and exciting plot, and the construction of a thoroughly involved mystery, baffle the reader in a maze of details and circumstances. He might lack humor, fail to appreciate the finer shades of character, but he certainly conceived some striking personalities; for his own type of story he was unsurpassed by any of his contemporaries.

"The Woman in White" (1860) was his greatest success; "The Moonstone" (1868) was a close second in the opinion of a large and devoted following of readers.

Before the Mohammedan conquest the moon-god, in his Brahmin shrine, wore upon his forehead one of the most beautiful diamonds in creation. "Partly from its peculiar color, partly from a superstition which represented it as partaking of the nature of the deity whom it adorned, and growing and lessening in luster with the waxing and waning of the moon, it first gained the name by which it continues to be known in India to this day—the name of 'the moonstone.' After passing from one lawless hand to another, in 1850, 'after the lapse of eight centuries the moonstone looks forth over the walls of the sacred city in which its story first began.'"

Throughout this long period the moonstone had been sought diligently by three Brahmins and their successors. Their vigilance was, in 1848, rewarded by the sight of the resplendent gem gleaming on the bosom of a light-hearted girl. Rachel Verinder had received the moonstone as a legacy from an unscrupulous uncle who was in high disfavor with the family. And he, knowing that the moonstone brought ill-luck, had made the gift in revenge.

Although thoroughly admired at Miss Verinder's birthday dinner, the stone began to exert its uncanny influence on the atmosphere of the party. Two rival suitors were present—both cousins of Rachel Verinder. One, Godfrey Ablewhite, persuasive in manner and eloquent as chairman of many charitable organizations, lived in the neighborhood and had hitherto gained the advantage which propinquity gave him over Franklin Blake, lately returned to England, bringing the moonstone, after several years spent on the Continent. The latter was a guest of Mrs. Verinder three weeks before the birthday, where his graciousness and congeniality to Miss Verinder made him most welcome. Hence it was not surprising that Rachel fell in love with him and refused the importunities of Godfrey Ablewhite just before the birthday dinner. This major tension, accompanied by various misunderstandings on the part of other guests, ended in a dispute between the family physician and Franklin Blake over the latter's sleeplessness, in which the doctor failed to convince him that medicine could triumph over his nerves.

On hearing a drum, the guests rushed to the terrace to be confronted by three Indian jugglers. At a word from one of the diners, a celebrated Indian traveler, the intruders hurriedly retreated. This surprising turn of events argued for putting the moonstone into especially safe keeping, but Miss Rachel, with ideas of her own, insisted on placing it in an unlocked Indian cabinet in her dressing-room. The company then dispersed, leaving Franklin Blake, who looked wretched, and Mr. Ablewhite together. After much urging Mr. Blake decided to take brandy and water to help combat his sleeplessness.

The household was startled next morning at the disappearance of the moonstone. Franklin Blake, always alert, was instrumental in bringing in the nearest police. Rachel became exceedingly angry at their intrusion and was deeply offended with Franklin Blake for securing them. The chief of police succeeded in making a mess of affairs and was superseded by the famous detective Sergeant Cuff.

The chief of police had aroused the resentment of the servants by examining their boxes; Sergeant Cuff wished to begin with the personal effects of the family, not looking for the moonstone, but rather for an article of clothing bearing a paint stain from the door of Rachel's boudoir. Every one acceded but Miss Verinder, who gave a most decided refusal. The only servant suspected by the sergeant was Rosanna Spearman, who had been rescued from misfortune by Lady Verinder. She was discovered by Sergeant Cuff to have bought a quantity of plain white cloth and made and laundered a new garment in her room when supposed to be ill with a headache. Miss Rachel's point-blank refusal to have her possessions searched and her decision to leave her home ended in gaining her point and the dismissal of the detective, who left the Verinder home convinced that Miss Rachel had disposed of the diamond through the connivance of Rosanna Spearman in order to pay some pressing debt.

Rachel and Lady Verinder spent some little time in London, where Rachel was ordered by her physician to have as much gaiety as possible to counteract the depression of recent events. Franklin Blake left for the Continent and Godfrey Ablewhite again resumed his attentions to Rachel. Shortly after leaving Lady Verinder's country home for London, Godfrey Ablewhite was summoned to a strange house by an unknown person, bound, gagged, and searched by a tawny-skinned individual. On the same day a notorious money-lender met with a like experience in the exact spot where Mr. Able-white was maltreated, only that in his case a receipt for a valuable left at a banker's was removed from his loose papers. The news of the disappearance of the moonstone having reached London, an ugly suspicion began to attach itself to Godfrey Ablewhite, only to be dissipated by the emphatic assertion of Rachel Verinder: "I know that Godfrey Ablewhite is innocent!" Soon after this Rachel became engaged to Mr. Ablewhite, although she told him her heart was elsewhere. He seemed, however, to be quite satisfied with this condition until after Lady Verinder's death, when he had an opportunity to examine her will. When Rachel's lawyer found this out and communicated it to Rachel she dismissed Godfrey Ablewhite, on suspecting him of wishing to marry her for pecuniary reasons. He accepted his dismissal more gracefully than his father, in whose house Rachel was residing after the death of her mother. Mr. Bruff, her lawyer, then made arrangements for her to live with one of her aunts.

At this time Franklin Blake was quickly summoned to England by the death of his father. In his unhappiness he visited Lady Verinder's old home, where he found things sadly changed, with no one in charge except a faithful old steward. This servant told him that there was a letter waiting for him from Rosanna Spearman which her confidant would deliver into no other hands than his. The short letter contained direction to search on the seashore for a hidden box. The box held a garment stained with a smear of paint from Miss Rachel's boudoir and marked with the name of Franklin Blake. A long letter explained that the garment had been hidden there by Rosanna Spearman on account of her love for Franklin Blake and her hopes of shielding him from discovery. Immediately knowing that there must be some mistake, Mr. Blake tried in vain to see Rachel in London by all fair means. His resort to a trick to accomplish this ended unfortunately and they parted in great bitterness. Rachel's words, "You villain, I saw you take the diamond with my own eyes!" spurred him to do all in his power to prove his innocence.

He returned to the country house and soon met the assistant of the family physician, with whom he had disputed at the birthday dinner. Doctor Candy had caught a severe cold that night, which with complications still affected him mentally and bodily. His assistant had taken in shorthand the doctor's delirious ravings, and after studying them had found out what was preying upon the doc-

tor's mind. In the tumbler of water measured for Franklin Blake the
night of the birthday a small quantity of laudanum had been placed.
Sleep-walking results were immediately suspected and even Rachel
was persuaded to have the experiment repeated under conditions as
nearly possible like those of the year before. Her aunt came with
her to chaperon this strange house party, and all eagerly awaited the
experiment. Franklin Blake walked in his sleep as far as the cabinet,
which held a mock diamond. Although he let this stone drop to the
floor as the effects of the medicine wore off, his innocence was established and the two lovers were reconciled.

The time had nearly come when the money-lender was to take
from the banker's the valuable which he had deposited there. De-
tectives watched the bank and several people near the money-lender
were followed on wrong suspicion. A shrewd office-boy took upon
himself to follow a large man with a dark beard. This man had
taken refuge in a low-class boarding-house, awaiting the sailing of his
steamer for Rotterdam. Franklin Blake and Sergeant Cuff hastened
to this house and found the man had been murdered, presumably by
an Indian. The detective, on removing the black beard and pasty
complexion, revealed to the onlookers the fair hair and ruddy features
of Godfrey Ablewhite.

Thus the Brahmin priests, after patiently waiting for eight centuries, were able to restore to the moon-god his famous moonstone.

THE MYSTERIES OF PARIS

by

EUGÈNE SUE

CONDENSATION BY SARA WARE BASSETT

*EUGÈNE SUE was born at Paris, January 20, 1804.
His father was a distinguished surgeon in Napoleon's army.
He himself served in a like capacity at the battle of Navarino
in 1826. After a varied experience in the army and navy, he*

inherited his father's fortune in 1829 and set up to follow Cooper's example in the telling of tales of the sea, for which his experience well fitted him. The great romantic movement included him in its all-embracing sweep. Many thought him the equal of Dumas, but facility of composition is probably the only point on which he was fully able to meet his great contemporary. Socialism greatly attracted him, and in pleading for the cause of the working classes he won a large audience. He sat in the French Assembly, but his opposition to the coup d'état of Napoleon III sent him into exile. He died at Annecy in Savoy, August 3, 1857.

His "Mysteries of Paris" and "The Wandering Jew" reached enormous length and enormous numbers of readers as they appeared in newspapers, in book form, and on the stage.

To interpret justly the works of Eugène Sue, one must not forget to take into consideration the epoch at which they won their place in world literature.

When Sue was born the novel was still a comparatively new product. There had, it is true, been books before its advent, for the invention of printing had put reading-matter within the reach of the people; but until fiction made its appearance most of the material published had been of a religious trend, consisting of lives of the saints and treatises on theology and science. Even then such volumes were costly, to say nothing of their being of far too ponderous a nature to answer the cravings of a public scantily educated and desirous for entertainment at a time when amusements were few.

Therefore, when out of this arid literary waste the novel sprung into being, we can easily picture the eagerness with which the hungering masses fell upon it. Here, at last, was something human and within the scope of the every-day man's understanding; here, in fascinating form, were presented not only characters from the life with which he was familiar, but also adventures in those mystic realms of romance that he had imagined. It was like water to the thirsty!

Hence, if, when reading the very early novels, or even those of the later decades to which Sue belonged, we are conscious of stilted dialogue and melodramatic and improbable situations, let us remember that the writers of this era were to no small extent pioneers in a sparsely trodden wilderness of art; and that when "the world was so new and all" in literary development it is a marvel that their handiwork has endured for so many years. Sue's *Mysteries of Paris* penned in 1842, seems touched with the fires of everlasting youth. Indeed, it must possess the charm of universal appeal or it would never have held its place for almost a century. When we consider how few of our present-day novels survive a second season, we are forced to doff our caps to this artist of the past who, like Stevenson, so well merits the sobriquet of "Tusitala, a Teller of Tales," and the secret of whose spell lies in the eternal child in us answering to the sorceries of a master story-teller.

The book in question is a labyrinth of exciting and dramatic happenings, which, cleverly woven together, embody the author's unique philosophy that the quest for good may be made quite as seductive a crusade as the quest for evil, the only difference lying in the goal toward which one turns his steps. Certainly the story bears out this theory, for we are swept along by the magician's cunning page after page, chapter after chapter, until his creative resources seem limitless. Never for an instant does our interest lag. When the book is finished we feel that, had Sue so ordained, he could have evolved just as many more plots with an equal degree of ease.

He opens his narrative with a scene in the slums of Paris, where Fleur-de-Marie, a beautiful girl of the streets, is being viciously attacked by the Slasher, a brute of the underworld. A trivial quarrel between the two has arisen and the man is about to strike this helpless creature when suddenly a stranger intervenes and by superior strength and wit lays low the assailant. The new-comer is a M. Rudolph, who styles himself a painter of fans. Although poorly garbed and speaking the jargon of the pavements, we speedily realize that he is something other than he pretends; and in this supposition we are soon justified, for presently we learn that in truth M. Rudolph is no other personage than his Royal Highness the Grand Duke of Gerolstein in disguise. The Slasher, however, does not know this, and neither does his pretty companion, and we soon find the three cronies seated amiably at a café table, relating for one another's amusement the stories of their past lives.

Rudolph has little to say. He is an artisan, he declares. The Slasher frankly admits himself to be an escaped convict who has served in the galleys for murder; but with the inconsistency of human nature he announces that while he has no scruples against murder, he will not steal. Fleur-de-Marie, or Goualeuse, as her comrades term her, is a sixteen-year-old waif who has never known any parent save Screech Owl, a cruel woman from whom she had fled when a child; nor has she had any home save prison walls and the haunts of vice. Nevertheless, despite her vile surroundings, she has kept her soul untainted and is essentially pure of heart, being the victim of environment and circumstances rather than its votary.

Observing this, Rudolph, whose aim is ever to give another chance to those in whom good is apparent, transplants her to a home in the country, where, under the care of Mrs. George, his old nurse, she may grow up in a wholesome atmosphere. At the same time he binds the Slasher to him for life by offering him his hand with the remark that the convict has honor and a heart.

Here our story begins.

Rudolph, we soon learn, has two aims in venturing incognito into the filth of Paris. The first is to discover, if he can, the whereabouts of Mrs. George's son, Germain, who has been taken from her in his youth by a vicious husband. The second is to trace, if possible, his lost daughter, who is supposed to have died in infancy. It is around these two themes that the romance moves. In pursuing them M. Rudolph is beset by every imaginable adventure. He is locked up in a subterranean cellar, where the waters of the Seine slowly creep up to his neck, and from which predicament the faithful Slasher rescues him.

Innumerable traps are laid for his feet; but from each successive snare he miraculously escapes. And throughout this series of entanglements he never abandons his premise that no matter how depraved the individual, there is potential good in all humanity, which, if nurtured, will blossom into virtue. In consequence he becomes a sort of "inferior Providence" to those whom he meets. He saves the blameless debtor from prison, and places an honest livelihood within his reach. He does a thousand kindnesses. On the other hand, he does not hesitate to bring the unworthy to justice. Relentlessly he causes the eyes of a wretch who has been pitiless to the weak to be put out that he may know what it means to be helpless and the prey of the strong.

The story is a network of crimes and their eventual punishment, and everywhere triumphant we find the creed that in the breast of humankind burns a spark of the divine.

The portion of the tale dealing with the kidnapping of Fleur-de-Marie from her home with Mrs. George by Screech Owl, the blinded schoolmaster, and the imp Hoppy is a novel in itself. How these wretches wait for the innocent girl, convey her to Paris by coach, and thrust her into the arms of the police, who in turn deposit her in prison, is exciting reading. From prison she is released by a written order, only to fall a victim to a band of hired ruffians who try to drown her in the Seine. As she is floating down the river, one of her old comrades from Saint-Lazare leaps in and saves her life. Next we see her in a great Paris hospital, and it is at this juncture that the Grand Duke Rudolph of Gerolstein obtains traces of her, discovers that she is his own daughter, and bears her in triumph to his magnificent palace to be transformed from a fugitive of the streets to her Royal Highness Princess Amelia. Here, for a brief period, we behold our little Fleur-de-Marie the idol of the court and sought in marriage by a prince of the realm.

But the stigma of the past is ever fresh in the girl's mind. She cannot shake it off. Though she adores her lover, she refuses to wed him, saying that she "loves him too much to give him a hand that has been touched by the ruffians of the city." Poor, brave Fleur-de-Marie! She at last seeks peace in a convent; and when she dies there we have no regrets that her blameless but troubled life is ended.

In the mean time what of Germain?

We search for him through an equally ingenious train of happenings. With all M. Rudolph's wealth and astuteness it is no easy task to find this missing boy who is lost in the great city of Paris. But he is found. Like Goualeuse, the young hero has kept his soul unsullied by evil. Urged to rob his employer, he has not only refused, but has given information against those who plotted the crime, that they might be brought to justice. As a result of this good deed, however, he has been hounded from one end of Paris to the other. At last he falls victim to a monster of crime, Jacques Ferrand, a corrupt notary, who casts him into prison on a fictitious charge. Here he is no favorite, for by scorning to mingle with the vicious creatures about him he incurs their wrath and suspicion, until at length they dub him a spy and resolve to murder him. From this fate he is saved by the Slasher, who appears in the prison just in time to fell his assailants and pilot him to liberty. Eventually he is restored to his mother's arms and to his pretty sweetheart, Rigolette, whom he now marries.

The skill with which Sue constructs his story, introducing character after character, and bringing these varied elements into a unified whole, is a marvel of artistry It is also interesting to note throughout the novel the author's knowledge of medicine—his handling of drugs, his portrayal of hospital practices, and other technical touches relative to his profession. Wherever such data can be turned to use he does not hesitate to employ them, fearlessly setting forth in black and white specific evils of the day that should be righted. Nor does he shrink from proclaiming to France, as did Dickens to England, the defects of the legal and penal systems of his country.

A voice so boldly upraised at a time when injustices were many must have won a hearing, and we honor Eugène Sue not only as a pioneer in the novel-writing field, not alone as a prince of storytellers, but as a reformer of the social and political evils of his generation.

THE NEWCOMES

by

WILLIAM MAKEPEACE THACKERAY*

CONDENSATION BY CHARLES K. BOLTON

Col. Thomas Newcome, the hero of Argom, and of Bhartpour, had loved the beautiful Leonore de Blois, but, having incurred the wrath of his stepmother, he fled to India to carve out his career. There he married the widow, Mrs. Casey, and a few years later sent their son Clive to England. He regaled the ladies of the regiment with Clive's letters; sporting young men would give or take odds that the colonel would mention Clive's name once before five minutes, or three times in ten minutes. But those who laughed at Clive's father laughed very kindly.

At last the happy time came for which the colonel had been longing, and he took leave of his regiment. In England, he had in his family circle two half-brothers, Sir Brian, who had married Lady Ann, daughter of the Earl of Kew, and Hobson Newcome.

One morning at breakfast while Sir Brian chumped his dry

* For biographical information see page 143.

toast, Barnes, the son, said to his sister Ethel: "My uncle, the colonel of sepoys, and his amiable son have been paying a visit to Newcome."

"You are always sneering about our uncle," broke in Ethel, "and saying unkind things about Clive. Our uncle is a dear, good, kind man, and I love him."

At Hobson Newcome's and elsewhere the family party often assembled—the colonel; his friend Mr. Binnie and Binnie's sister Mrs. Mackenzie, with her daughter Rosey; Sir Brian and Lady Ann; and Clive, who had become a painter. From one of these parties Clive and I, his friend Arthur Pendennis, walked with the usual Havana to light us home. "I can't help thinking," said the astute Clive, "that they fancied I was in love with Ethel. Now, I suppose, they think I am engaged to Rosey. She is as good a little creature as can be, and never out of temper, though I fancy Mrs. Mackenzie tries her."

Time passed and our Mr. Clive went to Baden, where he found old Lady Kew with her granddaughter Ethel. "You have no taste for pictures, only for painters, I suppose," said Lady Kew one day to Ethel.

"I was not looking at the picture," said Ethel, "but at the little green ticket in the corner. I think, grandmamma," she said, "we young ladies in the world ought to have little green tickets pinned on our backs, with 'sold' written on them."

Barnes Newcome, too, was at Baden, for he was to marry pretty little Lady Clara Pulleyn, free at last from that undesirable Jack Belsize, Lord Highgate's son. Lady Kew had plans which Clive's growing regard for his cousin Ethel put in jeopardy.

"My good young man, I think it is time you were off," Lady Kew said to Clive with great good humor. "I have been to see that poor little creature to whom Captain Belsize behaved so cruelly. She does not care a fig for him—not one fig. She is engaged, as you know, to my grandson Barnes, in all respects a most eligible union; and Ethel's engagement to my grandson, Lord Kew, has long been settled. When we saw you in London, we heard that you, too, were engaged, to a young lady in your own rank of life—Miss Mackenzie."

Clive's departure led to more flirtations by Ethel than old Lady Kew could countenance, but Ethel had found out how undesirable a man Lord Kew was, and broke the engagement so dear to her grandmother's heart.

When Clive heard that the engagement was over between Kew and Ethel he set out in haste for London. I was installed as confidant, and to me Clive said: "Mrs. Mackenzie bothers me so I hardly know where to turn, and poor little Rosey is made to write me a note about something twice a day. Oh, Pen! I'm up another tree now!"

Clive met his cousin Ethel at a party or two in the ensuing weeks of the season, and at one of their meetings Ethel told him that her grandmother would not receive him. It was then that Clive thought Ethel worldly, although much of her attitude was due to the keen and unrelenting Lady Kew. The colonel and James Binnie during all this time put their two fond heads together, and Mrs. Mackenzie flattered both of them, and Clive as well.

Meanwhile the Lady Clara was not happy with her Barnes. All the life and spirit had been crushed out of the girl, consigned to cruel usage, loneliness, and to bitter recollections of the past. Jack Belsize, now Lord Highgate, could stand the strain no longer, and took Lady Clara away from her bullying but cowardly husband. The elopement of Clara opened Ethel's eyes to the misery of loveless marriages, and the mamma of her new love, the Marquis of Farintosh, already distressed over the unpleasant notoriety of the proposed Newcome alliance, received a letter from Ethel which set her son free.

Ethel then turned to the lonely, motherless children of her brother Barnes, and found comfort in devoting herself to them. Clive married his Rosey, and his father determined to become a member of Parliament in place of Sir Barnes. One night the colonel, returning from his electioneering, met Clive, candle in hand. As each saw each other's face, it was so very sad and worn and pale, that Colonel Newcome, with quite the tenderness of old days, cried: "God bless me! my boy, how ill you look! Come and warm yourself, Clivy!"

"I have seen a ghost, father," Clive said, "the ghost of my youth, father, the ghost of my happiness, and the best days of my life. I saw Ethel to-day."

"Nay, my boy, you mustn't talk to me so. You have the dearest little wife at home, a dear little wife and child."

"You have a wife; but that doesn't prevent other—other thoughts. Do you know you never spoke twice in your life about my mother? You didn't care for her."

"I—I did my duty by her," interposed the colonel.

"I know, but your heart was with the other. So is mine. It's fatal, it runs in the family, father."

The shares of the Bundelcund Banking Company in which the colonel had made his fortune now declined steadily, and at last the crash came, wiping out all the colonel's money and with it all Rosey's fortune. The impoverished Newcomes settled down first at Boulogne, and then in London, the colonel weary, feeble, white-haired, Mrs. Mackenzie a perfect termagant, Rosey pale and ailing, and little Tommy, the baby, a comfort and a care to the hard-worked Clive.

The colonel, no longer able to live under the same roof with Mrs. Mackenzie, found a home with the Grey Friars, and here I saw him. His dear old head was bent down over his prayer-book. He wore the black gown of the pensioners of the hospital of Grey Friars.

When the colonel's misfortunes were at their worst, Ethel, in reading an old book, found a letter from the colonel's stepmother between the covers. It was a memorandum of a proposed bequest to Clive. Ethel at once determined to carry out this intended bequest, and so she and I hastened to Clive's home; but not even good news could soften Mrs. Mackenzie's evil temper. That was a sad and wretched night, in which Mrs. Mackenzie stormed until the poor, delicate Rosey fell into the fever to which she owed her death. We soon repaired to the Grey Friars, where we found that the colonel was in his last illness. He talked loudly, he gave the word of command, spoke Hindustanee as if to his men. Then he spoke words in French rapidly, seizing a hand that was near him, crying, *"Toujours! Toujours!"* Ethel and Clive and the nurse were in the room with him. The old man talked on rapidly for a while; then again he would sigh and be still; once more I heard him say, hurriedly, "Take care of him when I'm in India"; and then with a heart-rending voice he called for the love of his youth, "Leonore! Leonore!" The patient's voice sank into faint murmurs; only a moan now and then announced that he was not asleep.

At the usual evening hour the chapel bell began to toll, and Thomas Newcome's hands outside the bed feebly beat a time. And just as the last bell struck, a peculiar sweet smile shone over his face, and he lifted up his head a little, and quickly said, *"Adsum,"* and fell back. It was the word we used at school, when names were called; and, lo! he whose heart was as that of a little child had answered to his name in the presence of The Master.

HOMER'S* ODYSSEY

CONDENSATION BY PROF. WILLIAM FENWICK HARRIS

It is the tenth year since Troy has fallen. Though the "Iliad" did not go beyond the death of Hector at Achilles's hands, other stories carried on the tale through the death of Achilles, the capture of Troy by the Greeks by means of the stratagem of the wooden horse, the sacking and burning of the city, the death of Priam and his queen, the slavery of Andromache which Hector had foreseen, the slaughter of the little son he loved so dearly, the escape of Æneas with his aged father.

After the booty had been divided, the Greek chiefs took leisurely courses to their homes. The great King Agamemnon sent his dramatic night letter, announcing to his queen at home by the light of flames leaping from hilltop to hilltop across the sea that Troy had fallen; for his pains he met the dramatic death at the hand of Queen Klytaimnestra which Æschylus has made forever famous in his great play, "Agamemnon"; the latter has in it the beginning of the story of Orestes, the close Greek counterpart of Hamlet. The king's brother, Menelaus, had better fortune; he had journeyed homeward with his erstwhile Queen Helen, as if the great Trojan episode had never been, and was reigning again in peace and quiet with The World's Desire by his side at Sparta, with no dread of a marauding Paris sent on the quest of Beauty by Aphrodite. And so, too, the other princes had returned with varying fortunes

But not so the Great Adventurer. Troy had taken ten years to capture; ten years more still found the wily Odysseus detained in the Isle of Ogygia by the fair Calypso. Meanwhile the patient Penelope bides at home, beset by the riotous suitors who make Liberty Hall of the absent king's palace and would force the queen

* For biographical information see page 163.

to wed one of them. She, ever as alert and resourceful as her wandering lord, puts off her promise till she has woven a web—of which she each night unravels what she has done during the day.

This first great story of wandering adventure has a much more perfect unity than the "Iliad." It centers closely about the person of Odysseus, and divides itself into three parts, the adventures of Telemachus in quest of Odysseus, the wanderings of the hero, and his return home, where with the few still faithful to him he makes himself his own detective, lays the scene for the destruction of the villains, and finally brings about the happy ending which has so constantly distressed critics of the novel and the theater since man began to write and ordinary folk to listen or to read.

In the first chapter, which comprises the first four "books" of the "Odyssey," young Telemachus, amidst the mockery of the suitors, starts in quest of his father and makes the rounds of the courts of our old friend Nestor, King of Pylos, and of Menelaus and Helen at Sparta, where he learns the whereabouts of his father, and then starts homeward.

At this moment it is at last made possible for Odysseus to start on his way home. But the sea, ever his enemy, again plays him false, and he is wrecked once more, though he is cast ashore on the land of the Phæacians. There begins in the land of this fabulous folk one of the most marvelous adventures of the man of marvels. Probably the scene that remains in the minds of the great majority of readers of Greek literature as the fairest bit of idealized beauty in it all is the picture of the young Princess Nausicaa. She had gone down to the river mouth with her handmaidens to wash linen; their work done, they fell to playing ball upon the shore, where Odysseus, beneath the shade of the bushes, was sleeping off the weary travail of his long swim. "Then having bathed and anointed themselves sleekly with olive-oil, they took their meal by the banks of the river and waited for the clothes to dry in the bright rays of the sun. And when they had cheered themselves with food, maids and mistress alike, they began to play at ball, casting aside their veils. And for them fair-armed Nausicaa began the song. As Artemis the archer-goddess goeth down from a mountain, either lofty Taygetus or Erymanthus, taking her sport with boars and swift deer, and with her the wood-nymphs sport, daughters of ægis-bearing Zeus, and Leto rejoiceth in heart, and over all she holdeth head and brows, and easy to mark is she, though all be fair—so was the unwed maid conspicuous among her attendants."

The day's work and the sport were over; they were about to depart and leave the weary sleeper under the bushes—when one last throw sent the ball spinning into the water. Instant and unanimous scream from princess and from maids!

So Odysseus was introduced to Phæacia, and the introduction proved well that the hero knew not only the ways of men, but of maids as well. Of the many pleasing things he said to the princess to win her favor, one stands out conspicuous—his comparison of her perfect youth to the young shoot of a palm-tree he had seen in Delos. Whoever has a gardener's eye knows instantly the perfect tribute.

Then followed the presentation of the royal wanderer at the court of King Alcinous and Queen Arete and the tale of his adventures since leaving Calypso's isle. The king is moved and promises to help the stranger on his way. A feast is held; the court bard sings of Troy —the stranger weeps; the king presses him to tell his story. It was a wondrous tale he had to tell, the like of which was never heard before or since. Beginning with the fall of Troy, he had made his course to Thrace, to the Lotus-eaters, to the land of the Cyclops, when befell the adventure with Polyphemus, whose one eye he put out; next the trying experience with the perverse winds of Æolus, with the Læstrygonians, and with the enchantress Circe, who turned her visitors into swine. Then came the descent to Hades, which set the fashion for Virgil and for Dante and all the others who have essayed that great adventure. The sirens, Scylla and Charybdis, and other adventures brought the tale up to Calypso once more.

Alcinous and the Phæacians sent Odysseus on his way to his home at Ithaca. But his old enemy, Poseidon, turned the ship to stone, and the wanderer reached home alone, in the guise of an old beggarman, where he arrived as his son Telemachus was returning from his travels.

Then began the thrilling tale of the wiles and guiles to win his own from the suitors who had taken his place, the harbor of refuge with faithful old Eumæus, the swineherd, the recognition by Telemachus, the death of the true old dog Argos on sight of his long-absent master, the interview with Penelope, the recognition by his old nurse who knows him by a scar upon his leg, the final great trial of strength between the old beggarman and the suitors; they cannot even bend the famous bow of Eurytus; he, however, strings it with ease and sends an arrow singing through the holes of twelve battle-axes set up one behind another.

At that instance the beggarman throws off his disguise and, with Telemachus and only two faithful followers, slays the evil suitors, wins back his true wife, who has waited patiently all these long years, and hastens to greet his old father Laertes.

Impossible romance? I dare say. Yet one of the most human stories ever told.

OF HUMAN BONDAGE*

by

W. SOMERSET MAUGHAM

CONDENSATION BY LAWRENCE FALCONER

WILLIAM SOMERSET MAUGHAM (1874–   ), whose father was a solicitor to the British Embassy in Paris at the time of his son's birth, was orphaned before he was ten and brought up by a clergyman uncle in Kent. The boy spoke French before he spoke English, and his insecurity with the language when he went to school in England may have had something to do with the stammer he developed which caused him so much embarrassment at prep school in Canterbury, as well as later at Heidelberg.

When he returned to England from the Continent, Maugham had a brief apprenticeship at accounting before he transferred to medicine as a career. Although he received his medical degree, he never practiced except as a student in the London slums where he got his background for his first novel, "Liza of Lambeth" (1897). After he succeeded in getting this book published, he was diverted from medicine to writing.

*In 1915, the year that "Of Human Bondage" was pub-
lished, the author was married. During World War I he
served in the British Intelligence. His novel of the South
Seas, "The Moon and Sixpence" (1919), was inspired by a
subsequent journey to Tahiti. In addition to his novels he
has written many travel sketches, essays, and short stories,
of which his best known is probably "Rain." Maugham has
visited the United States frequently and lived there for a
while during World War II. He has given the manuscript
of "Of Human Bondage" to the Library of Congress. Although this autobiographical novel is probably his most
widely read book, "Cakes and Ale" (1930), "The Razor's
Edge" (1944), and "Catalina" (1948) have been well received. His comedies of manners, "The Circle" (1921),
"Our Betters" (1923), etc., staged in London and later
collected in three volumes (1951), brought him wide acclaim
even before his novels.*

*In recognition of his contribution to English letters,
Maugham was honored by Queen Elizabeth in 1954. His
skill in describing life's bitter realities has been commended
by critics who have sometimes labeled him the English
Maupassant.*

Philip Carey, an only child, was orphaned in 1885 when he was
nine. He then went to live with his Uncle William and Aunt Louise,
who lived in Blackstable, sixty miles from London. Both of them
were about fifty years old.

William Carey was a vicar, tight-fisted and narrow-minded. His
wife was a little, wrinkled, and childless woman. She loved Philip
but knew nothing about children and was shy of showing her affection. The boy preferred to be with the jolly housekeeper, Mary Ann,
a fisherman's daughter.

One Sunday afternoon when the vicar was napping, Philip built
a monstrous castle with his play bricks; it collapsed and woke his
uncle up.

"What are you doing with those bricks, Philip? You know you're
not allowed to play games on Sunday."

Philip stared at him with frightened eyes and flushed deeply.

"I always used to play at home," he answered.

"I'm sure your dear mamma never allowed you to do such a wicked thing as that." Mr. Carey stood over Philip while he put the bricks away.

In the evening the vicar said: "I don't wish you to go to church tonight, Philip. I don't think you're in a proper frame of mind to enter the House of God."

When the vicar had left for church, Mrs. Carey said to Philip, "Shall you and I read the service together, Philip, and we'll sing the hymns at the harmonium? Would you like that?"

"I want to be left alone," he said.

"Philip, how can you say anything so unkind? Don't you know that your uncle and I only want your good? Don't you love me at all?"

"I hate you. I wish you was dead."

Soon Philip discovered the vicarage library. His uncle was not a reader, but he collected books. Philip found adventure and happiness in reading.

In September Mr. Carey enrolled Philip in the preparatory section of King's School in Tercanbury, where he would be trained for the ministry.

Philip had a club-foot. The first boy he met in the school kicked him in the shin because he wouldn't remove his shoe and show his foot. A bully in the dormitory forced him to exhibit his deformity to all the boys in the room. Philip could not participate in sports. At first the boys thought it great fun to imitate Philip's hobbling walk. Later they accepted Philip's being crippled just as they accepted another boy's being fat. But Philip, horribly sensitive, withdrew into himself and made no friends. He continued to derive his chief pleasure from reading and study. After two years he became the head boy in the junior school.

A wave of religiosity passed through the school. Philip began to read the Bible regularly. One night he came upon the passage about faith being able to move mountains. He brooded over it and when home on vacation asked his uncle about the power of faith. The vicar assured him that if it says so in the Bible it is so. Philip began to pray, every night: "Oh, God, in Thy loving mercy and goodness, if it be Thy will, please make my foot all right on the night before I go back to school." He looked forward eagerly to returning to school with a normal foot and being able to play football. When the miracle didn't happen, Philip felt that his uncle had played a practical joke on him. His religious ardor cooled.

Philip did well as he moved through the senior school and he was expected to win a scholarship to Oxford. In his last term he became a devoted friend of a good-natured and charming boy named Rose. But when he returned to school after a six-weeks' illness Rose had found another friend and snubbed him.

Because of this disappointment in friendship and his spiritual aridity, Philip lost interest in his school work. Finally he decided to give up his religious vocation and leave the school. But the prefect persuaded him to stay out the school year and finish his course.

After many arguments with his uncle, Philip was allowed to use some of his own money—he had inherited two thousand pounds or so—to spend a year at Heidelberg. It was arranged for him to live with Professor Erlin and his family. The professor had two lively young daughters and had as boarders in his home some interesting students from abroad. Philip spent a happy year there and learned German and French. He studied under a famous philosopher and ceased to believe in God. When he lost his religious faith he felt that a great weight had been taken from his shoulders; he experienced a vivid sense of liberty.

After returning to England, Philip found a Miss Wilkinson visiting in the vicarage; she was the daughter of a clergyman who had been a close friend of Philip's uncle. This woman, who was clever, amusing, and gay and who dressed elegantly, fascinated Philip. Though almost twenty he had never had a sweetheart. Soon he found himself in love with Miss Wilkinson, though she was twice his age. She allowed herself to be seduced—or rather, she seduced Philip, who was pleased with himself and happy and flattered by the devotion of this mature and sophisticated woman. But she had to return to Germany, where she was a governess.

Now, after much debate about possible careers, it was decided that Philip should become a chartered accountant. He went to London to begin a five years' apprenticeship. In London Philip was lonely and wretched. The other clerks were uncouth fellows who resented his superior education. Philip was bored by the work and not successful at it; he determined to abandon his apprenticeship at the end of the first year. His employer took him to Paris for a week, on business, and Philip decided that he must go to Paris to study art. (While at Heidelberg he had done water colors which people admired.)

Philip's uncle was adamant in opposition to the plan. He regarded the young man as irresponsible and thought the wicked city of Paris would ruin him. Philip was not yet of age and his uncle refused to grant him an allowance from his inheritance. Philip thought of selling the valuable watch and some jewelry his father had left him, in order to live in Paris until he came of age. However, his Aunt Louise prevailed upon him to accept a hundred pounds of her own money. He went to Paris.

Philip lived the life of the poor art student. He had faith in his talent and worked hard to make an artist of himself. He enjoyed the companionship and stimulating conversation of struggling young artists and writers. He longed for a mistress, that essential ingredient of the life of the Bohemian artist, but he could not afford one. And he did not envy his friend Cronshaw, a poet and hack writer, who lived with a fat and vulgar trollop who deceived him with hairdressers and *garçons de café.*

Philip had made the acquaintance of Fanny Price, a homely and bad-tempered girl who had given him helpful advice when he first tried to sketch a model. She was a wretched artist but regarded herself as a genius. One day she asked Foinet, the instructor, for a frank opinion of her work. He told her she would never be an artist. Philip lost track of her for a while, but one day he received a note from her asking him to come to her place. He found her dead; she had run out of money and had hanged herself.

The tragedy of Fanny Price made a profound impression upon Philip. He began to question his talent and his choice of a career. Finally he went to the ruthlessly honest Foinet and asked the artist's opinion of his work. Foinet told him that he could become a competent artist but that he had no talent. Philip decided to abandon his artistic career, for there is nothing so terrible as the pursuit of art by those who have no talent. He had spent two years in Paris, and his inheritance had shrunk to sixteen hundred pounds.

Just at this time his aunt died, and he returned to England for the funeral. He made a new start in life, this time with his uncle's blessing. He decided to follow his father's profession, medicine, and enrolled in St. Luke's Hospital, in London.

Things went smoothly for a while; Philip enjoyed the study of medicine and did well at it. But suddenly he was helplessly and completely in love with a waitress, Mildred Rogers. She had a beautiful profile and lovely blond hair. But she was pale, thin, and flat-chested as a boy; she was ignorant, stupid, bad-tempered, cold, and heartless. Philip was fully aware of her defects.

Because of his preoccupation with Mildred, Philip failed his examinations. Not long after, Mildred informed him that she was going to marry a German named Miller.

Philip recovered soon from the shock, loathing himself for his folly and weakness. He accepted the consolation of a young widow named Norah, who was intelligent and kind and good; she loved him and was also a true friend. He was happy, though he did not love Norah.

Then Mildred reappeared with a tragic story. Miller had deceived her: he was a married man and was not well-to-do as he had professed to be. And he had left her when she became pregnant.

To his dismay Philip found that he still loved Mildred. He discarded Norah and took Mildred into his rooms. He paid the expenses of her pregnancy and delivery. He accepted Mildred and her baby as his wife and daughter.

Mildred was grateful to the extent of her capacity for gratitude, but she did not love Philip. Soon she and Griffiths, a philandering friend of Philip's, became attached to each other. There were quarrels, and Mildred told Philip: "I never liked you, not from the beginning, but you forced yourself on me, I always hated it when you kissed me. I wouldn't let you touch me now not if I was starving." She deserted Philip for Griffiths, for whom she had conceived a violent passion. Philip learned later that Griffiths had tired of her quickly and had had a devil of a time getting rid of her.

Again Philip was doing well at the hospital and enjoying his work. The patients liked him. A young man came to the hospital for an operation on his club-foot. The surgeon who performed the operation persuaded Philip to have the same operation. Thereafter Philip was able to wear a more normal boot and to walk with only a slight limp.

Philip made the acquaintance of a patient of forty-eight, Thorpe Athelny. This man, an eccentric character, became very fond of Philip. He was married to a jolly, fat, and ignorant woman, and he had nine lovable children. Philip had Sunday dinner with them regularly, and the children began to call him Uncle Philip.

One evening Philip saw Mildred sauntering along the street glancing at men, obviously a common prostitute. Though he no longer lover her, he offered her shelter, and she and her little girl moved in with him. Mildred, in return, was to look after his apartment and cook for him. But Mildred became more and more resentful because he refused to renew their sexual relations. He came home one day to find Mildred gone and everything in the apartment destroyed.

Philip took a room across the street from the hospital. His inheritance was dwindling. On the advice of a friend, a shrewd Scot who worked for an investment firm, he had a profitable flutter on the Stock Exchange. Later, during the Boer War, on the advice of this man he invested heavily in a South African mine that was sure to flourish after the end of the war—which seemed imminent. But the war dragged on and the stocks became practically worthless. Philip found himself almost penniless and had to leave the hospital.

After a period of starvation and fruitless job-hunting the Athelnys took him in. Athelny got him a job as shop-walker at the linendraper's where Athelny himself worked. Philip hated the work, but after a time utilized his art training, designing posters and even dresses. He lived in anticipation of his uncle's death; his uncle's small estate would enable him to complete his medical training.

Finally the uncle died and left him five hundred pounds. Philip completed his medical course. He was now nearly thirty. Eager to see more of the world, he hoped for an appointment as a ship's doctor. However, he was assigned as a temporary assistant to an elderly physician in Dorsetshire whose regular assistant was ill. After four weeks the old man offered Philip a partnership, with the prospect of taking over his practice when he retired. Philip refused the offer because of his longing to travel.

But fate stepped in. Philip went to the country with the Athelnys and there, with no romantic preliminaries, he and the eldest daughter Sally became lovers. Sally was a magnificently healthy, practical girl; the relationship was a simple, passionate one. When Sally told Philip that she was pregnant, he decided to sacrifice his dreams of travel and do his duty by marrying her. Later Sally informed him that it was a false alarm—and Philip found that he was deeply disappointed. So he asked her to marry him and she immediately consented.

"I'm so happy," said Philip.

"I want my lunch," she said.

He smiled and took her hand. They stood for a moment and looked at Trafalgar Square. Cabs and omnibuses hurried to and fro, and crowds passed, hastening in every direction, and the sun was shining.

* * *

(When Philip was in Paris as an art student, he and Cronshaw were once discussing the meaning of life. Cronshaw said to him:

"Have you ever been to the Cluny museum? There you will see Persian carpets of the most exquisite hue and of a pattern the beautiful intricacy of which delights and amazes the eye. In them you will see the mystery and the sensual beauty of the East; but presently you will see more. You were asking just now what was the meaning of life. Go and look at those Persian carpets, and one of these days the answer will come to you."

Philip often pondered over what Cronshaw had said. Years later it came to him suddenly what Cronshaw had meant: Life has no meaning, except the beauty of its intricate pattern.)

THE OLD WIVES' TALE

by

ARNOLD BENNETT

CONDENSATION BY MARGARET GILLETT

ARNOLD BENNETT (1867–1931), English prose writer whose name is always linked with the Five Towns he made famous in his novels, was born in one of them, Hanley, North Staffordshire, where his father was a solicitor. In his youth, Arnold studied law and worked in his father's office. After a family quarrel, he left for London and was a solicitor's clerk until 1893 when he gave up law for journalism. Next he served for six years as the editor of the magazine "Woman," an experience which may have helped him develop the special insight he later showed in his portrayal of female characters. In 1900 he moved to France, where he lived for eight years. Always a lady's man, in 1907 Bennett married a French actress, from whom he was separated in 1921.

With his flair for high living, the author of "Imperial

Palace" spent the income from his many successful novels lavishly to indulge himself, and he died of typhoid fever in a flamboyantly luxurious hotel not unlike the one he commemorated in his well-known book.

In addition to his early novels, "Man From the North," (1898), "Anna of the Five Towns" (1901), "Grand Baby-lon Hotel" (1902), his best-known are "The Old Wives' Tale" (1908), "Clayhanger" (1910), and "Imperial Palace" (1930). Bennett also wrote plays, dramatizations of his novels, short stories, and "common-sense books" such as "How to Live on Twenty-four Hours a Day," etc. Bennett admitted indebtedness to Stendahl and Flaubert. He had a prodigious memory and great skill in describing realistic detail. "The Old Wives' Tale" is perhaps one of the most impressive records of Life in Time—of birth, change, and decay. It is really a history of a community, as well as of its heroines, and Time makes its mark on the setting as well as on the people of the story.

Constance and Sophia Baines were the lively and attractive daughters of a respected draper of St. Luke's Square in the midlands town of Bursley. Their ages were sixteen and fifteen, years of complete wisdom and utter conceit.

Reared in a comfortable home, the girls were expected by their sensible parents to leave school and help in the shop. Constance was quite willing but Sophia, the younger, and a passionate, proud beauty, wanted to be a teacher. This ambition was looked on by the family as utter madness. Teaching was for needy widows and unmarriageable spinsters.

For a time after Constance took her place behind the counter, Sophia had her way and was apprenticed to the local schoolmistress. In her free time she took her turn sitting with her paralyzed father, who could not be left alone. One day when Sophia was supposed to keep vigil while her mother and sister were out, she left the room for a moment to greet handsome Gerald Scales, a commercial traveller from Manchester. In the brief interval of Sophia's absence, the patient somehow slipped from his pillow and was asphyxiated. Poor Sophia blamed herself for leaving her father's side and in a fit of terrible remorse abandoned her teaching career to help her widowed mother in the family enterprise.

Three months after her father's death, when she found herself spending more and more time in the shop, Sophia realized her sacrifice had really been selfishly motivated because she was mainly interested in Gerald rather than in doing penance for her neglect of duty. Nevertheless, she continued to see the young man during the next two years, on his occasional visits to Bursley, until her mother expressly forbade her to speak to him again. In some alarm over her daughter's infatuation, Mrs. Baines had finally inquired about Mr. Scales and she was not at all satisfied with the reports of his character. Fearing that Sophia would not obey, she arranged with her sister in Axe to invite her unruly daughter away for a long holiday.

But within a fortnight, the willful Sophia had run off with Gerald, who had providentially come into a tidy inheritance and was able to resign his employment.

Almost immediately, as if to cover up the disgrace of the unheralded marriage, Constance was wed to Mr. Samuel Povey, long-time manager of the Baines' shop. As husband and wife the Poveys led a dull but contented life, and the drapery business prospered under Samuel's diligent effort. After seven years, the couple had a son, Cyril. While he was yet a baby, his grandmother, Mrs. Baines, died of the dropsy, and half of her substantial wealth passed to Cyril's mother, the other portion being held in trust for a hypothetical Sophia who had not been heard from since she left, except for one Christmas card from Paris.

Doted on by his mother, Cyril grew into a husky, selfish, and clever boy with a special talent for drawing, and life continued undisturbed for the Poveys for more than a decade. Suddenly tragedy struck the household. Sam's cousin who lived nearby and who had for years borne the burden of a drunken wife, finally killed her. With great family loyalty, Sam embraced the cause of the convicted man; and, while rushing about on the legal affairs of the trial, which took place in very bad weather, he neglected a cold and died of pneumonia. Overnight Constance was a widow.

After twenty-one years of married life, her husband's death was an amputation. Although she faced it with calmness, she was very slow to adjust to the havoc of change. The widow was further dismayed as she saw her son gradually growing away from her and moving into another world that she did not understand. With what seemed to her strange and heartless persistence, Cyril insisted on attending Art School every evening of the week. Since he held an apprenticeship in design at the local pottery during the day, he was almost never home. Constance, trying to grow accustomed to the loneliness, saw little of him but lived for those moments when he was home and willing to share a few words of conversation with her. It was a frightful blow, then, when he won the National Scholarship in Art, an award which would take him at only nineteen to London. Hers was a grief that as a proud mother she was compelled to conceal.

* * * * * * * *

Meanwhile Sophia had tailored for herself a very different but equally tragic fate. After four years of high living, Gerald had come to the end of his fortune, and their marriage had turned out to be the folly prophesied. Sophia loathed her husband, and he resented her. Finally, he deserted her in a dingy Paris hotel when she refused to write home for money. The shock of his abandonment brought on a fever and for weeks she hovered between life and death. During her illness she had been transferred to a private pension by a sympathetic friend of her vanished husband. There she had been nursed by two women of doubtful reputation but genuine kindness.

When she regained her health, Sophia discovered that the elder of the two who had cared for her so well was in dire financial straits and about to lose all her furniture, which she had mortgaged. Fortunately, Sophia had previously had the foresight to salvage two hundred pounds from her husband during one of his drunken stupors. With part of the notes, which she had sewn into the hem of one of her gowns, she redeemed the furniture and became a partner in the proprietorship of the lodging house. However, it was not long before her partner ran off with one of her former lovers, and the entire responsibility of running the place fell to the young Englishwoman.

This abrupt change in Sophia's life took place during the siege of Paris by the Germans in 1870, a time when rooms were in great demand and she had no trouble keeping her establishment fully rented at any price. But after the war crisis was over and things returned to normal, the bad reputation of the street prevailed and good lodgers were increasingly scarce. Sophia, who loved her independence and found hotel management suited her very well, decided to invest her savings, which were by now considerable, in another pension in a better location.

In due course she found a place for sale that admirably suited her needs and bargained for it so astutely that she was able to buy it for a song. With the improved location and enlarged facilities, she very soon amassed a sizable fortune. At the height of her career, after a quarter of a century of hotel management, when she was widely respected for her sagacity and admired for her great dignity of manner, she was discovered by a friend of her nephew, Cyril, who promptly informed Constance of her whereabouts. Immediately Sophia received a long and affectionate letter from her sister, inviting her to come home to Bursley for a visit. At first she did not want to go, fearing her pension would suffer in her absence, but she was finally persuaded to make the trip to England when a corporation offered to buy her hotel at such a profitable figure that she did not dare refuse.

Although not much had happened to St. Luke's Square in her absence, a great deal had happened to Sophia's appreciation of it. As she returned to it now, a middle-aged and experienced woman, it seemed small, dirty, dingy, and wholly unbearable. Constance she found to be fat and a bit fatuous but kindly as ever and in an appalling rut. She tried to argue her into moving to Paris or London or even a nearby seaside resort, but in vain. Constance only accused Sophia of trying to dominate her. The two women had more money than they could ever spend and yet Constance's inertia forced them to remain in the old-fashioned, unhealthy house in that decaying provincial town, and there they lived together for nine dull years.

During this period Cyril was seldom seen in Bursley. With a substantial allowance from his mother, he spent his time in travel and dabbling in art. He wrote infrequently and then only the barest of messages.

On a very dull day in a succession of dull days, Sophia received a telegram from Manchester saying that Gerald Scales was dying there. She went there to see him feeling, as his wife, an obligation to go to his bedside. When she arrived at the address given in the telegram, she was met by a portly, middle-aged man.

"Mrs. Scales?" he said, in a very quiet, very benevolent voice. Sophia nodded.

"I'm afraid I've got bad news for you, Mrs. Scales."

"He's dead?" she asked.

"He's dead," he replied.

"What was it?" Sophia inquired briefly.

"Exhaustion, I suppose, and malnutrition. He was penniless," he explained and then continued. "He just came to the door last night as we were closing. We had a very heavy rain here. He was wet, in a dreadful state, simply dreadful. Of course I didn't know who he was, I'd never seen him before." He led her to the door of a room and opened it to let her pass. She found the body of a very old man in a terrible state of emaciation. The sight made her feel very old, too, and decrepit.

On the return journey to Bursley, Sophia had a stroke and within a few hours was dead. Numbed by the sudden loss, Constance took it stoically at first, rather relieved to be mistress again in her own house. Then she fell into a general decline, plagued by all the changes that were going on too rapidly about her and by the two fiends, sciatica and rheumatism. To add to her distress, she received no news from her son.

Cyril did not get home in time for his mother's funeral. It had been impossible to reach him on his last Italian tour. When the servants left the house for their mistress' burial, only Sophia's ancient French poodle was there to guard the empty place.

OLIVER TWIST
by
CHARLES DICKENS*

CONDENSATION BY REV. HOWARD LAFIELD

Oliver Twist was born about seventy-five miles from London, in the lying-in room of the almshouse. His mother, worn and exhausted from a long and painful journey on foot, had been found unconscious in the road, and had been carried to the only place of refuge for such as she seemed to be. His name he owed to the inventive genius of the parish beadle, who remarked, "The last one was a 's'—Swubble I named him, the next one as comes will be Unwin, and I've got names ready made to the end of the alphabet, and all the way through it again, when we come to 'z'."

*For biographical information see page 81.

The wronged and unhappy mother died without revealing her name, and the only proofs of the boy's identity, a locket and ring, kept even at the price of starvation, were stolen from the corpse before it was cold by the old crone who had been in attendance.

The orphan's childhood, passed in cruel neglect and semi-starvation, was brought to an abrupt close by his own unparalleled act. Desperate through hunger, he and his companions determine that some of them shall secure for all an extra helping of the thin and watery gruel which is their principal diet. The lot falls upon Oliver. Nine-year-old child though he was, he was "reckless with misery." He rose from the table, and, advancing to the workhouse-master, basin and spoon in hand, he said, "Please, sir, I want some more!"

Such unheard-of daring receives speedy treatment. The next morning a bill, posted upon the gate, offers five pounds to any one who will take Oliver Twist off the hands of the parish.

Then there follows a brief stay as the apprentice of a coffin-maker and undertaker, who, with an eye to the effect, promptly makes of the sad-faced little waif a chief mourner at the funerals of children, and "many were the processions which little Oliver headed, in a hatband reaching down to his knees, to the admiration of all the mothers in the town."

His master is, on the whole, well disposed toward him, but a fight with a bullying older apprentice brings him into unmerited disgrace and punishment and he runs away.

On the outskirts of London he chances upon the fascinatingly droll Artful Dodger, pickpocket and pupil of Fagin. The curious behavior of his new associates is only a game to the innocent boy, when Fagin places snuff-boxes, jewelry, watches, and handkerchiefs in his pockets, and then stands looking in imaginary store-windows while (in an unbelievably short time) every one of the things is taken from him. The true meaning of it all bursts upon the horrified Oliver when he is taken on an expedition and sees the "game" in full operation. Dazed and confused, he is the only one captured and taken before a magistrate. His innocence is established, but he faints in the court-room, and is taken home by the remorseful Mr. Brownlow, the man whose pocket he was supposed to have picked. In his new friend's house Oliver is nursed through a serious illness, and better days seemed to have dawned for him, when he again falls into the hands of Fagin. This is no chance happening, for the old crook, dreading the information which the boy may give, has him kidnapped, while on an errand for Mr. Brownlow, by Nancy, a wretched girl of the streets, pupil of Fagin, and mistress of Bill Sikes, the greatest ruffian of the whole gang.

In order to close Oliver's mouth, by making him also a criminal, he is taken along on a housebreaking attempt. Protesting, he is put through a small window that he may open the door to his companions. He is firmly determined to warn the people of the house, but the burglary is a failure, and Oliver, wounded by a stray shot, is left in a ditch by the fleeing gangsters. The next morning he crawls, injured as he is, to the same house, where his story is believed and he finds new and lasting friends.

Again the lad is sought out by Fagin, aided by a mysterious man who has shown great emotion at a chance sight of Oliver in the street, and who now plots with Fagin, not merely for the possession of the boy, but for his moral ruin, which seems to be desired especially by this so-called Monks.

Their whispered plottings are overheard by Nancy, who atones for her former kidnapping of Oliver by risking her life to inform his new friends of his true parentage.

The interview between this scorned street-girl and the beautiful Rose Maylie, adopted niece of Oliver's protectress, gives Dickens a splendid opportunity to which he does not fail to do full justice. "Coldly and harshly treated by Mrs. Maylie's self-righteous servants, the girl is in a defiant mood when finally admitted, and remarks, with a toss of the head, 'It's a hard matter to get to see you, lady. If I had taken offense and gone away, as many would have done, you'd have been sorry for it one day, and not without reason.' "

But "the kind tone of the answer she received, the sweet voice, the gentle manner, the absence of any accent of haughtiness or displeasure, took the girl completely by surprise and she burst into tears. 'Oh, lady, lady,' she said, clasping her hands passionately before her face, 'if there was more like you, there would be fewer like me, there would, there would!' "

Then comes the startling account of what Nancy had overheard: Monks has secured by clever inquiry and bribery, the locket and the ring: he recognized Oliver; he alludes to his father's will and speaks of the gratification it will be to him (Monks) to make a common felon of his young brother, Oliver. He also says with a laugh that there is some comfort in the fact that his identity has been kept from his latest friends, "since how many thousands and hundreds of thousands of pounds they would give to know who their two-legged spaniel is."

Rejecting all Rose's efforts to place her in some safe refuge from her horrible associates, and refusing all rewards, the weeping girl returns to the only life she has ever known, arranging to repeat her evidence to some discreet man whom Rose is to bring to London Bridge.

Nancy keeps the appointment with Rose and Mr. Brownlow, but it costs her her life, as suspicious Fagin has had her followed and watched. Sikes, insane with rage, brutally disregards her protestations that she has shielded him and has remained faithful to him. Disbelieving her, he beats her to death with a club, then flees vainly from the terrors of his own memory of the deed, and dies by an accident as he is trying to escape arrest.

OUR MUTUAL FRIEND
by
CHARLES DICKENS*

CONDENSATION BY ALFRED S. CLARK

A sinister bird of prey seemed Jesse Hexam, crouched in the stern of a dirty row boat, his eyes fixed upon the broad waters of the Thames, his arms bare, his hair matted, his clothes mud-begrimed. Twilight deepened the shadows cast by the huddled buildings of London, but his gaze did not swerve. His daughter, a girl of twenty, rowing in obedience to his nods, regarded him with fascinated dread. Suddenly he stiffened; the bird of prey had sighted the quarry. A few minutes later behind the boat a body bobbed and lunged. Hexam had found another corpse, the pockets of another drowned soul to rifle. It was this grisly livelihood that was reflected in the frightened eyes of Lizzie Hexam.

* For biographical information see page 81.

The story of that find was to be talked about in drawing-rooms; in dingy homes along the waterside and in the comfortable bar of the Six Jolly Fellowship-Porters; in the musty shop of Mr. Venus where skeletons leaped out of corners as the fire brightened; in Boffin's Bower, behind which rose the dust-mounds that had created the Harmon fortune. For the body was identified as that of John Harmon, returning to England to claim a fortune left him by an eccentric father upon condition that he wed a girl whom he had never seen.

John Harmon was decreed dead and the fortune came to Nicodemus Boffin. He remained the same unaffected and lovable man he had been in the past when he was foreman in charge of the dust-heaps. They were singularly happy, were Mr. and Mrs. Boffin. Men and women laughed at their oddities, but never with malice. Commonplace as they were, there was a sterling worth to them.

Eager to atone for his lack of schooling, Mr. Boffin hired Silas Wegg, wooden-legged vender of sweets and ballads, to read aloud Gibbon's story of Rome. His eyes popped with astonishment as Wegg plowed stolidly ahead making sad havoc of Roman names.

"I didn't think there was half so many Scarers in print," Mr. Boffin muttered, sagely.

He acquired, too, a ward and a secretary. Bella Wilfer had been named in the Harmon will as the son's future bride. Her blighted hopes so troubled Mr. Boffin that he installed her in his home, treating her like a beloved daughter. And soon after John Harmon disappeared there came into London a mysterious John Rokesmith, who obtained the position of secretary. A secretive man was John Rokesmith, unwilling to speak of his past.

Rogue Riderhood, former partner and now sworn enemy to Jesse Hexam, set afoot suspicions that Hexam had murdered John Harmon, and the law trailed the vulture of the Thames. It found Jesse dangling behind his boat, as so many had dangled there before, swept overboard and caught in his rope. Eugene Wrayburn was one of the trailers and again he looked into the clear eyes of Lizzie Hexam.

Lizzie found refuge with Fanny Cleaver, better known as the Dolls' Dressmaker, a fantastic little creature with a tongue as sharp as the needle she so incessantly plied. Intruding into Lizzie's life came the love of Bradley Headstone, a morose man, and of Eugene Wrayburn, conscious that she was too far below him for marriage, unwilling to do her harm, and yet unable to resist his longing to be near her.

Rejected, Bradley Headstone vowed vengeance upon the man whom he believed responsible. In the Boffin home, too, unhappiness was brooding. Bella Wilfer, her head turned by wealth, remembering poverty at home, set her heart upon wedding a rich man and discouraged John Rokesmith. The secretary had other troubles. He was trying to put together the past. He recalled a voyage, a ship upon which he was known as John Harmon. He remembered coming ashore and going with a mate to the house of Rogue Riderhood. Somewhere was a room where he drank coffee. Then stupefaction, with gleams of memory concerned with a fight, a slide, cold water swirling about him, a rescue, and a decision to test Bella by taking another name. After that the discovery of the mate's body, mistaken for that of John Harmon.

Suddenly Mr. Boffin seemed to lose his amiability. He was gruff with his secretary; he turned to stories about misers. "The more I save, the more you shall have," he said to Bella, but she did not like the cunning look in his eyes. Nor was Silas Wegg aloof from the lust for money. He cast covetous eyes upon the mounds that had made Mr. Boffin "the Golden Dustman." He explored their lowlands and their summits, poking about for treasure. Perhaps there might be another will. He did find a later Harmon will and cherished it as a weapon wherewith he would bleed his benefactor.

Lizzie Hexam, frightened by her lovers, disappeared. Neither Headstone nor Eugene could trace her. But Headstone fancied that Eugene would find her, and for weeks he trailed his rival. Eugene was aware of this morose figure that was never far behind him and he took an impish delight in roaming after nightfall through all the four quarters of London.

At the same time matters were approaching a climax with the Boffins. Silas Wegg was preparing his trap; Mr. Boffin was daily growing more surly. At last he blazed forth and discharged John Rokesmith for aspiring to the hand of Bella to secure the Harmon fortune. But Bella took the part of the dismissed secretary and cried bitterly as she recalled the lovable Mr. Boffin, now transformed into this terrible monster of greed. She sought again the poverty of her childhood home. It did not take John Rokesmith long to find her, and the cherubic Mr. Wilfer felt happily faint when he saw his Bella's head find what seemed a natural resting-place upon John's breast.

Meanwhile Eugene had found Lizzie's hiding-place, near Plashwater Weir Mill Lock. Eugene rowed up the river to the hamlet, but he did not notice the interested lockkeeper who swung open the gates for him. Nor did he know that a man dressed like the lock-keeper was near, watching him with baleful eyes. The latter was Bradley Headstone; the gatekeeper was Rogue Riderhood, who was known to hate Eugene. Riderhood puzzled more than a little when he saw Headstone, with murder in his eyes, in clothes precisely like his own.

Eugene walked at nightfall with Lizzie by the banks of the river. Headstone could not know that Lizzie had begged Eugene to go away, but he saw their lips meet. A shadowy figure kept close to Eugene after that until something seemed suddenly to crash in his head and the stars and moon reeled in his sight. He closed with his assailant; there was a scuffle and a splash. Lizzie, tormented by her talk, had not gone to her room. She heard the splash and rushed to the river-bank. When she saw a face in the river she hurriedly leaped into a boat. No man could have been more skilful with oars. She reached the floating body, caught it by the hair, secured it, and screamed for help. Help did not come before she had bound and kissed that face that was so dear to her.

Scarred and marred as he was, Eugene struggled back from the borderland of death. He did not expect to recover when he asked Lizzie to marry him, but she was as proud of him when she was made his wife as though he had been standing in full strength by her side instead of lying helplessly in bed.

Rogue Riderhood remembered that Headstone had intended him to suffer for the crime. So he announced that he would dog Head-stone until he was paid handsomely. Headstone knew that the scoundrel would trail him forever, as he had trailed Eugene. He walked away without a word, with Riderhood at his heels. He stepped out upon the bridge that held back the Thames and then suddenly caught his tormentor with a grip that could not be shaken. They wrestled back and forth on the brink, steadily nearing the edge. Riderhood tried in vain to draw a knife. He fought, he tried to squirm free from that relentless embrace. At last he went over backward, with Headstone gripping him. They found the bodies locked together.

In the meantime Silas Wegg tightened his screws upon the hapless Boffin. But the dramatic scene that he had planned did not work out, for there was a later will than the one he had found, giving everything to Mr. Boffin. So Mr. Wegg was suddenly swung out of the house and into a passing scavenger's cart. His wooden leg waved a gyrating farewell as he passed out of the Boffin house.

Bella Wilfer had become Bella Rokesmith and there was a wonderful, tiny Bella before she understood Mr. Boffin's strange miserliness. Not till then did she learn that her name was Bella Harmon and that Mr. Boffin had been troubled by her hardness of heart. So he had decided to try her. It was for that reason that he had been so gruff and miserly. He was glad he had done it, for it had proved Bella's worth and given her to the man who loved her. And now, although the Harmon fortune had been left by the last will to Mr. Boffin, he resolutely refused to take it. He kept only money enough to live comfortably for the rest of his happy days.

The magnificence of the new home where Bella was to live impressed even her impressive mother, and the cherubic father was made John's secretary and released from the numbing life that had been his for many years. But perhaps John and Bella, and the Boffins, too, who were living with them, were made happiest by the long visit that they had from Mr. and Mrs. Eugene Wrayburn. Eugene was slowly winning his way back to health and the old affected cynicism had departed. He was prouder of his wife from the slums than he was of his own distinguished family and the place in society that had been his.

PAUL AND VIRGINIA
by
BERNARDIN DE SAINT-PIERRE

CONDENSATION BY IRVING BACHELLER

JACQUES HENRI BERNARDIN DE SAINT-PIERRE was born at Havre in 1737 and died at Eragny, near Pontois, in 1814.

An emotional dreamer, an irascible personification of the

rolling stone, Bernardin de Saint-Pierre was constantly wandering from one thing and place to another.

Educated for an engineer's profession, he went to sea, served in the army, was dismissed, received an appointment at Malta, held various posts at St. Petersburg, Warsaw, Dresden, Berlin, Mauritius, was superintendent of the Jardin des Plantes at Paris and professor of the École Normale, was a member of the Institute, and was ever meeting with tumultuous and romantic adventures.

Yet he found time to write many volumes, of which the world remembers one. In "Paul and Virginia" he created two figures which have caught the popular imagination, not only of France, but of every country where books are read.

The story inevitably suggests the Greek pastoral "Daphnis and Chloe" by Longus, and one sees in all his life the interest he took in Crusoe.

In the year 1726 a young man of Normandy brought to the Isle de France his young wife, whose family was of noble blood. Shortly afterward he was taken with the fever and died, leaving her alone on the isle.

Estranged from her family and without means, the young widow made her way to an uninhabited island where she could cultivate the soil without the payment of rent, and there she built a rude home for herself and her little child, a daughter whom she named Virginia.

At the same time another woman, with a little son named Paul, settled on the same island, and the two women, mutually grateful for aid and comfort, became fast friends, although they had been of different stations in life.

Marguerite's servant, named Domingo, a powerful black man, was the husband of Marie, who was Madame de la Tour's handmaid. Bound to each other by similar needs, the two lonely women spent much time together, and the two children were almost inseparable. Their attachment was very marked even from the cradle. If Virginia was in trouble, the cries of Paul made it known. When they learned to speak, the first names they learned to give each other were brother and sister. For the rest, they went almost naked, and could neither read nor write.

From the beauty of their bare limbs one might fancy them two of Niobe's children escaped from the marble.

As Madame de la Tour saw the unfolding charms of her daughter she became alarmed for her future and humbled herself to write to an old aunt in France, asking for aid for Virginia's sake.

The aunt replied coldly, commending her to the governor of the island, adding, "Your disgraceful marriage has brought its righteous punishment."

Deserted by her kinsfolk, the poor widow took Paul and Virginia to her arms.

Paul became a planter, busy and skilful, while Virginia spun or tended the goats and helped in the house. Thus passed their innocent youth.

To them Madame de la Tour read the stories which time had hallowed, teaching them to find their happiness in serving others.

Their lives seemed bound up in that of the trees. They knew no historical epochs, no chronology save that of their orchards. No care wrinkled their brows, no intemperance poisoned their blood. They had all the freshness of the morning of life. They loved each other naturally and purely.

It was wise Marguerite who said: "Let us marry our children. Soon Paul will be a man, and then we will have much to fear."

Madame de la Tour hesitated. "Let us wait. Let us send Paul to India for a time. There he will be able to earn money with which to provide a home for himself and Virginia."

To this plan Paul would not consent. "I am needed here. Domingo is old and our mothers are alone. I shall stay."

At this moment came another letter from the aunt in Normandy asking that Virginia be sent to her for education. "If she follows my wishes," the aunt wrote, "she may look forward to being my heiress."

Virginia was alarmed at this offer and Paul was angry. The madame decided against it.

The governor of the island now urged that Virginia be sent.

A missionary of the island joined the governor in urging that Virginia go to her kinswoman, and at last with a heart filled with anguish, mother and daughter, thinking it God's will, consented.

Paul was puzzled by all this secret council.

Meanwhile Virginia's consent had brought from her aunt gold to pay for clothes and jewels and her passage, and she was a transformed being. In her muslin and taffeta, with her hair in the manner of the period, she looked the duchess, and Paul was thrown into despair at sight of her beauty and her alien magnificence.

Distressed by his grief and hoping to cure him of his false hopes, Marguerite now told him that he was only the illegitimate son of a peasant, while Virginia was the daughter of a noblewoman.

Paul, pressing her in his arms, assured her that, as he had no other relative, he would love her the more. "But I see now why Madame de la Tour avoids me."

As the thought of losing Virginia came to him, Paul lost control of himself. Clasping her in his arms, he said: "I am going with you. Nothing shall part us. I swear it by the sea that I must cross, by the air to which I have never breathed a lie."

Nevertheless, Virginia was taken away from him while he was wandering in the forest, mad with his fears. When he returned to the cabin and found her gone, he rushed to a high point from which the outgoing vessel could be seen, and there he stood till the darkness fell and the night winds began to sing their songs in his ear.

Thereafter when he saw the two mothers weeping he bitterly said, "Seek some one else to wipe away your tears."

At last he turned his thought to the garden and to a new task. He determined to learn to read. He wished to be able to read of the country to which his love had gone. In a very short time he was able to read, and when at last a letter came from Virginia he was able to read it for himself. It was a sweet letter, but not a cheerful one. The girl's heart was in her happy island, and she asked Paul to plant the flower seeds which she sent, upon the spot where they had last talked together—a place she called Farewell Rock.

As the months passed, envious folk began to whisper that Virginia was about to marry a nobleman, and Paul was a prey to doubt and despair.

One morning at daybreak Paul saw a white flag flying on Mount Discovery. It was a sign that a ship was in the offing. A little later a letter from Virginia to Madame de la Tour was handed to Paul. Rapturously kissing it, he thrust it into his bosom and hastened to his home! To all the household madame read the letter. Virginia was coming home! She would soon land. Masters and servants all embraced.

"My son," said Madame de la Tour, "go tell all our neighbors Virginia is coming home."

To this happy household a negro messenger came to say that the

ship was in distress and firing guns for help. A storm was approaching. By midnight the sea was hammering the rocks with fearful
roar. The sound of the signal guns was dreadful in Paul's ears. All
night long he and his faithful Domingo waited for the dawn in
silence and dread.

At dawn the governor with a file of soldiers arrived at a point
near which the ship could be dimly seen in the fog. All signs pointed
to a hurricane, and the people gathered in the hope of assisting the
ship to land its passengers.

At nine o'clock a whirlwind swept the harbor clear of fog and
the ship was seen moored near the rocks. Her head was set toward
the billows which rolled from the open sea.

Suddenly, in the midst of a terrible rush of sea, the cables parted.
The ship was thrown upon the rocks. A cry of despair arose among
those who stood on shore. Paul, in frenzy, was about to throw himself into the sea when a strong hand prevented him. In order to save
his life they bound him fast with a long rope and let him leap into
the water. He tried to reach the ship, only to be flung back upon the
sands.

The crew threw themselves into the sea. Those on shore saw a
young woman stretching out her arms in piteous entreaty. It was
Virginia, almost the last to remain on board. In a moment she, too,
was struggling in the cruel sea.

Paul, unconscious and bleeding from his last attempt to reach the
ship, was carried to a neighboring house, while old Domingo and
other friends searched the beach for the body of Virginia.

At last in despair they started back to tell Virginia's mother of
the girl's tragic death. On the way some negroes told them that
wreckage had been driven in at Palm River Valley, and so Domingo
and his companions turned aside to look once again for the body.

There on the sand, half buried, yet with a serene and beautiful
face, lay the maiden, richly clad. One hand rested upon her gown,
the other was pressed to her heart and covered a picture of Paul.

Lifting her gently, the servants carried her to a fisherman's hut
and left her.

In the morning Paul was brought home. He had regained his
senses, but he could not utter a word. His coming brought a ray of
hope.

After a beautiful and touching ceremony, in which the black
people took a part, they buried the lovely body on the western side

of the church, at a point where she had often rested when on her way to Mass, with Paul, and there a few weeks later they brought his body in order that he might rest forever by her side.

~◈~

PEG WOFFINGTON

by

CHARLES READE

CONDENSATION BY EDWARD H. CROSBY

CHARLES READE, English dramatist and novelist, was born at Ipsden, Oxfordshire, on June 8, 1814.

It was his wish that the word "dramatist" should stand first in the description of his occupations, and recorded on his tombstone, and in his aims as an author, was dramatist first and novelist afterward. He always had an eye for stage effect in scene and situation; yet it has been claimed that he was wrong in his own conception of his power as dramatist, and his plays were often failures, while his novels have endured the test of time.

His first comedy, "The Ladies' Battle," appeared at the Olympic Theater in 1851; but his reputation as dramatist was made by the two-act comedy, "Masks and Faces," in which he collaborated with Tom Taylor. By the advice of the actress, Laura Symons, he turned it into a prose story, which appeared in 1853 as "Peg Woffington." A little later "Art" appeared, afterward known as "Nance Oldfield."

Reade was assured of a reputation as a novelist when he published "It's Never Too Late to Mend." This is a novel which he wrote for the purpose of reforming abuses in prison discipline, and the treatment of criminals. Five other novels followed in quick succession: "The Course of True Love Never Did Run Smooth," "Jack of All Trades," "The Autobiography of a Thief," "Love Me Little, Love Me

Long," and "White Lies," dramatized as "The Double Marriage." Then appeared "The Cloister and the Hearth," relating the adventures of the father of Erasmus, a story of the fifteenth century. His next novel of note was "Hard Cash," a story of modern English life.

Reade produced three elaborate studies of character— "Griffith Gaunt," "A Terrible Temptation," and "A Simpleton." He introduced himself in "A Terrible Temptation" as Doctor Rolfe.

He was an amateur of the violin, and among his works is an essay on Cremona violins, which is entitled "A Lost Art Revived."

For some years Reade's health gradually failed. He died on the 11th of April, 1884, leaving behind him a complete novel, "A Perilous Secret," which showed no falling off in the art of weaving a complicated plot and devising thrilling situations.

Peg Woffington stood before the mirror in her dressing room at the Theater Royal, Covent Garden, London. She was alone with her thoughts and they were both serious and pleasant, if the play on her mobile features could be taken as a criterion. She was summing up her eventful career from the time when but a child of eight, cold, ragged, and hungry, she had been found on the Desmond Quay in Dublin by an actress who undertook her professional education, to the present moment, when, as the reigning actress of the British capital, she had the world at her feet. She was supreme in tragedy and captivating in comedy, and in private life brilliant as a conversationalist, with a wit as keen as it was delightful.

And the reflection her glass threw back was one of rare beauty. An oval face crowned by tresses which equaled the ebon of the raven's plumage, lustrous eyes in which the emotions constantly played, and a poise that nothing apparently could disturb. Yet there was a curious expression on her handsome features, a look which she had never before witnessed. For Peg Woffington, for the first time in her life, was in love.

She had many admirers and quite a few flirtations, but they had all been ephemeral, as Peg Woffington could quickly detect idle flattery and the sycophancies of the *jeunesse dorée* which hung about her shrine. She was a woman of the world, keen, suspicious, and cynical, and while she toyed with her gallants, her heart and soul were in her work. But one evening she noticed in a box a face new to the theatre. He was a man evidently from the provinces, but he gazed at her with undisguised admiration. Night after night he was at his post, listening attentively to every word she spoke and with an unmistakable air of respect.

She waited, thinking like all the others he would seek an interview, but as time went on and he made no attempt to bring an acquaintance, Peg's curiosity was piqued and by guarded inquiries she learned that he was Ernest Vane, a country gentleman of means and reputed a bachelor. One night, however, Mr. Vane was brought to the greenroom by Sir Charles Pomander, a man about town who had long but unsuccessfully sought to win Peg's favor. Miss Woffington was not in the room when Mr. Vane first arrived. He quickly adapted himself to the novel surroundings and launched into a eulogy of Peg's personal charms and histrionic ability.

During Mr. Vane's remarks Peg had entered the room and overheard her praises so eloquently sung, and, knowing that Mr. Vane was unaware of her presence, she was impressed with his sincerity. Then they were introduced and Mr. Vane was almost speechless with admiration. All that his imagination had painted was more than realized. Her beauty, her intelligence, her graciousness, were overpowering and Mr. Vane, in his embarrassment, could only stammer a few commonplaces. Here indeed was a novelty and her curiosity turned to interest.

She was still cautious and would treat her new-found friend with varying moods, sometimes cordial and then again coldly, but all the while she was learning more and more of the man who had come into her life.

As she stood before her mirror she was awaiting the arrival of Mr. Vane. They had become warm friends, much more on the part of Mr. Vane, who had openly declared his love and had sent her many tokens of his affection, which Peg had accepted, but with her peculiar whim she had declined anything save some inexpensive gift, telling her lover that it was the sentiment which she desired, not the intrinsic value of the present. She had decided to reveal to Mr. Vane that she, in turn, loved him, but the old, suspicious feeling would not leave her.

When they were alone together Peg placed her hands on Vane's shoulders and, gazing fixedly into his eyes, said:

"Ernest, we actresses make good the old proverb 'many lovers, few friends,' but no one outside our circle knows how much we need a friend. Will you be one to me?"

And Ernest promised faithfully that he would, while life remained.

Then she gave herself up to the intoxication of the moment. With all her adulation Peg was lonely. There had been no one to whom she could go and open her heart with a sense of security, and when Vane poured into her willing ear his avowals of undying love and devotion, Peg's hungry soul drank in his words as the thirsty earth absorbs refreshing showers. She was supremely happy, more so than she had ever dared to be, and the thought almost frightened her as she built dreams for a bright future.

Sir Charles Pomander did not at all relish the turn affairs had taken. He had planned many schemes to win Peg's affection, and when he witnessed the triumph of one he regarded as a rank outsider his love turned to hate. He endeavored insidiously to poison Vane's mind with stories of Peg Woffington's past life, and on one occasion he was nearly successful. James Triplet, a hanger-on at Covent Garden, was recognized by Peg as one who had befriended her in the early days of poverty. Triplet was a playwright and scene-painter, and to give him assistance Peg offered him a commission to paint her portrait. Peg's visits to Triplet's studio were told by Sir Charles to Vane, as evidences of Peg's faithlessness, but the falsity of the charges was soon proved and Vane's infatuation was stronger than ever. Sir Charles had almost abandoned hope of defeating his rival until one day, when returning to London from the country, he gave assistance to a woman whose coach had become disabled.

The beauty of the lady so impressed Sir Charles that he sent his servant to learn her identity, and the man brought back word that she was Mrs. Ernest Vane. A deadly weapon was thus placed in Sir Charles's hands, but he refrained from making public his information until the proper moment. A banquet had been arranged by Mr. Vane in honor of Peg Woffington, and Sir Charles managed to have Mrs. Vane appear when the festivities were at their height.

His scheme was successful and the effect of Mrs. Vane's advent was electric. Mr. Vane, not knowing that his wife was in town, was filled with consternation, but Peg's tact did not desert her even in this trying moment and she introduced those present as members of the nobility. Mrs. Vane was not suspicious and accepted the situation in good faith, but Triplet, who had brought verses in honor of Miss Woffington and being unaware of Mrs. Vane's identity, revealed the true facts and the wife was heartbroken at her husband's inconstancy.

As for Peg, she was furious at the deception placed upon her. She fully believed that Mr. Vane was free to woo her, and then in a moment her dreams were rudely shattered and her faith in mankind destroyed. She determined to take desperate revenge. She would keep Vane at her side in spite of the wife, and then, when he was firmly in her toils, she would publicly discard him. Filled with these thoughts, she went to Triplet's studio, where the portrait he had painted was to be exhibited.

The first glance showed the picture to be a wretched failure and even Triplet acknowledged his defeat. But there was no time to lose, for the critics were already approaching the studio. Peg, with a sudden inspiration, cut the face from the portrait and, having arranged the draperies so that her body would be concealed, she placed her own features in the aperture. The comments of the connoisseurs were ludicrous, some declaring there was not the slightest resemblance to the original, others that the flesh tints were imperfect, and still others that the drawing was out of all proportions. When the opinions had been expressed, Peg came from behind the easel and expressed her views in true Milesian manner.

Peg remained after the others had departed and told Triplet of her intentions toward Mr. Vane. Unexpectedly Mrs. Vane knocked at the door of the studio. She had been followed by Sir Charles Pomander and had sought refuge from his attentions. Peg had no desire to meet Mrs. Vane, but there was not sufficient time to escape, so once more she went behind the easel and placed her face in the portrait. Mrs. Vane, after explaining her presence, noticed the picture and exclaimed:

"You are a great artist, Mr. Triplet; the likeness actually breathes. Oh, that she were here, instead of this wonderful image of her. I would speak to her. I am not wise or learned, but orators never pleaded as I would plead to her for my Ernest's heart."

She paused for a moment, and then, addressing the picture, she continued:

"Oh yes, you are beautiful, you are gifted, and the eyes of thousands wait on your every word and look. What wonder that he, ardent, refined, and genial, should lay his heart at your feet. I cannot take him from you, but, oh, be generous to the weak and give him back to me! Give him back to me, beautiful, terrible woman and I will love you longer than men can love!"

Suddenly she started back with a wild scream.

"It is alive!" she cried, and, running to Triplet, hid her face on his shoulder.

For Peg had been so affected by the piteous appeal of the heart-broken woman that with all her self-control she could not check the tears which coursed down her cheeks. Peg ordered Triplet to leave the room, and when the two women were alone Peg turned to Mrs. Vane and said, calmly:

"I trust, madam, you will do me the justice to believe I did not know Mr. Vane was married?"

"I am sure of it," replied Mrs. Vane. "You are as good as you are gifted."

Peg then promised to so degrade herself in Vane's eyes that he would leave her in disgust, but to this plan Mrs. Vane refused to agree. Finally Peg arrayed herself in Mrs. Vane's cloak and hood, threw a note from the window to Sir Charles, who was waiting below, which she knew would bring that worthy into the room, and then despatched Triplet to summon Mr. Vane to the studio, Mrs. Vane concealing herself in an adjoining apartment. Sir Charles responded to the summons immediately, and in a moment was making violent love to Peg, whom he mistook for Mrs. Vane.

In the height of a most impassioned scene Vane entered and made the same error as did Sir Charles. Swords were drawn, but Peg disclosed herself before matters became serious. The thought that his wife was beloved by another produced such a shock to Mr. Vane that he realized he still loved her and the two departed together, leaving Peg with her unhappy thoughts.

Peg Woffington never recovered from this episode. She plunged once more into her work, but life had lost all its interest. She did not remain long on the stage, but retired to private life and devoted herself to charity, Mr. and Mrs. Vane being her stanch friends while she lived. Her grave in the little churchyard of Teddington, England, is the Mecca of thousands who pay tribute to the memory of the actress and the woman.

PENDENNIS

by

WILLIAM MAKEPEACE THACKERAY*

CONDENSATION BY RICHARD HENRY DANA

One fine morning in the full London season, Major Arthur Pendennis (retired on half pay) came to breakfast at his accustomed
corner in his Pall Mall Club. His were the best blacked boots in
London. His buff waistcoat, checked cravat, spotless linen, white
gloves, his whiskers, his very cane, were perfect of their kind.

He seemed thirty years old, until you saw the factitious nature
of his rich brown hair and the crow's feet around the eyes of his
handsome face with its Wellington nose. His long white cuffs showed
the gold sleeve buttons given him by His Royal Highness, the Duke
of York.

Through his gold double eye-glasses, he read his letters, one an
invitation from the Marquis of Steyne, one from the Bishop of Ealing
and Mrs. Trail, another from an earl, and so on, and last of all,
two others, one from his widowed sister-in-law, and the other from
her only child, Arthur Pendennis, Jr. The first begs him to "come
immediately" to Fair Oaks, Clavering, St. Mary's, "to entreat, nay
command" the "wretched boy" to give up his engagement to marry
Miss Costigan, an actress twelve years the senior of this lad of eighteen. The second from this same lad beseeching his uncle to remove
his mother's objections to his proposed union with his "dear Emily,"
a descendant of the old Irish Royalty, the most beautiful woman in
the world. "A love like mine, sir," writes young Pen, "I feel is contracted once and forever—I shall die without ever knowing another
passion."

The major, inwardly in a rage, ruefully sends refusals to the
marquis, the earl, the bishop, and other entertainers, and takes a
sleepless and tiring trip in the tight, smelly night mail-coach for
Clavering.

* For biographical information see page 143.

On arrival Major Pendennis is most affable to Pen and his mother. He does not "entreat" or "command" his nephew, but wins the boy's confidence and talks familiarly of his own noble friends and the brilliant career he has in mind for Pen. The major then "faces the enemy," Captain Costigan, the half-tipsy, imaginative old Irish soldier, the father and protector of "Emily." To him and his beautiful, honest, but dull daughter the major is equally suave. Beautiful she is, with broad brow, large, melting eyes, black wavy hair, white complexion, rosy cheeks, and the arms of a "Venus." Pen had come to see and know her through Foker, a school friend, a lad homely and kindly, dull at his books, but bright in every-day matters, whose father, the great brewer, furnished him money, and Lady Agnes, his mother, social position. Verses Pen had been writing to the Greek goddesses he now dedicates to his new divinity.

Major Pendennis, as his next move, lets slip, in the presence of the Costigans, the fact that Pen has no means beyond what his mother allows him out of her slender income. Costigan is then indignant that Pen "should have had the face to offer himself to his dear beguiled daughter." Pen cannot believe his adored Emily has calmly thrown him over, until the Costigans openly "cut" him in the street. He almost dies, or believes he is dying of despised love, with all the symptoms of sleepless nights and feverish days, and is scarcely consoled by his mother and little cousin Laura.

Laura is five years younger than Pen, his second cousin on the side of his mother, who adopted her on the death of her parents, perhaps because of a romance of early unmarried days with Laura's father.

Miss Costigan secures an engagement at a London theater through Major Pendennis's influence. The magnetic attraction being thus removed, Pen goes to "Oxbridge." Then through Foker and with the major's encouragement Pen makes rich and aristocratic friends and begins a brilliant career at the Debating Union, at dinners and late suppers, with his wit, eloquence, poems, and commanding self-confidence. Wild without being vulgar, extravagant beyond his means and neglecting his studies, he becomes deeply in debt and is "plucked" in his degree examination, though many a fellow he has despised for dullness or crushed in debate passes with honors.

Unselfish, he would leave the gayest party to go and sit with a sick friend, and yet, selfish, he forces his mother to pinch herself to keep him in college and he accepts Laura's savings to pay his debts. He flees "Oxbridge" in disgrace, though later he tries again and passes his "exams" with fair credit.

Coming home from college, Pen, now a young man of good figure, medium height, blue eyes, and auburn whiskers, finds Laura grown from the simple little girl into a tall, slim, handsome young lady with large gray eyes, long black lashes, pale face with rose tinge in her cheeks which flushes easily into a deep blush.

Now comes on the scene Sir Francis Clavering, Bart., who opens Clavering Park, which has long been closed. The papers a few years before announced his marriage with the rich widow of the late J. Amory, Esquire, from India. He brings Lady Clavering, her daughter Miss Blanche Amory, a young lady, and his son and heir, little Frank Clavering. Blanche has fair hair, dark eyebrows, long black lashes veiling brown eyes, slim figure, small feet, and constant smiles showing sweet pearly teeth and deep dimples. Sir Francis himself is a weak creature, a gambler, fond of low company, and rapidly wasting his wife's property with constant demands on her generosity. Lady Clavering, a good, kind soul, illiterate and murdering the King's English, is hardly more fortunate in her second marriage than in her first with the sailor and convict Amory.

Shadowing the Claverings is a mysterious Colonel Altamont, with a strange influence over Sir Francis and a power to get money from him, despite the baronet's lack of ready cash.

Pen becomes enamoured of Blanche, writes her love poems, and meanwhile she leads him on, only to drop him again for any one with better prospects. When thus dropped, Pen offers himself to Laura, but in a half-hearted way. Laura replies, "When next you offer yourself, do not say as you have done to me, 'I have no heart— I do not love you; but I am ready to marry you because my mother wishes for the match.'" After Laura's refusal, Pen tires of the country and goes to London to study law. He settles in chambers at the Lamb Court Temple and makes a friend of and rooms with George Warrington, an older graduate of "Oxbridge." In London Pen leads a life not of study, but of joviality, though not of vice. He is too lofty to stoop to vulgar intrigue. When reduced to his least few pounds, Pen, by Warrington's help, gets a poem accepted in a magazine, is given books to review, becomes a contributor to the new *Pall Mall Gazette,* writes the popular novel *Walter Lor-*

raine and becomes well off and well known. His uncle is proud of him, gets him invitations to dine in high society, and introduces him, among other celebrities, to the great Duke of Wellington.

One night, the mysterious Colonel Altamont, half drunk, forces his way into the Clavering dining-room in London and Major Pendennis recognizes him as an Indian acquaintance. Soon after this, he urges Pen to marry for money, saying, "It is as easy to get a rich wife as a poor one," and encourages him to court Miss Blanche Amory. Somehow the Major persuades Sir Francis to give up his seat in Parliament in favor of Pen and to arrange for a large dowry for Miss Blanche. Finally, in lieu of any better prospect, she accepts Pen.

The secret of Colonel Altamont's influence over Sir Francis becomes public property and reaches Pen's ears, for Altamont is none other than Amory, the husband of Lady Clavering. He was reported to have died, but in reality is alive. This makes the Clavering marriage invalid and Miss Amory heir to the fortune instead of young Frank. Pen then refuses to benefit by the fortune or to take the seat in Parliament, and writes Blanche he is still willing to marry her, though he admits he does not love her deeply. Later, when he calls, he finds his old schoolmate, Foker, rich through his father's death, now installed in Miss Blanche's affections. Still, the fair Blanche confidentially confesses to Pen that she would prefer him if he could lay aside his "absurd scruples." This he refuses to do, so the Foker and Amory wedding is arranged.

Then Pen, freed from this mercenary alliance, finds his heart all the while was really devoted to Laura, so he proposes to her in earnest and this time is accepted. Foker in turn finds by accident the secret of Amory's survival, and, what is worse, that Blanche knew and yet concealed it from him. For this lack of confidence he leaves the fickle Blanche, so that there is only one wedding at Clavering and that not at the baronet's hall. It turns out that Altamont, alias Amory, already had a wife living when he went through the form of marriage with the future Lady Clavering; so, after all, Sir Francis and she are legally husband and wife.

Sir Francis reforms. Miss Blanche goes abroad and marries in Paris a count with doubtful title. Pen is elected to Parliament on his own merits, the new railroad buys some of Pen's lands and greatly increases the value of the rest, so he is well off and most happy with the adorable, high-minded, and devoted Laura.

THE PICKWICK PAPERS

by

CHARLES DICKENS*

CONDENSATION BY MARGARET GILLETT

At sunrise on May 13, 1827, Mr. Pickwick, a man of mature years and imposing financial resources, looked out upon Goswell Street, London, with an air of tranquility and profound self-satisfaction. Putting himself into his clothes and his clothes into his portmanteau, he shaved, drank his coffee leisurely, left the house, and hailed a cab.

At the Golden Cross he was met by three other members of the Pickwick Club (named after him as its respected founder): Mr. Tupman, Mr. Snodgrass, and Mr. Winkle. These worthy gentlemen, with their respective interests in women, poetry, and sports, had joined together for a tour of the countryside, in which they were intent on making certain observations and researches in character and manners to be collected by the Club for scientific study. Accompanying them in their coach on this day was a green-coated stranger, Mr. Jingle, a rather mysterious sort, who seemed to know his way about very well.

One of the first adventures of the little party was set down in the notebook of Mr. Snodgrass. It concerned a military review which took place near the town of Rochester and in which our four companions inadvertently took part when they were caught quite unexpectedly in the midst of a mock battle staged between two charging regiments. After extricating themselves from this uncomfortable position, they very fortunately met an acquaintance—a Mr. Wardle—accompanied by several ladies in an open barouche, who took them aboard where they could have a better view of the proceedings and retain their status as spectators without being drawn into the fray.

Mr. Wardle very hospitably invited them to visit his country place, Manor Farm at Dingley Dell. There they had a pleasant eve-

* For biographical information see page 81.

301

ning of cards, collected some fine material for study, and had a splendid supper, after which one of the guests, an elderly clergyman, told
a tragic tale called "The Convict's Return."

The next day, the company set out on a before-breakfast shoot
which ended rather abruptly by Mr. Winkle's accidentally firing a
charge into Mr. Tupman's arm. Fortunately for the latter, the wound
was a minor one which he counted as almost a blessing since it provided a capital excuse for great sympathy and much attention from
the ladies. While the victim was recovering under their kind minis-
trations, the other gentlemen were taken by their host to a cricket
match at nearby Muggleton, followed by a convivial dinner at the
Blue Lion, with much toasting of both players and spectators.

Being something of a lady's man, Mr. Tupman took his opportunity to engage the affections of Miss Rachel Wardle, the spinster
sister of his host. All went well between the pair, and their affair
might have blossomed into a blessed union had it not been for the
interference of Mr. Jingle, who interjected himself into the household
as a friend of Mr. Pickwick. With great cunning this imposter
wormed his way into Miss Rachel's heart and, after borrowing ten
pounds from the unsuspecting Tupman, persuaded her to elope with
him to London. A vigorous chase ensued in which Mr. Wardle and
Mr. Pickwick pursued the fleeing couple to their destination in the
City. There they bought off the wily suitor and restored Miss Rachel
to her home and family quite unharmed.

When they returned, they found that Mr. Tupman, who had been
so abruptly deserted by his lady, had departed and left a grief-
stricken note threatening suicide. Mr. Pickwick was, of course, very
upset by his friend's condition and immediately went to the address
given in the note, to find him at the Leathern Bottle lost in profound
melancholy. With some effort Mr. Pickwick was able to bring him
back to his senses, as it were, and persuade him to rejoin the club
members in their scientific studies.

At this point Mr. Pickwick hired a man-servant, by the name of
Sam Weller, formerly boot-black at the White Hart Inn, a fellow of
very considerable knowledge of the world. Somehow when Pickwick
informed Mrs. Bardell, his landlady, of his intentions to add another
member to his household, the good woman misunderstood his declaration as a proposal and promptly fell into his arms in a deep swoon.
Surprised almost out of his wits, the poor man was even more dis-
comfitted when he found himself discovered in this awkwardly com-

promising predicament by his three friends, whose suspicions were seemingly confirmed when the disappointed Mrs. Bardell subsequently sued him for breach of promise. This was, of course, a completely unfounded litigation based entirely on the romantic imagination of the lady herself and carried forward by a pair of wily lawyers.

So incriminating were the circumstances of this case that even Sam, who was not yet fully acquainted with his master's sterling character, was for a time deluded into thinking him a veritable reprobate.

"Rum feller, the hemperor," Mr. Weller said to himself as he walked slowly up the street. "Think o' his making up to that ere Mrs. Bardell—with a little boy, too! Always the vay vith these here old 'uns hows'ever, as is such steady goers to look at. I didn't think he'd ha done it, though—I didn't think he'd ha done it!"

The trial, set for the fourteenth of February, which is, after all, Valentine's Day, came off, unhappily, in favor of the plaintiff who was awarded damages to the extent of 750 pounds. Speechless with indignation the defendant vowed he would never pay a farthing, preferring to spend the rest of his life in debtor's prison. Upon this decision, Mr. Pickwick, his valet whom he had recently acquired, and his traveling friends immediately set out for the curative waters of Bath where he contemplated a stay of at least two months until his term at the debtor's prison should begin. This it did on the exact date specified in the judge's decision and Mr. Pickwick, accompanied by his faithful servant, entered Fleet Street Prison for an indefinite period. In due course they were joined by the plaintiff, who was finally incarcerated herself because of her inability to pay the costs of the case.

At the suggestion of his solicitor, Mr. Pickwick paid the costs himself, thus obligating the plaintiff, who promptly withdrew her case out of gratitude. By this clever arrangement, both plaintiff and defendent were released from prison.

However, Mr. Pickwick and his loyal retainer, Sam, did not leave their Fleet Street abode before meeting up with the nefarious Mr. Jingle and *his* man, who were, indeed, in a pathetic condition, almost on the brink of starvation. Their plight so touched Mr. Pickwick's heart that, in spite of their past misdeeds, he forgave them, paid off the sum of their indebtedness, and set them on the straight path as free men.

Finally, after distributing all these benefits out of his great generosity and sympathy for his fellow man, the well-loved hero of our story settled down in a house in Dulwich to spend quietly and in peace his declining years. Without him the Pickwick Club, of course, dissolved, but its Chairman was quick to point out:

"I shall never regret having devoted the greater part of two years to mixing with different varieties and shades of human character."

And so he had been witness to many dramatic events during this period. Among them were the marriages of two of his closest associates—Mr. Winkle and Sam, his own "gentlemen's gentleman." Mr. Snodgrass was about to embark on the matrimonial sea with Miss Emily Wardle, daughter of his old friend. In all of the festivities attendant upon these joyous events, Mr. Pickwick took an enthusiastic part and derived great and lasting satisfaction from all the personal happiness of his many and faithful friends.

THE PILGRIM'S PROGRESS
by
JOHN BUNYAN

CONDENSATION BY BASIL KING

JOHN BUNYAN was born at Elston, England, in November, 1628. His father was a rough tinker but managed to send the boy to the village school. In the crude home, current religious notions were so vividly impressed upon the child's mind that he frequently had terrifying visions of evil spirits bearing him away to eternal torment.

At seventeen, he served for a year in the army. Two years later he married a woman whose only dowry was two religious books. They intensified his religious fervor. After a long and terrible spiritual struggle he conquered his sins, the worst of which were liking to ring the church-bell and dancing on the village green.

The spirit of preaching now lay such hold upon him that

he attracted great crowds. In 1660 he was arrested as a Dissenter and thrown into the Bedford jail, where he spent the greater part of twelve years. He enjoyed occasional precarious freedom, and was allowed to preach to sixty other Dissenters in prison, but he worried much about his wife and four little children. Nevertheless, his confinement was a boon, for it gave him leisure for the thinking, out of which grew his incomparable "Pilgrim's Progress." He began to write it in jail, but it was not published until six years later. The irresistible charm of the thrilling, fairy-tale quality, combined with its "reverence for God and sympathy for man," won immense popularity at once.

The last years of his life were rich in activity and acclaim. He preached to great audiences in London and elsewhere, but remained simple and passionately earnest to his death in 1688.

As I walked through the wilderness of this world I lighted on a certain place where was a Den and laid me down to sleep. As I slept I dreamed a dream. I saw a man clothed with rags, a book in his hand, and a burden on his back. Reading in the book, he broke out with a cry: "What shall I do to be saved?"

Going home, he opened his trouble to his wife and children, who at first pitied but presently chided him. This continuing for many days, he walked in the fields, where he saw coming to him a man named Evangelist, who advised him to flee the City of Destruction, which was to be burnt with fire and brimstone, and make for the City of Zion.

Then was there much ado in the family of Christian, for such was his name, that he should run from his home on a way which all knew to be perilous. Two of his neighbors did Christian implore to accompany him. The name of the one was Obstinate, that of the other Pliable. "What," cried Obstinate, "leave our friends and comforts behind us?" But Pliable went with him for a space, till they reached a quag named the Slough of Despond. Having wallowed here for a time Pliable, getting out on the side nearest to his home, turned back. But Christian struggling on alone, one Help came to his rescue and led him to solid ground.

Here as Christian was walking he espied afar off a Mr. Worldly Wiseman, of the town of Carnal Policy. To his questions as to where he would be going Christian replied that he sought means to be rid of the burden on his back. "Why, in yonder village, Morality," said the gentleman, "there dwells one whose name is Legality, and who hath a pretty young man, Civility, to his son. These will ease thee of thy burden." So saying he directed Christian to a high hill, the which, on his reaching it, bent over so much that it was like to fall on and bury him.

Now Christian began to be sorry that he had taken Mr. Worldly Wiseman's counsel; whereupon he again saw Evangelist, who encouraged him to go back and seek the Gate for which he had been making when urged to go out of the way. So in process of time Christian got up to this Gate, over which was written, "Knock and it shall be opened unto you." He knocked, therefore, and one named Good-will came to answer.

Then did Christian recite the perils through which he had come in seeking to be rid of his burden. "Be content to bear it," said Good-will, "until thou come to the place of deliverance, for there it will fall off of itself."

So was he sent on his way again, walking along a road which ended in a cross and a sepulcher. I saw in my dreams that as he came up with the cross his burden loosed from his back till it fell into the sepulcher, where I saw it no more.

Then Christian gave three leaps for joy and went on singing, coming to the hill Difficulty. About midway to the top of this hill was an arbor in which he sat him down to rest, but soon fell asleep. Losing under the settle the roll in which he had begun to read, he started hastily, when he awoke, on his way again. At the top of the hill there met him two men running amain. These were Mistrust and Timorous, who warned him to go back, since there were lions in the way. Then was Christian in a great quandary, since to go back to his own city would mean to be burnt with fire and brimstone, while to go on would be to risk death at the mouths of lions. Thus troubled, he sought comfort in reading in his roll, but, lo! it was not in his bosom.

Then was much time lost while Christian returned to the arbor to find his book; but while he was thus bewailing his miscarriage he lifted up his eyes and saw a stately palace, the name of which was Beautiful. Here dwelt the damsels Discretion, Prudence, Piety, and Charity, who made Christian welcome, laying him in the chamber called Peace. Next day they showed him the armory of their house, as well as such ancient treasures as Moses' rod, the hammer and nail with which Jael slew Sisera, and the jaw-bone with which Samson did mighty feats. Likewise did they take him up to the top of their house and bid him look at the pleasant countries of the Delectable Mountains and Emmanuel's Land. "When thou comest there," said they, "thou mayest see the Gate of the Celestial City."

Going on thence, he entered the Valley of Humiliation, where met him the foul fiend, Apollyon. Apollyon claiming Christian as his subject, the latter could in no wise deny the fact, seeing that he had been born in the City of Destruction, over which the monster ruled. Nevertheless, Christian renounced his allegiance to this wicked prince, claiming that he had sworn himself to the King of Princes, who dwelt in the City of Zion. Then ensued a dreadful fight between Christian and the fiend, during which the fiend was like to have worsted the pilgrim had it not been for the weapons furnished him from their armory by the fair damsels in the Castle Beautiful. The battle being over, there came a hand with some of the leaves of the Tree of Life, wherewith Christian stanched his wounds.

Now at the end of this valley was another still more dread, called the Valley of the Shadow of Death. On its right was a very deep ditch into which the blind have led the blind in all ages, while on the left was a dangerous quag, the which if even a good man were to fall into it he could find no bottom for his foot to stand on. Good Christian was the more put to it, seeing that the pathway was exceeding narrow, and as he went on he sighed bitterly. About the middle of this valley was there also the mouth of Hell, out of which came dismal flame and smoke. When the fiends came up to this entrance he cried out in a vehement voice, "I will walk in the strength of the Lord God," whereat they gave back.

Having passed through this valley, he came up with his friend Faithful, who had, though Christian knew it not, followed him out of the City of Destruction. Then was there much discourse between the two pilgrims as to the perils through which they had come, with Faithful telling of his escape from Madame Wanton, as well as from the old man with the three daughters, the Lust of the Flesh, the Lust of the Eyes, and the Pride of Life. Also did Faithful tell of his encounters with Arrogancy, Pride, and Worldlyglory. But the worst of them all was with Shame, a bold-faced fellow who would never have done speaking against all good men and things.

Then I saw in my dream that they presently came to the town

of Vanity, where is a fair kept called Vanity Fair. Here is there at all times such noise and folly, with the buying and selling of such foolish wares as have given the town its fame. The people of the fair, taking the pilgrims for outlandish men and bedlams, made a great gazing at them. Likewise were they not a little amused that Christian and Faithful, setting very light by all their merchandise, did speak exhortingly. Much hubbub did follow thereon, during which the pilgrims were cast into jail. At a convenient time they were brought forth to trial before the Lord Hategood, witness being given against them by such base fellows as Envy, Superstition, and Pickthank. Among the jurors were Mr. Nogood, Mr. Malice, Mr. Lovelust, and such like, by whom good Faithful was condemned. After much persecution they burned him to ashes at the stake, whereat I saw in my dream that a chariot with horses carried him up to the Celestial Gate by the nearest way.

As for Christian, He that overrules all things released him from prison, so that he went on his way in company with one Hopeful, who had followed him from that town. Soon they came to a great fortress called Doubting Castle, the owner of which was Giant Despair, who took them prisoners. Now Giant Despair had to his wife a woman named Diffidence. So when he was gone to bed he told her what he had done, to wit that he had taken a couple of prisoners, and asked her what he should do with them. Her counsel was that he should advise them to make away with themselves. So when morning was come he goes to them with a very surly manner, telling them that, as they were never like to get out of this dungeon, they should end themselves with knife, halter, or poison. When they desired him to let them go he looked very ugly upon them, and, rushing at them, had doubtless made an end to them himself, but that he fell in a fit to which he was subject, and lost the use of his hand.

Thus escaping from Giant Despair, they came to the Delectable Mountains, where met them certain shepherds, Knowledge, Experience, Watchful, and Sincere, who took them by the hand and led them to their tents. Also did they lead them forth to the top of a hill called Clear, from the which they might spy the Celestial Gate through a perspective glass.

Then I saw in my dream that Christian and Hopeful, going down the mountains, and passing through the country of Conceit, got over to a land called the Enchanted Ground, and thus into the country of

Beulah, whose air was sweet. Their way lying directly through it, they solaced themselves there, listening to the singing of birds and seeing the flowers appear in the earth.

Here they had a distant view of the City of Zion, which was built of pearls and precious stones, and the street paved with gold. Also I saw that as they went on there met them two men in raiment that shone. "You have but two difficulties more to meet," said they, "and then you are in the City."

Now I further saw that betwixt them and the gate was the River of Death. There was no bridge to go over it, and the river was deep. At sight thereof the pilgrims were much stunned, asking if there was no other way. Being told there was none, they addressed themselves to the water.

Having entered it, Christian began to sink; but Hopeful cried, "Be of good cheer, my brother; I feel the bottom." But as for Christian, a great darkness and horror fell upon him, in which he was troubled by hobgoblins and evil spirits. Hopeful, therefore, had much ado to keep his friend's head above water, repeating to him the words of the roll, "When thou passest through the waters I will be with you." Thus after much struggle they got over.

Now the City stood on a mighty hill; but up that hill the pilgrims went with ease because they had two Shining Ones to lead them. Also had they left their mortal garments behind them in the flood. "You are going now," said the Shining Ones, as they climbed, "to the Paradise of God, wherein you shall see the Tree of Life and eat of the fruits thereof." And while they were drawing toward the gate behold a company of the Heavenly Host came out to meet them, some before, some behind, and some on the right and left, continually sounding as they went with melodious noises, so that the sight was as if Heaven itself had come down to meet them.

Now I saw in my dream that these two pilgrims went in at the gate, and, lo! as they entered, they were transfigured, and had raiment given them that shone like gold. There were also that met them with harps and crowns, and all the bells in the City rang for mirth, while it was said, "Enter ye into the joy of your Lord." Now just as the gates were open to let the men in I looked in after them, and behold the City shone like the sun. In the streets walked many men with crowns on their heads, and golden harps to sing praises withal. After that they shut up the gates, which, when I had seen it, I wished myself among the Redeemed.

THE PILOT

by

JAMES FENIMORE COOPER*

CONDENSATION BY ALFRED S. CLARK

On a late afternoon of a winter's day during the American Revolution, a rakish schooner and a majestic frigate anchored well inside a little bay on the northeastern coast of England. A whale-boat drove shoreward, a young officer scrambled up the steep cliffs, and a few minutes later a mysterious stranger was transferred to the frigate's deck. He answered to the name of "Mr. Gray" and was said to be merely a pilot, but he was greeted with surprising deference.

For no ordinary man would these vessels have ventured so near that coast of sandbars and hidden rocks. The wind was a mere ruffle of air. But the incessant mutter of the long, slow waves foretold that a storm was brewing. Ever more fitfully and faintly blew the land breeze; the mutter of the waters grew deeper. Only here and there did a few stars twinkle between the fast gathering clouds. It was time to beat out to open sea, if it were not even now too late. Men swarmed aloft and hung upon the yards; sails fluttered out; the anchor was pulled in; the frigate gathered headway. Then the faint breeze died. The spread of canvas hung useless; the currents drove the ship shoreward.

With a roar the wind came suddenly from the east. White spray dashed from the bow. Yet the pilot paced the quarter-deck, seemingly oblivious to danger. But open water was far ahead and suddenly from the forecastle came that dreaded cry, "Breakers! Breakers dead ahead!" The pilot shook off his trance of thought. His orders thundered forth, sailors sprang hither and thither at his bidding, the frigate swung about at his cry of "Hold on everything!" Tortuously she picked her way through the twisting channels, in darkness amid the howlings of the great winds.

She shivered from bow to stern as a hundred men loosed the huge

* For biographical information see page 86.

mainsail. The jib was torn free with a crash like a cannon's blast, but the big sail held and the frigate bowed like a reed in the wind. White foam showed dimly upon both sides, but the pilot kept the ship, as by a miracle, within a narrow ribbon of dark water. He took the wheel himself. Time and again the frigate seemed to have reeled free from peril; time and again she plunged anew toward a welter of white water. But she drove ever on and at last she rode the great waves of the open sea.

Not the storm alone had these ships dared. They were American vessels, lurking about an enemy's coast. This little bay had a peculiar fascination for two young lieutenants aboard—Edward Griffith and Richard Barnstable. Not far inland lived Colonel Howard, a Tory who had fled from America when the Colonists revolted. With him dwelt his niece, Cecilia Howard, beloved by Griffith, and his ward, Katherine Plowden, betrothed to Barnstable. In St. Ruth's Abbey lingered, too, Christopher Dillon, a poor kinsman anxious to better his condition by wedding the wealthy Cecilia. Redcoats lent a picturesqueness to the venerable abbey, for a small garrison under Captain Borroughcliffe had been summoned by the owner. For aught that men knew, John Paul Jones himself might be aboard these ships hovering near by.

While reconnoitering the next night, "Mr. Gray" and Griffith were captured, but Borroughcliffe's drunkenness enabled them to escape. Griffith was, however, retaken.

The impetuous Barnstable, fretting offshore with his enormous coxswain, Long Tom Coffin, had been nearly cut off from his schooner by an English cutter, but he scrambled aboard safely and the drum beat to quarters. While broadsides roared and the decks grew slippery with blood, the little fighting ships met and grappled. Before Barnstable could lead his boarders to the enemy's deck, Coffin tumbled into the sea. Shouting, "Revenge Long Tom!" the lieutenant rushed with his men upon the foe. It was fighting at close quarters and the issue was in doubt when the drenched and furious coxswain emerged from the sea and with his harpoon pinioned the English captain to his mast. In a few minutes the Americans were masters of the cutter. Cowering in that scene of bloodshed the victors discovered the crafty Dillon, who pleaded to be sent off as a hostage, promising to return in person or to have Griffith delivered in his stead.

His word of honor was trusted and he was sent away with Long

Tim. He luckily overheard Dillon's treacherous plot to entrap Barnstable's waiting party. The resourceful old seaman gagged Borroughcliffe and drove Dillon, at the point of his harpoon, back to the waiting schooner. By this time, however, a battery on the cliff brought down the schooner's mainmast. She was driven from her course by heavy seas. The masts were felled and anchors dropped, but she plunged on like a bobbing cork in rapids. Barnstable would have stayed by his ship, but suddenly Long Tom seized him and hurled him over the bulwarks. "God's will be done with me," Coffin cried, above the wind's roar. Dillon's lifeless body was rolled upon the shore, but Long Tom's stayed with the sea to which he had dedicated his life.

Surprise succeeded surprise at the abbey. Barnstable marched his shipwrecked mariners into the building and they took possession, but they were soon made prisoners by the redcoats. Then the mysterious figure of the pilot appeared at the door and behind him loomed marines from the frigate. Colonel Howard, an unwilling prisoner, was marched away with Cecilia and Katherine, who could not be downcast at the triumph of their lovers.

Captain Borroughcliffe was freed, as was another inmate of the abbey, Alice Duscombe. She had recognized the pilot in his disguise when he was first captured. They had been lovers, but she was so stanch in her love for her king and she so hated bloodshed that she had broken her troth to this "Mr. Gray," whom she addressed as John. She reminded him that, did she but once call aloud his true name, the whole countryside would ring with it. What that name was is never revealed, but there was but one sea-rover who could strike stark terror into all English hearts.

On board the frigate repeated conferences were held between the captain, Griffith, and "Mr. Gray." Suddenly out of the fog drove a mountainous ship of the line. The drum beat aboard the frigate, sailors leaped nimbly about the deck, clearing for action. The women were led below and gradually order resolved itself out of the chaos of shouting men. A terrific roar filled the air as three tiers of guns blazed a broadside from the English ship. A few sails and ropes were cut, but the frigate's sailing power was hardly affected. One chance ball struck the captain and hurled him to death. Griffith succeeded to the command and he was appalled as he saw the frigate hemmed about. To the east loomed the great ship of war and far in the northeast the sails of another frigate.

"What are we to do?" cried Griffith. "Fight them! Fight them!" shouted the pilot. "Let me proclaim your name to the men," Griffith appealed. But the pilot refused. "Should we come to a grapple," he said, "I will give forth the name as a war-cry and these English will quail before it."

The ship of war was distanced, but she cut off a retreat and the frigate ahead had been reinforced by two others. The foremost maneuvered with the American frigate for position. Broadsides crashed and they grappled. The American guns raked her foe and left her helpless, with useless ropes dangling from shattered masts. The deck was cleared and as another enemy appeared, Griffith shouted, "Hoist away of everything!" Fifty men flew aloft upon the spars, and white canvas was spread from every mast. The frigate lunged ahead, but it could not outstrip its rival, and the halt to give battle had enabled the ship of the line to draw up.

Then for a few breathless moments the pilot leaped into command. Breakers loomed ahead, but he drove the vessel straight into the shoals, into narrow passages where white foam bubbled perilously close. The enemy dared not follow, and when night fell pursuit was hopeless.

Colonel Howard, fatally wounded in the battle, lived long enough to see Cecilia Howard and Katherine Plowden wedded by the chaplain to their lovers. His last words were spoken to Griffith. "Perhaps I may have mistaken my duty to America—but I was too old to change my politics or my religion; I—I—I loved the king— God bless him—"

The frigate drove on to Holland, where the pilot landed in a small boat that dwindled into a black speck and disappeared in the setting sun. Twelve years later Cecilia Griffith saw her husband's face cloud as he read in the newspaper of the death of a great man, but not even then did he divulge his name. He had promised to keep it secret. He said only, "Our happiness might have been wrecked in the voyage of life had we not met the unknown Pilot of the German Ocean."

POINT OF NO RETURN*

by

JOHN P. MARQUAND

CONDENSATION BY MARGARET GILLETT

JOHN P. MARQUAND (1893–1960), was born in Wilmington, Delaware, lived at Rye, New York until he was fourteen, then attended high school in Newburyport, Massachusetts. Although his family finances were limited, he was able to get a scholarship and attend Harvard, where he took his B.A. in 1915. From there he became a reporter on the "Boston Transcript" until he entered West Point in 1917. Marquand served in France in World War I as a First Lieutenant in the AEF. When he returned he went back into journalism and spent two years in the magazine department of the "New York Tribune" (1919–20). He then worked for one year with a New York advertising agency before he retired to New England to write his first novel, a thriller, "The Unspeakable Gentleman" (1922). During this period he also sold stories to the "Ladies Home Journal" and the "Saturday Evening Post."

On the income from his writing, Marquand managed to marry (1922) and, as his royalties increased, to travel all around the world. The "Mr. Moto" mystery story series based on the author's visit to the Far East proved very popular, and "The Late George Apley" (1937), in which he attacked Boston society, won him the Pulitzer prize for fiction. The novelist also received wide recognition in academic circles, with five honorary degrees conferred on him between 1940 and 1950.

Marquand's breezy sociological approach and deftness of style have made many of his books long-term best sellers and good movie material. His best-known titles are, perhaps:

"H. M. Pulham, Esquire" (1941), "So Little Time" (1943), "Point of No Return" (1949), which became a Broadway hit, and "Sincerely, Willis Wayde" (1955).

Marquand was divorced in 1935, remarried in 1937 and that marriage dissolved in 1958. He had two children by his first marriage and three by his second. He was a member of the editorial board of the Book-of-the-Month Club.

Charles Gray had not thought for a long time about his home town, Clyde, Massachusetts, until one morning in mid-April of 1947. It was the bathroom there that came into his mind while he was shaving. Before his father had added others in 1928, there had been only one and everybody had used it. It was just like Grand Central Station . . . to which he would never get on time if he didn't hurry and catch the 8:30.

Charles was a commuter who lived in a fashionable suburb of New York with his wife and two adolescent children. He went into the city every morning to sit at his desk in the Stuyvesant Bank, where he was an assistant vice-president, and wait for Burton, the president, to tap him on the shoulder and say, "You're the new vice-president, move up one." Or at least that was the way Nancy made him feel practically every morning when he left home.

"Darling," she would say as she drove him to the station, "Why don't you ask Burton what the score is? Aren't you tired of waiting?"

The question made him edgy the first thing. Of course he was tired of waiting, but he just had to sit it out. "That would be stupid," he said. "Naturally he knows I want to know."

Maybe thinking about Clyde that morning was a premonition because, that very day, someone he had known in Clyde long ago came in to see him at the bank. Malcolm Bryant, anthropologist—or was he a sociologist?—who had made some kind of a study of the little old home town before the war. Now he had come into the bank to get a draft cashed and he needed to be identified. He was off to New Guinea, he explained, on another of his expeditions among the head hunters. Then Clyde came up again in the afternoon. One of the bank's clients wanted a loan and was offering as collateral a sizable interest in a cordage company in Clyde. Mr. Burton had called him over to his desk to tell him he wanted him to go up for a day or two and get some information—make sure that the company was all right.

After the president let him go, he remembered he still had to see the Whitakers before he went home. He'd try to catch the 6:30 for Sycamore Park so he wouldn't be too late at the country club party. The Blakesleys would be there—Roger, the other assistant v.p. at the bank, was running neck-and-neck with Charley for promotion to the empty desk—and he'd have to dance with Molly Blakesley so everything would look friendly. It was just too tiresome, this jockeying for the right to sit at the slightly bigger desk, move to a slightly more pretentious house, join a little snootier club, drive a new Cadillac instead of an old Buick. It made him sick. He wished he had the courage to resign and tell them all to go to hell.

When Nancy and he got home after the party, Charley wasn't sleepy, so he stayed up to read awhile. Malcolm had given him a copy of *Yankee Persepolis,* the study of Clyde that the Foundation had finally printed, and Charley wanted to have a look at it, especially since he was going up there tomorrow morning. As he leafed through the pages, memories flooded back—Jessica Lovell, his brother Sam, who had been killed in the war, Spruce Street, all the rest.

His family had lived on Spruce Street when he was growing up and he saw again, as if it were yesterday, the old house that his father had remodeled on the spending spree he had gone on in the late 20's. That was where his father, who had played the sky-rocketing stock market with compulsive abandon, had died at the time of the crash—the crash that had not only ended his father's life but had changed his own completely. Apparently because of certain suspicious aspects of his father's death, officially reported as a heart attack, Jessica's father had persuaded her not to marry him even after they had been secretly engaged for some time. But he realized now it was probably not just that. The Lovells lived on Johnson Street and, even though Charley had been to Dartmouth, the Grays were still Spruce Street people. *Yankee Persepolis* spelled out the class difference pretty clearly.

He had come to New York then in January of 1930—he couldn't very well stay on in Clyde after his mother had gone out to Kansas to live with his sister Dorothea and her husband—to the Stuyvesant Bank and he had been there ever since. He wondered how much longer he'd be there. If Roger got the promotion there would be nothing for him to do but resign. He had no plans. He thought of Nancy and the kids and the mortgage. It was frightening.

"Charley." It was Nancy. She was standing in the doorway in her quilted-silk wrapper. "It's two o'clock. Come on, put out the light. The neighbors will think we're having a fight."

"All right, Nance," he said, and he put his arm around her as they walked upstairs.

The next day he went back to Clyde not in fantasy but in reality. He stopped at what used to be called "the hotel" but was now referred to as "the inn." Things in general looked pretty much the same. From the inn he phoned the Masons, who lived still next door to the old house on Spruce Street and had always been good friends of the family. He knew they'd be hurt if he didn't call as soon as he got in. Jackie Mason had been his chum all through high school. Of course, as soon as Mrs. Mason heard his voice she said he must come right over, supper was ready and Jack was home. Charley was glad because it seemed dreary being in the hotel among strangers in the old home town. He walked around to Spruce Street as soon as she hung up. The clock on the Episcopal Church was striking. The sound was very familiar.

After supper when they had talked about everything and everybody in Clyde, except the Lovells, Jack walked back to the hotel with Charley. He seemed to be getting along well in Clyde. He had just been made head of the accounting department at Wright-Sherwin's, where Charley used to work as a kid, and he was in Rotary, a member of the Shore Club, and a library trustee. But Charley was hardly prepared to hear he was going to marry Jessica Lovell. He was thinking of what Jessica used to say about the bourgeois Masons, but, then, things change in twenty years even in Clyde.

Before Charley went to sleep that night, he phoned Nancy.

"Did I wake you up?"

"Yes, you did," his wife said. "Never mind. Are you all right?"

"I'm fine," he replied. "Are you all right?" He knew Nancy always hated wasting money talking aimlessly long distance but he didn't want to let her go.

"What about the company?"

"I'm attending to it tomorrow."

"All right, don't worry about anything."

"About what?" he asked, knowing full well what she meant.

"You know what . . . the bank . . ."

"Why, have you heard anything?"

"No," she answered, then added, "Don't sit alone there worrying. I'll see you Friday. Good night, dear."

Friday night was the night the Burtons had invited them to dinner, and Tony had said he and Charley would have a long talk. When the time came and they were sitting opposite each other, alone in the Burton library, their brandy and cigars in their hands, Charley was no longer thinking clearly nor really caring any more. His interest in the conclusion to the interview was rather academic. Nevertheless, he was a little startled when the older man asked him point blank what he thought of Roger Blakesley.

"What do you want me to think?" he asked, almost impertinently.

"It isn't what I want," Tony Burton shook his head. "It's just that he's been on my conscience lately. I suppose he'll not have too much trouble finding another place after he resigns." Tony's voice seemed to come from a long way off and later, when Charley tried to reconstruct that evening, he could never remember what happened after that.

THE PORTRAIT OF A LADY

by

HENRY JAMES

CONDENSATION BY MARGARET GILLETT

HENRY JAMES (1843–1916) came from a well-to-do, intellectual New York family (his father was a theological writer of some importance in his day, and his brother William, was the famous philosopher-psychologist). Henry had a generally unsystematic education provided by tutors and interrupted by a long visit to Europe during his boyhood. It also included a brief study of law at Harvard.

Preferring writing as a career, he began doing reviews, sketches, and short stories while still in his teens and, in the 'sixties, he contributed to the "Nation," the "North American Review," and the "Atlantic." His first novel, "Watch and Ward" (1871) appeared serially. A few years after the publication of "Roderick Hudson" (1875), he settled in London, where he remained for the next twenty years. He never married. Except for several sojourns in America, he lived abroad until his death. In 1915 he became a British subject.

The novels of Henry James fall into three periods: the first, beginning with "Roderick Hudson" (1876), and covering "The Portrait of a Lady" (1881) and his other novels through "The Bostonians" (1886), often called his American period and concerned with the impact of Americans on the older European way of life; the second, on English themes, stretching from 1890, with the publication of "The Tragic Muse," through "The Awkward Age" (1899); and the third, in which he makes a contrast between European and American characters with more psychological interplay and less action, including "The Wings of a Dove" (1902), "The Ambassadors" (1903), "The Golden Bowl" (1904), and two unfinished novels, "The Ivory Tower" and "The Sense of the Past."

James also wrote numerous essays, reminiscences, and short stories which tended to become novelettes in length. Of these "The Turn of the Screw" is perhaps the best-known. He was a fastidious craftsman, and his care for form and technique was essentially French. On the other hand, his relatively protected, orderly, and uneventful existence, free of any business or domestic entanglements, left him without those profound emotional experiences that often constitute themes of French literature.

Under certain circumstances there are few hours of life more agreeable than the hour dedicated to the ceremony known as afternoon tea. So it was that mid-summer day on the lawn of the old English country-house, some forty miles from London, where three gentlemen were gathered in the lengthening shadows. The old man seated in the cushioned chair with the shawl across his knees was

Mr. Touchett, owner of the impressive Tudor mansion in the background. An expatriate American banker, he was afflicted with the gout, but his disposition had none of the crotchety humor usually associated with that ailment. With him were his son, Ralph, a fragile young man with a weak chest, and a visitor from the neighboring estate, Lord Warburton. They were all chatting comfortably when a young woman appeared at the door of the house. They did not notice her at first, perhaps because they were not expecting her so soon. Although they knew Mrs. Touchett planned to bring her recently orphaned niece back with her from the United States, they had not been warned of their arrival. It was the American girl, Isabel Archer, who stood alone in the doorway.

Lord Warburton was immediately struck with her grace and charm, and it was not long before this eligible bachelor was visiting Gardencourt to call upon the attractive girl and quite precipitately to offer her marriage. But Isabel was an independent character and somehow could not see herself linked harmoniously with such a noble "personage" as the young Lord. Indeed, she was disinclined to be linked with anyone just yet and had already refused one proposal from a wealthy young Bostonian, Caspar Goodwood, who was so persevering as to follow her to England to press his suit further. As she put it to her cousin, Ralph, when he inquired about her plans, "I don't want to begin life by marrying. There are other things a woman can do." She may have been thinking of her friend, Henrietta Stackpole, who was a newspaper writer and quite happily independent. But even Henrietta, who had also recently come to England, thought Isabel was making a mistake in taking such a haughty position.

"Do you know where you're drifting?" she had asked once when they were together in London a few months later.

"No, and I find it pleasant not to know," Isabel replied, somewhat irritated at Henrietta's interference.

Still the importunities of her lovers upset Isabel. She realized that a girl like herself, without property or expectations, ought to be grateful for the financial security that these alliances could provide. But she was reluctant to enter upon a contract that seemed to require the surrender of so much individuality. She was certainly not without emotional response to the struggle even though she took a good deal of quietly deliberate satisfaction from having declined two very eligible suitors in a fortnight. At least she had taken a stand in defense of her independence!

Then Mme. Merle appeared on the scene, and Isabel was temporarily distracted from her marriage problems. Mme. Merle, another member of the American colony abroad, was visiting Mrs. Touchett at Gardencourt and brought with her exciting news from all the social centers on the continent. This cosmopolitan woman seemed to Isabel the epitome of all admirable traits and talents. But their initial friendship was interrupted by the death of dear, kindly Mr. Touchett, who had been failing rapidly during the past months. Immediately after the funeral of her beloved uncle, Isabel found herself whisked off to Florence with her aunt, and, almost before she could catch her breath, she was informed that she had been left a handsome legacy by Mr. Touchett. It was not until much later that she learned he had been persuaded to make the bequest by his son, Ralph, who was secretly in love with Isabel himself and wanted her to be able to realize her ambitions in her own way.

Meanwhile Mme. Merle turned up again in Florence to congratulate Isabel on her inheritance, and it was through her that Gilbert Osmond came into Isabel's life. He was still another American, permanently resident in Italy with his fifteen-year-old daughter, Pansy. Something of a dilettante in the arts, he lived on a small income, serenely fastidious and surrounded by precious objects which he collected as a hobby. Like the others, he soon fell into the habit of calling on Isabel, who seemed to receive him with a good deal more geniality and encouragement than she had her previous suitors. For some reason she found him more acceptable; he was so clever and agreeable, and his daughter was such a darling child. Inevitably he confessed his love, although he did not propose marriage in so many words. Isabel thought him extremely refined and interpreted his avoidance of formalities as delicacy—after all, she was now a wealthy woman while he was a gentleman in comparatively poor circumstances, without name or property; if he pressed his suit, she might suspect him of a vulgar interest in her property. Thus she excused his apparent diffidence.

At any rate, she heard him as she had heard the others, in some distress. This saying "No" presented her with a perpetual conflict, and this time she wanted to consider the matter even more carefully. She spent a year on a tour, visiting such romantic places as Greece, Turkey, and Egypt with her mentor, Mme. Merle. On her return to

Florence, and against the advice of her aunt and her cousin, she decided to marry the distinguished widower with the impeccable manners and the gentle voice.

Meanwhile the prospective match was discussed by various interested parties. To Mme. Merle, Osmond conceded that Isabel was "not disagreeable."

"Is that all you can find to say about that fine creature?"

"All? Isn't it enough? Of how many people have you heard me say more?"

She made no answer to this. "You're unfathomable," she murmured at last. "I'm frightened at the abyss into which I shall have cast her."

"You can't draw back—you've gone too far."

"Very good; but you shall do the rest yourself."

"I shall do it," said Gilbert Osmond. Later he went further. "She's really very charming. . . . She has only one fault—too many ideas."

The Countess Gemini, Osmond's sister, opposed the match. To Mme. Merle she said: "Of course he's a gentleman. But does he think he can marry any girl he happens to pick out? I must say I've never seen such pretensions! Who is he, if you please? What has he ever done? . . . Osmond has always appeared to believe that he's descended from the gods."

The wedding was very simple, but soon after, the couple bought a splendid palace in Rome, where Mrs. Osmond's Thursday evenings became famous. Gradually and almost imperceptibly, her husband began to find fault with her friends—"that dreadful newspaper-woman" and "your sickly cousin"—and expressed disapproval of her even seeing them away from home. Isabel felt these restrictions keenly but offered no resistance to her husband's wishes. She followed his instructions, but he knew he could never subjugate her mind. Nevertheless, her soul was filled with terrors. Osmond seemed to have the faculty of making everything wither that he touched. He was not violent, he was not cruel, except in a very subtle way that revealed his hate for his wife. She had a certain way of looking at life which he took as a personal offense. His ideal was one of high prosperity and propriety forming the aristocratic life. Her notion of it was simply the union of great knowledge with great liberty; the knowledge would give one a sense of duty and the liberty a sense of enjoyment. But for Osmond it was altogether a thing of forms, a conscious, calculated attitude. He regarded her mind as vulgar while, on her part, some of his amoral attitudes shocked her.

Under Osmond's influence Isabel changed without knowing it. When Pansy and a nice young gentleman of Mrs. Osmond's aquaintance fell in love and Pansy's father refused to accept him as a suitor because he was not a wealthy nobleman, Isabel felt obliged to urge her to obey her papa in all things; the docile young lady, another of Osmond's works of art, dutifully and uncomplainingly abandoned her hope of happiness.

It was a great shock to Isabel when she finally learned from her sister-in-law, the Countess, that Pansy's mother was Mme. Merle. But even before this revelation, the Osmond marriage had deteriorated until it was a mere shell holding two miserable people in a brittle, meaningless relationship. However, Isabel was determined to keep the shell intact, and she continued to observe all the external formalities of married life. In spite of these efforts, it became known to her friends that she was unhappy. Warburton, Ralph, Henrietta, and Caspar sensed it on their visits to her villa in Rome. Warburton became interested in Pansy and thought of marrying her—was it in order to have a permanent tie with the girl's step-mother? Osmond was frightfully disappointed when Warburton, having learned from Isabel where Pansy's affections lay, returned to England and abandoned his suit. Ralph also returned to England very ill.

When word arrived that Ralph was dying, Isabel left for England against her husband's express command. Arriving at Gardencourt in a very disturbed state, she found some solace in being with her cousin during the last days of his life. Before Ralph died, they acknowledged their love for each other and were happy even though he lay on his death bed. After the funeral Isabel lingered on in England, reluctant to return to Rome. For the last time Caspar pleaded with her to leave her husband and flee with him back to America. But Isabel's conscience was too strong. She returned to Rome and to her duty. She had made an independent choice when she decided to marry Osmond and would see it through.

PRIDE AND PREJUDICE

by

JANE AUSTEN

CONDENSATION BY MARGARET GILLETT

JANE AUSTEN (1775–1817) was born at Steventon Parsonage in Hampshire, England. Her father, a learned clergyman, tutored her until she was nine, when she joined her sister, Cassandra, at school in Reading. While Jane was still in her teens she wrote an epistolary novelette, "Love and Friendship," a kind of miniature farce, not published until 1922. In 1801 the family moved to Bath, where, the following year, the author of "Pride and Prejudice" (which had been written but not yet published) had a proposal of marriage which she declined. Except for occasional jaunts to London and changes of residence to Southampton and Chawton, Jane's life from then on seems to have been uneventful. Threatened with tuberculosis, she finally went for medical treatment to Winchester, where she died at forty-two.

Jane Austen's literary production includes six novels: "Pride and Prejudice" (written in 1796–97 but not published until 1813), full of infectious wit and acute observation of people and places; "Sense and Sensibility" (begun in 1797, published in 1811), a satire on the sentimental novel; "Northanger Abbey" (published posthumously in 1818), an anti-romantic parody; "Mansfield Park" (1814), a complex plot woven around the author's favorite theme of repentance; "Emma" (1816), a character study, humorous and objective; "Persuasion" (1818), her most sentimental story. In addition to these, there are a volume of short sketches and several unfinished prose pieces which were published after the author's death.

The most remarkable characteristic of Jane Austen's writing is probably her ability to paint delicate, satirical

324

portraits of the foibles of her time. Without any specific references to the events of the period, she is able to re-create the eighteenth-century background that provides the setting for her stories. She is especially deft at describing the feelings and characters of the ordinary English country life that she knew best.

It is a truth universally acknowledged, that a single man in possession of a good fortune must be in want of a wife.

"My dear Mr. Bennet," said his lady to him one day, "have you heard that Netherfield Park is let at last?"

Mr. Bennet replied that he had not. Whereupon Mrs. Bennet promptly began to tell him that a wealthy young gentleman, a Mr. Bingley, was taking up residence in the Longbourn neighborhood and she commented enthusiastically, "What a fine thing for our girls!"

Mr. Bennet pretended not to understand, though he privately hoped that Mr. Bingley would have the good sense to choose the favorite of his five daughters, Elizabeth. He was so odd a mixture of quick parts, sarcastic humor, reserve, and caprice, that the experience of three-and-twenty years had been insufficient to make his wife understand his character. She was a woman of mean understanding, little information, and uncertain temper. The business of her life was to get her daughters married; its solace was visiting and news.

Mr. Bingley was everything Mrs. Bennet could wish for. He was lively and personable and appeared at the Assembly Rooms for the very first ball with a large party—his two sisters, the husband of one of them, and another young man, Mr. Fitzwilliam Darcy, who was tall and handsome with a rumored fortune of ten thousand pounds a year. Mr. Bingley enjoyed himself. He danced every dance, including two with Jane, the eldest Miss Bennet, whom he declared to be the most beautiful creature he ever beheld. But Mr. Darcy soon showed that he was proud and above being pleased. He danced only once with each of Mr. Bingley's sisters and declined to be introduced to any other lady. Elizabeth, the Bennets' second daughter, had been obliged, by the scarcity of gentlemen, to sit down for two dances, but when Mr. Bingley offered to arrange an introduction, Mr. Darcy said coldly, "She is tolerable, but not handsome enough to tempt me." Elizabeth, who had overheard this conversation, of course had no very cordial feelings toward the haughty Mr. Darcy. She told the story, however, with great spirit among her friends; for she had a lively playful disposition which delighted in anything ridiculous.

It soon became evident that Mr. Bingley admired Jane. They met tolerably often—though never for many hours together and always in company. Elizabeth was unaware that the fastidious Mr. Darcy had now discovered that her features were not only tolerable, but that her face was rendered uncommonly intelligent by the beautiful expression in her dark eyes. He began to believe that if it were not for the inferiority of her family, he would be in some danger. *Her* opinion of him was unchanged and even hardened when she heard from Mr. Wickham, a new officer in the ——Shire Regiment, stationed in nearby Meryton, that Mr. Darcy had dishonored his father's wishes and denied Wickham the legacy the old gentleman had intended for him. Wickham, who had known Darcy all his life, assured Elizabeth he was both proud and prejudiced.

Mr. Wickham had a fine countenance, good figure and a pleasing manner of address. Elizabeth enjoyed his attention to herself, though when this was suddenly transferred to a lady who had just inherited a small fortune, she was not unduly hurt.

Quite unannounced, Mr. Bingley and his party suddenly removed from Netherfield to London. Elizabeth was convinced that his condescending sisters and the abominable Mr. Darcy had persuaded him to stay in London so he would not marry Jane. Jane herself resolved not to repine, but she gladly accepted an aunt's invitation to spend the winter in town, secretly hoping to see Mr. Bingley there. In this, the dearest wish of her heart, she was disappointed.

Elizabeth, meanwhile, had another suitor, her cousin, Mr. Collins. He was not a sensible man and this deficiency of Nature had been but little mitigated by education or society. He was presently resident clergyman at Rosings, the estate of Lady Catherine de Bourgh, aunt of the intolerable Mr. Darcy. Despite Mrs. Bennet's remonstrances, Elizabeth refused Mr. Collins's offer and she was surprised but not distressed when, within a few days, he announced his engagement to her best friend, Charlotte Lucas. However, she agreed to visit them at the Rosings' parsonage shortly after Christmas.

Her pleasure in this visit was somewhat diminished by the sudden arrival of Lady Catherine's nephew. There were not many of her acquaintances whom she did not prefer to Mr. Darcy, and whenever she met him in the park on a ramble, she felt all the perverseness of mischance.

One evening when she was alone at the parsonage, the doorbell rang and much to Elizabeth's surprise, Mr. Darcy entered the room. After a silence of several minutes he came toward her in an agitated manner and began:

"In vain have I struggled. It will not do. My feelings will not be repressed. You must allow me to tell you how ardently I admire and love you."

Elizabeth's astonishment was beyond expression. Yet, in spite of her deep-rooted dislike for Darcy and the proud, ungracious manner of his proposal, she could not be insensible to the compliment of such a man's affections. Still, he had told her he had made his declaration against his will, against his reason, against his character, and in spite of her low connections, and so she made little effort to be civil in her rejection of his suit. She assured him that she could never be tempted to accept the offer of a man who had the means of ruining the happiness of her beloved sister, Jane, and had so cruelly deprived Mr. Wickham of his inheritance. The interview ended as abruptly as it had begun.

The following morning, as Elizabeth sought solace for her agitated spirits by walking in the park, she was distressed to meet him whom she most wished to avoid. Mr. Darcy came forward, presented her with a letter, turned and was soon out of sight. With a contrariety of emotion Elizabeth read Darcy's confession that he had indeed persuaded Bingley not to see Jane again, but he had done so because he believed the lady to be indifferent. The second charge Elizabeth had laid against him, Darcy refuted entirely. He had given Wickham three thousand pounds, which amply accorded with his late father's wishes, but Wickham had wasted it on loose living and had repaid the kindness only with abuse. The letter contained no repetition of the sentiments that Darcy had avowed the previous evening.

Elizabeth had begun reading with a strong prejudice against anything Darcy might say. Then she began to reflect that to those who did not know Jane, her manner might indeed seem detached and even indifferent, for her feelings, though fervent, were little displayed. As for Wickham, she suddenly realized he had been most indiscreet in criticizing Darcy to strangers, and she herself had already seen that he had a great attachment for money. Horror at such duplicity, mortification at her own obtuseness, and shame for her rudeness to Mr. Darcy swept over Elizabeth. She was glad her visit was almost at an end so she would not have to face him again.

Though reunited, the Bennet family was depressed. Mrs. Bennet had not succeeded in marrying any of her daughters, Jane had not heard from Bingley, Elizabeth could not confide the burden of Darcy's letter even to Jane, and the younger girls were disconsolate because the regiment had moved to Brighton. Only Lydia was herself, cheerful and boisterous. She had received an invitation to stay with the Colonel's wife in Brighton.

For Elizabeth, the gloom was broken by a tour of neighbouring counties with her aunt and uncle. However, her embarrassment was acute when her aunt, innocent of what had passed between Elizabeth and Mr. Darcy, wished to visit that gentleman's estate. Elizabeth would only consent to this on receiving reliable intelligence that the owner was not at home. They inspected the mansion without incident, then as they walked across the lawn, Elizabeth turned back. Mr. Darcy appeared so suddenly that it was impossible to avoid his sight. Their eyes instantly met and the cheeks of each were overspread with the deepest blush. The impropriety of her being found viewing the estate of which she might have been mistress caused Elizabeth extreme discomfort, but Darcy's behaviour was strikingly altered and he could hardly have been more cordial.

He was extremely gracious to her aunt and uncle and arranged to call on them later at the nearby inn where they were staying. Thus it happened that Darcy was with Elizabeth when Jane's letter arrived. The news was disastrous—Lydia had eloped, and with Wickham. In her extremity Elizabeth told Mr. Darcy. Later she realized that this could only deepen his disgust for her family and she hardly expected to see him again, once she and her aunt and uncle left to offer what comfort they could to her mother.

Many days passed with no news of Lydia and Wickham. There was no reason to suppose they were married. At last, however, they were found and, as man and wife, returned to the Bennet household where Mrs. Bennet, delighted to have one daughter married, welcomed them extravagantly. Lydia was unabashed and in her flighty and foolish accounts of the wedding accidentally disclosed a secret to Elizabeth. It had been Mr. Darcy who had found them in London, persuaded Wickham to marry her, paid his bills, procured him a commission in another regiment, and provided her with a dowry.

This revelation threw Elizabeth into a flutter of spirits, in which it was difficult to determine whether pleasure or pain bore the greatest share. Oh! how heartily did she grieve over every ungracious sensation she had ever encouraged toward Darcy. For herself she was humbled, but she was proud of him.

After the flurry of Lydia's wedding, all was quiet until rumor spread in Meryton that Mr. Bingley was returning to Netherfield. Within a few days Mrs. Bennet saw him from her dressing-room window enter the paddock and ride toward the house. With him she saw that insufferable Mr. Darcy.

It was clear that Jane's beauty soon rekindled the admiration of her former lover and Mrs. Bennet, contriving for them to be alone but unaware of the double felicity of her plan, arranged for Elizabeth to take Mr. Darcy for a walk. Elizabeth discovered that her sentiments had undergone a material change—prejudice had gone and gratitude and admiration for Mr. Darcy had ripened into love.

It was not long before Mr. Bennet was being applied for the hands of his daughters—by Mr. Bingley for Jane's and, to the surprise of all, by the once proud and odious Mr. Darcy for his favorite, Elizabeth's.

~◁◯▷~

THE PRISONER OF ZENDA*

by

ANTHONY HOPE

CONDENSATION BY PROF. WILLIAM FENWICK HARRIS

ANTHONY HOPE, known outside the world of books as Sir Anthony Hope Hawkins, was born in London, February 9, 1863, the son of a clergyman. He married an American woman.

He was educated at Marlborough, and at Balliol College, Oxford, where he took honors in letters and was president of the Oxford Union, which means that he was already a man

* Printed by permission of, and arrangement with, Henry Holt & Co., authorized publishers.

of mark in his under-graduate days. By way of a profession he became a barrister of the Middle Temple in 1887.

His first book was "The Prisoner of Zenda," which has probably remained his best-known one. It had a large hearing when he turned to the stage, and the public demanded a sequel, which, came in "Rupert of Hentzau." After Zenda quickly followed "The Dolly Dialogues," which, by their easy and debonair grace, inevitably suggest Lawrence Sterne. His books have been numerous, as "The King's Mirror" and "Tristam of Blent," and he has written plays as well, as "The Adventure of Lady Ursula." A touch of sureness and precision lends distinction to his prose; he has an unusual power of interesting his readers in his personages and their doings.

Hope died on July 8, 1933.

Ruritania was not England, or the quarrel between Duke Michael and Rudolf Rassendyll could not have gone on, with the remarkable incidents which marked it, without more public notice being directed to it. It is perhaps as strange a thing as has ever been in the history of a country that the king's brother and the king's personator, in a time of profound peace, near a placid, undisturbed country town, under semblance of amity, should wage a desperate war for the person and life of the king.

Yet there was the struggle between Black Michael and Rudolf Rassendyll, both of the royal house of Elphberg, but of very differing antecedents. The one was well known to the royal palace at Strelsau; the other was at home at No. 305 Park Lane, London, West. The kinship between the two was quite an accident, dating from the year 1733, when a dashing young prince, later known to fame as Rudolf the Third of Ruritania, paid a visit to London. There he was courteously entertained and was a great favorite with the ladies, especially Amelia, Countess of Burlesdon, and Baroness Rassendyll. In the end the prince left England rather hastily under a cloud, but not before he had fought a somewhat sanguinary duel with Countess Amelia's husband. In the years since there have appeared at intervals in the family of the Rassendylls certain sons who have been marked by the long, sharp, straight nose and the dark-red hair of the royal house of Ruritania.

The years pass, many of them, and another Rudolf of Elphberg is about to be crowned King of Ruritania. The same nose, the same red hair distinguish him. The loyal half of the population of Ruritania could not sleep at night till the coronation was safely over. For the late king had left another son, by a second and morganatic marriage, Black Michael, Duke of Streslau and Lord of Zenda. Though Michael bore none of the marks of the Elphbergs, he had been his father's favorite, and he cast a longing eye on the throne; all the cutthroats and blackguards of Ruritania seconded his wish, for Michael was a man after their own hearts.

Curious that young Rudolf Rassendyll should be moved by an idle curiosity to witness the coronation of Rudolf of Ruritania; still more curious that he, too, should bear the familiar nose, the same red hair. So thought Colonel Sapt, aide to the king, and Fritz von Tarlenheim, his close friend, as they came upon the young Englishman in the forest of Zenda, making his way afoot to Strelsau. So, too, thought the king when he appeared a moment later. But scandals of the past can no more be concealed in Ruritania than in England. As young Rassendyll later told the tale, first the king frowned, "then gradually the corners of his mouth began to twitch, his nose came down (as mine does when I laugh), his eyes twinkled, and, behold, he burst into the merriest fit of irrepressible laughter, which rang through the woods and proclaimed him a jovial soul.

" 'Well met, cousin!' he cried, stepping up to me, clapping me on the back, and laughing still. 'You must forgive me if I was taken aback. A man doesn't expect to see double at this time of day. Eh, Fritz?'

" 'I must pray pardon, sire, for my presumption,' said I. 'I trust it will not forfeit your Majesty's favor.'

" 'By heaven! you'll always enjoy the king's countenance,' he laughed, 'whether I like it or not.' "

All the good-fellowship in the world, however, could not permit royal scandals of the past to be raked up at a coronation. Rudolf Rassendyll must not show his face at this moment in the capital of Rudolf of Ruritania. "But by thunder," cried the king, "you sha'n't leave Ruritania to-day. For you shall dine with me to-night, happen what will afterward."

That was just the trouble, "happen what will afterward." One bottle led to another, until they were all as full of wine as they had any right to be. At last the king set down his glass and leaned back in his chair.

" 'I have drunk enough,' said he.

" 'Far be it from me to contradict the king,' said I. Indeed, his remark was most absolutely true—so far as it went." But still another bottle!—this from Black Michael, praying that he drink for the love that he bears his brother. Could the king refuse? He could not. Was the wine drugged? The morning answered yes.

" 'If he's not crowned to-day,' cried Sapt, 'I'll lay a crown he's never crowned.'

" 'By heavens, why?'

" 'The whole nation's there to meet him; half the army—aye, and Black Michael at the head. Shall we send word that the king's drunk?'

" 'That he's ill,' said I in correction.

" 'Ill!' echoed Sapt, with a scornful laugh. 'They know his illness too well. He's been ill before! As a man grows old he believes in Fate. Fate sent you here. Fate sends you now to Strelsau. You'll go?'

" 'Yes, I'll go,' said I, and I turned my eyes on the prostrate figure of the king.

" 'To-night,' Sapt went on in a hasty whisper, 'we are to lodge in the palace. The moment they leave us you and I will mount our horses and ride here at a gallop. The king will be ready, and he must ride back with me to Strelsau, and you ride as if the devil were behind you to the frontier.' "

So began those wondrous days of adventure which saw the throne of Ruritania occupied by an Elphberg with all the traces of the stock, though not "of the blood." "The play actor," Rupert of Hentzau called him, when he came to know the secret, but "as good an Elphberg as ever sat upon it," declared Sapt at the end.

The wild ride to Strelsau, with Sapt instructing the English Rudolf most minutely in his past life, his family, his tastes, pursuits, weaknesses, friends, companions, and servants—as Ruritania knew them—the etiquette of the court what would be expected at the coronation—and above all of the Princess Flavia.

"God save the king!" cried the people after the coronation had been safely managed.

"God save 'em both!" whispered Sapt, as his mouth wrinkled into a smile.

But if things went well at Strelsau with Rudolf Rassendyll, now crowned as Rudolf the Fifth of Ruritania and the accepted lover of the Princess Flavia, fortune did not smile on the other Rudolf at

Zenda. For Black Michael had had word from there that cleared for him the mystery of the coronation. Riding as fast as horses could lay feet to the ground, he seized poor Rudolf of Ruritania and held him prisoner. But then ensued a pretty pass.

"Aye, but he can't speak," roared Sapt in grim triumph. "We've got him. How can he denounce you without denouncing himself? 'This is not the king, because we have kidnapped the king and murdered his servant.' Can he say that? Hang me if Michael won't expose himself, if he tries to expose you."

But the most difficult situation for a loyal gentleman—and that was Rudolf Rassendyll—arose from the Princess Flavia. "I had to keep the princess devoted to me—and yet indifferent to me; I had to show affection for her—and not feel it. I had to make love for another; and that to a girl who—princess or no princess—was the most beautiful I had ever seen. How I succeeded in carrying out my program will appear hereafter."

How they fell in love, he with her and she with him, is part of the story. And how, forgetting self, he rescued the king, and robbed himself of love and throne and almost life. When he had fallen sorely wounded:

"Fritz," he called, "is the king still alive?"

"Aye, friend—dear friend," said he, tender as a woman; "thanks to the most gallant gentleman that lives, the king is alive!"

All's well that ends well. But of the Princess Flavia?

"If I can never hold sweet converse again with her, or look upon her face, or know from her her love, why, then, this side the grave I will live as becomes the man she loves; and for the other side I must pray a dreamless sleep."

PUDD'NHEAD WILSON*

by

MARK TWAIN†

CONDENSATION BY JOHN KENDRICK BANGS

Dawson's Landing, on the Missouri side of the Mississippi, in 1830, was a modest village with few claims to distinction. Conspicuous among her first citizens was York Leicester Driscoll, forty years of age, judge of the county court, of unblemished Virginia stock, unhappily childless, and esteemed by everybody that knew him. Another citizen of repute was Col. Cecil Burleigh Essex, who, except for one important particular later disclosed, has nothing to do with this story. Resident here also was a certain Percy Northumberland Driscoll, brother to the judge, married, and prosperous owner of slaves, among whom was a likely wench of twenty, Roxana by name, into whose home on the first day of February, 1830, two boy babies were born. One of these, christened Tom, was the son of Percy Northumberland. The other, tagged with the name of Valet de Chambre, or "Chambers" for short, was the son of the slave girl Roxana, by a father at first unknown, but later revealed to be Colonel Essex. Within a week of the birth of Driscoll's son the mother died, and in the natural course of events both boys were entrusted to the maternal care of the slave mother.

About the same time into this quiet community came one David Wilson, hopefully anticipating a successful legal career, a hope blasted in the borning, since a gift of irony, one of David's most tangible assets, fell upon ears so literal as to be unappreciative and suspicious of humor.

"I wish I owned half of that dog," said David one morning, when a snarling yellow cur disturbed him.

"Why?" asked somebody.

"Because then I would kill my half!" replied David.

*Printed by permission of, and arrangement with, Harper & Bros., authorized publishers.

† For biographical information see page 158.

His hearers fell away from him in alarm. How could a man kill half of a dog without killing the other half also? Surely this man must be out of his mind.

"A lummox," said one.

"A perfect jackass," said another.

"He's a pudd'nhead, that's what he is!" said a third.

And from that day forward 'Pudd'nhead Wilson" he was.

Now Pudd'nhead had two fads—palmistry and finger-prints. The first he occasionally practised, lacking clients to practise law upon, and the second he collected with great assiduity. No man, woman, or child ever entered the circle of Pudd'nhead's acquaintance without leaving a finger-print, or his thumb-mark, behind, and all of these were carefully named, recorded, dated, and filed. Thus it happened that one day came Roxana and her two charges, Tom, the son of Driscoll, and Chambers, the son of herself and another. As like as two peas were the babies, in color, size, and lineaments—so like that save to a mother's eyes they were indistinguishable, and the finger-prints of all were taken, labeled, dated, and added to the collection of Pudd'nhead Wilson.

What more natural than that the likeness of the two infants—Tom's own father could not tell him from the slave baby—should suggest to a mother's heart an interchange of the children by which the slave should become the master and the master the slave, especially when that heart was constantly oppressed by the fear that when her babe grew to manhood he might be "sold down the river," that ever-present tormenting dread of the slave of the upper waters? What more natural that, there being no chance of detection, Roxana, for love of her son, should yield to that temptation and forthwith turn Chambers into Tom and Tom into Chambers by a simple interchange of garments, these being the only outward and visible signs by which the boys were differentiated, anyhow? It was in this manner that it came to be the proud offspring of the house of Driscoll grew into the slave boy Chambers, abused and neglected, and that the seemingly white child of a negro slave and an unknown father became the scion of a family of unblemished lineage.

But a mere change of clothes and condition does not penetrate far below the surface. A silken gown cannot alter the currents of a shoddy soul, and while externally the spurious heir was all F. F. V., internally he was negro. After a few years, never having discovered the deception practised upon him by Roxana, Percy Driscoll died, penniless, but his brother, the judge, his prayer for children of his own denied, adopted the supposititious Tom and made the boy his heir. He sent him to college. He gave him every advantage that an affectionate father could have given a boy of his own, but the raw material which was the real Tom was poor, and the soil unfruitful. The boy acquired a taste for dissipation for which the simple life of Dawson's Landing offered no assuagements. He plunged into the gay whirl of St. Louis, garnering nothing but disgraceful gambling debts. Worst of all, he was at heart a snob, abused the real heir now become his slave, and acquired a profound detestation for his ancient nurse Roxana, of whose real relation to him he was unaware, until, goaded to intense resentment by his contemptuous and brutal treatment, she acquainted him with the terrible facts of his birth and ancestry, and demanded that he treat her as a mother on penalty of exposure.

The revelation prostrated the impostor for a brief period, but failed to spur him on to better behavior. He went from bad to worse, stooping even to housebreaking in order to obtain funds to pay his gambling debts. In his mother's power, and she not at all disinclined to blackmail, he was driven to all sorts of expedients to satisfy his own and her demands. But through it all he managed to maintain an outward appearance of superiority that enabled him to dazzle his inferiors and deceive his equals. The judge's love for the boy blinded him to the lad's evil character, but once he nearly disinherited him on the score of cowardice. A pair of mysterious Italian twins settled at Dawson's Landing, and at a public meeting, Tom having provoked him to action by his insolence, Luigi, the stronger of the two, had kicked the scion of the House of Driscoll off the stage into the audience, the stain of which insult a real F. F. V. would have wiped out upon the field of honor, but for which the cowardice of Tom found ample satisfaction in the police court, which proceeding so outraged the good judge that for the honor of his family he personally fought a duel with the offending Italian, wounding him and thus laying the foundations for much future trouble.

Came now the supreme touches in the career of the spurious Tom. For the payment of newly acquired gambling debts, with Roxana's consent, Tom sold his own mother back into the slavery from which at Driscoll's death she had been freed, but in violation of his promises he sold her "down the river," a crime that reacted upon his unfilial head when the resourceful Roxana escaped and, under threat of exposure of his real status in life, required him to indemnify her new master lest she be apprehended and returned to him. Having no other resources, Tom resolved upon the robbery of his benefactor, the judge, in the fulfilment of which venture he murdered him, his weapon being an Oriental knife of unusual design which he had stolen from Luigi, the Italian, in one of his theft-raids.

The murder of Judge Driscoll brought great excitement to Dawson's Landing and the Italian twins narrowly escaped lynching for the crime. The evidence was clearly against them. They were confessedly the owners of the gem-studded, ivory-handled knife with which the crime had been committed. What was worse, they had been found standing beside the body when the neighbors rushed in, having come to the judge's aid at his cry for help. Moreover, there was the clear motive of revenge growing out of the duel which Luigi had fought with the judge. The whole community adjudged them guilty—all but Pudd'nhead Wilson, who volunteered to defend them in court, a poor reliance, since they were his first and only clients. But Pudd'nhead was unafraid. The evidence against them was most convincing, but—

There were finger-prints upon the knife-handle, and they were not the finger-prints of the accused!

Whose finger-prints were they?

Tom, secure in his sense of safety because of the overwhelming evidence against the twins, ventured to taunt Pudd'nhead upon his confidence in winning his case. He entered his study, and, sitting himself at Pudd'nhead's side while he studied the prints in his collection, he picked up one of the records.

"Why, here's old Roxy's label," he said, contemptuously. "Nigger paws, eh? There's a line across her thumb-print. Now how comes that?"

Pudd'nhead, taking the glass from Tom's hand, held it up to the lamp. The blood sank suddenly out of his face. He gazed at the polished surface with the glassy stare of a corpse. *The mystery was solved!*

Tom's thumb-print standing clearly outlined before him on the glass and that on the handle of the blood-stained knife were identified.

"To the minutest detail," said the foreman of the jury, as he returned a verdict of murder against the unhappy lad.

The twins were acquitted, the defrauded heir lifted up out of slavery and restored to his inheritance, and Tom, forever branded as an impostor was "sold down the river" for the benefit of the creditors of the late Percy Northumberland Driscoll.

Which, all things considered, was not a strange fate, for, as Pudd'nhead Wilson himself has said in his famous calendar, "a cauliflower, after all, is nothing but a cabbage with a college education."

QUO VADIS*

by

HENRYK SIENKIEWICZ

CONDENSATION BY PROF. WILLIAM FENWICK HARRIS

HENRYK SIENKIEWICZ, so great a name in Poland that he has been coupled with Copernicus and Kosciuszko as the three Poles to whom Americans are most indebted, was born in Opreya in Russian Poland in 1846. He studied philosophy at Warsaw University, and soon afterward, in company with Helen Modjeska and other radical Poles, established a socialistic community in California. It was somewhat like the earlier Brook Farm experiment made by Hawthorne and his friends. It was no more successful and Sienkiewicz returned to Poland, where he wrote a series of articles for a Warsaw newspaper about his American experiences.

Then he turned to novel-writing. He wrote brilliantly and rapidly, turning with the utmost ease from realistic pictures of contemporary life to stories of romance and to historical novels. "Children of the Soil," which he called his best book, is a simple story of Polish life which won more favor with his own countrymen than it did abroad.

In the 1880's he completed his tremendous trilogy, "With

* Printed by permission of, and arrangement with, Little, Brown & Co., authorized publishers.

Fire and Sword," "The Deluge," and "Pan Michael." There
was an epic quality about these historical novels that made
many people in many lands hail him as a new Scott or a
new Dumas.

His international reputation, however, came with "Quo
Vadis," his masterpiece of ancient Roman life. It was
quickly translated into English and into nearly every Euro-
pean tongue. Then it passed to the stage, not only in
America and England, but also in France and Germany.
After that success Sienkiewicz traveled widely, visiting
England, France, Italy, Spain, Greece, Africa, and the Far
East. He received the Nobel prize for literature in 1905.
From the outbreak of the war to his death in November,
1916, he devoted himself to the relief of Polish war victims.

" 'I do not know to a certainty her name even—Lygia or Callina?
They call her Lygia in the house, for she comes of the Lygian nation; but she has her own barbarian name, Callina. It is a wonderful
house—that of those Plautiuses. There are many people in it; but
it is as quiet there as in the groves of Subiacum. For a number of
days I did not know that a divinity dwelt in the house. Once about
daybreak I saw her bathing in the garden fountain; and I swear
to thee by that foam from which Aphrodite rose, that the rays of
the dawn passed right through her body. I thought that when the
sun rose she would vanish before me in the light, as the twilight of
morning does. Since then I have seen her twice; and since then, too,
I know not what rest is, I know not what other desires are, I have
no wish to know what the city can give me. I want not women, nor
gold, nor Corinthian bronze, nor amber, nor pearls, nor wine, nor
feasts; I want only Lygia.' "

Thus did Vinicius, young Roman patrician of the time of Nero,
announce his love for Lygia, daughter of a king, beautiful hostage
from her nation, forgotten in the turmoil of the world-empire and
brought up as a Roman girl.

Vinicius was speaking to his uncle Petronius, known to his own
time as to us as Arbiter Elegantiarum, trained in all the art and
beauty of Greece, wise, witty, and learned, gaily staking his life in
his daily battle of wits with Tigellinus, who provided for the grosser
desires of the tyrant Nero as Petronius did for his finer and more
artistic ones.

It was a time when the conflicting tides of a pagan age sadly degenerate from the sturdy days of pristine Roman virtues mingled with those of a new era in the world only recently heralded from Judea. In the complicated threads of the picture of Rome, capital of the world, appear the figures of Peter and Paul, on their mission of spreading the new religion of Christ; Poppæa, wife of Nero, beautiful as a dream, but wicked as a nightmare; Eunice, the charming slave of Petronius; Chilo, wily Greek who can be Christian or pagan as profit leads him; Ursus, prodigious in his strength, simple as a child in his faith in Christ and his devotion to Lygia (from whom G. B. S. may have drawn a suggestion in *Androcles and the Lion*); and many minor folk who help to make the story stand out as unusually human among the numerous tales of Greco-Roman times.

When Vinicius told his uncle Petronius of his passion for Lygia, the latter thought nothing was easier than to provide his nephew with what he regarded as a new plaything; a word to Nero, who as emperor had all hostages in his care—summon the maiden to the palace—hand her over to the young patrician as her guardian—what more could be needed to satisfy every one's desires, especially as the maiden manifestly was pleased with Vinicius? But Petronius and his nephew reckoned without a new force that had entered into this Roman world. They could not understand a girl who fled from Nero's court and all its magnificence, fled even from the lover whom she loved. But "finally he understood this, which he and Petronius had not understood, that the new religion engrafted into the soul something unknown to that world in which he lived, and that Lygia, even if she loved him, would not sacrifice any of her Christian truths for his sake, and that, if pleasure existed for her, it was a pleasure different altogether from that which he and Petronius and Cæsar's court and all Rome were pursuing. Every other woman whom he knew might become his mistress, but that Christian would only become his victim. And when he thought of this, he felt anger and burning pain, for he felt that his anger was powerless. To carry off Lygia seemed to him possible; he was even sure that he could do so, but he was equally sure that, in view of her religion, he himself with his bravery was nothing, that his power was nothing, and that through it he could effect nothing. That Roman military tribune, convinced that the power of the sword and the fist which had conquered the world, would command it forever, said for the first time in his life that beyond that power there might be something else; hence he asked himself with amazement what it was."

It is a very definite and concrete way that the author has chosen to show the power of the new religion over human lives. Struggle as he would, backed by birth, by wealth and all the beauty, charm, and allurements that wealth could bring, by the ingenuity and wit of Petronius, by the strong-arm methods of Croton, champion bruiser of his time, even by the force of the known world in Nero's sway, Vinicius could accomplish nothing if all he could win to himself was a mere unwilling body, while soul and spirit were beyond his grasp. And the maddening part to him was that he owed all his troubles to the teachings of a parcel of Jewish fishermen or their likes, or slaves or humble folk who had never before entered into serious consideration in the thoughts of a patrician like himself. It was a long struggle with him, and as the reader follows the various people of the story through their part of the action, he gets an admirable picture of Rome—Nero, tyrant, actor, and artist, with all his magnificence and all his debaucheries; the poor and humble in their crowded quarters of the great city; the delight of all the senses in the life led by Petronius; the lawless streets of Rome by night; the pursuit of Lygia by Vinicius and his hirelings, resulting in the death of his professional bruiser Croton at the hands of the faithful Ursus, and the disaster to Vinicius which led to his nursing back to health by the Christians; his meeting with Peter and Paul; the gradual opening of his eyes, physical and spiritual; his discovery of Christians everywhere, among the people, among his own slaves, among soldiers and officers, even in the very court of Nero. And the growing worry and astonishment of Petronius:

" 'Vinicius, thou art losing sense, judgment, moderation,' exclaimed Petronius.

" 'I love only her in the world,' responded Vinicius.

" 'What of that?'

" 'This, that I wish no other love. I have no wish for your life, your feasts, your shamelessness, your crimes.'

" 'What is taking place in thee? Art thou a Christian?' "

And then the great fire of Rome, set by Tigellinus, that Nero might not lack the experience of Priam, who had seen Troy burn; the wild ride of Vinicius from Antium to the capital in the hope of rescuing Lygia from the flames; the persecution of the Christians with the thought of throwing on them the rage of the people at the burning of the city; the singling out of Lygia by the hate of Poppæa because Vinicius had spurned the Empress's proffered charms; the final rescue by a miracle of strength on the part of the ever-faithful Ursus, and the words of Vinicius to Peter:

" 'What thou commandest I will do.'

" 'Love men as thy own brothers,' answered the Apostle, 'for only with love mayest thou serve Him.' "

RAMONA

by

HELEN HUNT JACKSON

CONDENSATION BY MARY BROOKS

HELEN FISKE, born at Amherst, Massachusetts, October 18, 1831, was the daughter of Prof. N. W. Fiske. She was twice married, first to Major Edward B. Hunt of the United States Engineers; he died in 1863; it was while living as a widow at Newport that she made her pen name of "H. H." (Helen Hunt) well known. Years later she married W. S. Jackson, a banker of Colorado Springs.

She was a pen-woman of great industry and success. She first won attention by "Verses by H. H." Her poems were widely read and were praised by Emerson and T. W. Higginson. She wrote for the famous "No Name Stories" two novels, "Mercy Philbrick's Choice" and "Hetty's Strange History." She was author of books of many types, including those for children. She became greatly interested in the Indians. She was appointed a special commissioner to investigate their condition. From this work resulted "A Century of Dishonor," and the novel by which she will be remembered, "Ramona." She died August 12, 1885, in San Francisco. She possessed the affectionate regard of many readers.

"Ramona! The blessed child!" Father Salvierderra, nearing his journey's end, cried out with joy. Through the golden mustard tangle that overhung his path a dark-haired maiden came swiftly to meet him. At sight of Ramona's angelic face the aged Franciscan forgot his weariness, almost forgot his burden of grief over his beloved missions, despoiled and crumbling. A silent blessing, and he followed her contentedly to the Moreno ranch, where sheep-shearing had been delayed until his visit, that he might confess the shearing band.

Before Mexico's surrender of California, General Moreno's estates were lordly indeed; now huge portions had been lopped away by the United States Land Commission and the general's widow revenged her losses by denouncing all Americans as "hounds." A marvelous manager, the Señora Moreno, whom her handsome, gentle son Felipe obeyed in everything and knew it not! Yet she never suspected that Felipe's affection for Ramona could be more than brotherly; she had never loved the girl. For Ramona was not of Moreno blood. Her father was a tempestuous Scotchman who, cruelly jilted by the señora's sister, married an Indian woman. To his old love, childless and unhappy, he gave his beautiful blue-eyed baby to rear as her own. At Señora Ortegna's death the child came as a legacy to Señora Moreno, but at nineteen Ramona still waited to learn the mystery of her parentage. The stern, silent señora would not tell.

The Indian sheep-shearers arrived at sunset, just as Ramona hurried to the brook to wash an altar-cloth. Her face aglow, she bent over the stones, all unconscious that Alessandro, captain of the shearing band, beholding her, stood spellbound.

When Father Salvierderra led the household sunrise hymn next morning, a new rich barytone voice thrilled Ramona strangely.

"I never heard anything like it," she told Felipe.

"That is Alessandro, old Pablo's son—a splendid fellow. He plays the violin beautifully, the old San Luis Rey music. His father was bandmaster there."

Sheep-shearing began most unfortunately. Felipe, up too soon from a long illness, suffered a relapse while packing the dusty fleeces. Only Alessandro could soothe his delirium; accordingly, Alessandro was persuaded to remain until the invalid should recover.

As Felipe improved, he lived on the open veranda, lying on a rawhide bed that Alessandro made. The family sat near him. Alessandro, too, "his music a delight, his strength and fidelity a repose, his personal presence always agreeable, was freely welcome." The young Indian watched Ramona with dumb devotion.

"Such eyes," she mused, "like a saint, so solemn, so mild. I am sure he is very good." She ceased to regard him as an Indian. How could she understand this new feeling? Felipe was the only young man she had ever known.

One thought possessed Alessandro after old Juan Canito, the head shepherd, told him of Ramona's parentage: "The señorita has Indian blood. . . . The señora loves her not." When Ramona wept at the señora's unkindness, he trembled so that Felipe read his secret.

"If only my mother could think it," reflected generous Felipe, "it would be best to have Alessandro stay here as overseer, and then they might be married."

The crisis came when Ramona's eyes dimmed with tears because she feared Alessandro's father would not let him remain permanently on the ranch.

"Señorita," he cried, "tears have come into your eyes. Then you will not be angry if I say that I love you!"

"I know, Alessandro; I am glad of it. I love you!"

"Oh, señorita, do you mean that you will go with me? You cannot mean that!"

"Yes, I will go with you!"

And then, as they stood locked in each other's arms, the señora discovered them!

"Shameful creature!" she cried, smiting Ramona's protesting lips. She hustled the girl to her room and locked her in.

Alessandro, watching sadly all that night, heard two wood-doves calling, "Love?" "Here." "Love?" "Here." "My Ramona is like the gentle wood-dove," thought he. "If she is my wife my people will call her Majel the Wood-Dove."

In vain Felipe tried to persuade his mother. In vain she coaxed and threatened Ramona. The jewels which were to be Ramona's dowry, if she married worthily, were no temptation. When the señora scornfully declared, "Your mother was an Indian, a low, common Indian," the girl was truly glad.

"Why do you object to my marrying Alessandro?" she demanded. "I am of his people. The jewels you can give to the Church. I shall marry Alessandro."

Felipe sent Alessandro home to Temecula until the storm should blow over. But the long-dreaded Americans in their search for more land had just taken possession of that peaceful village. Dragged out of his own house by force, old Pablo died of grief. Alessandro buried him, and then in utter misery came back to bid Ramona farewell.

"Dearest señorita, I have no home," he faltered. "My father is dead; my people have been driven out of their village. I am only a beggar now."

But Ramona felt no fear of privations. "Take me with you!" she cried. After long pleading she overruled his wiser arguments, and that night they slipped away, with Baba, Ramona's own horse.

No trace of the lovers was found, for those Indians who knew Alessandro's whereabouts purposely misled inquirers; and at San Diego, where they were married, Ramona had given Alessandro's pet name for her, "Majella," to be entered on the register.

Their first home was near Alessandro's cousin in San Pasquale, where the Indians received Ramona gladly. She was very happy in her new life "under the sky." She accepted a tiny brush hut as cheerfully as the comfortable adobe which Alessandro soon built and which she beautified beyond belief. Gleefully she led Baba when he plowed the first furrows in their fields.

But Alessandro's anxiety rarely left him. When he heard that the Mexican pueblo paper of San Pasquale was worthless, that all the village lands belonged to the Americans in Washington, he lost hope. "I think I shall go mad," he said. When American ranchers appeared, he sold house and crop and moved to Saboba, seeking a place the Americans did not want.

On the way to Saboba they nearly perished in a snowstorm, but were saved by an easy-going Tennesseean family, the Hyers, with whom they became friends. Already Ramona's heart had been wrung at hearing of Father Salvierderra's death. Now came a new grief— she feared for Alessandro's reason. Could he bear another blow? "Eyes-of-the-Sky," their baby girl, never recovered from her exposure to the storm and died on the way to the agency doctor who would not come to her. White men began to encroach and to be insulting.

"We will hide forever," declared Alessandro. Leaving horses and wagon in San Bernardino with the Hyers for the winter, they went to a tiny valley almost inaccessible, folded high on Mt. San Jacinto's slopes. "Here we are safe!" exulted Ramona.

" 'Pears like she'd gone klar out 'er this yer world inter another," mused Aunt Ri Hyer, as she sat weaving carpets and gazing up at the shining mountain in the southern horizon.

When Alessandro saw the brown eyes of his second daughter he sighed, "It is an ill gift to have the eyes of Alessandro; they look ever on woe."

Now began attacks of mental distress—wild flights from imaginary white pursuers. Sometimes he tried to drive flocks he fancied were his own. One fatal day he galloped home on a strange horse, taken by mistake during one of his "sicknesses."

"Señor, I will explain—" But Farrar, the enraged owner, shot him dead in the midst of his explanations.

Child in arms, Ramona ran for help to the nearest village, Cahuilla. Then came oblivion.

Ten days afterward she opened her eyes. Aunt Ri was beside her and—Felipe! He had recognized Baba in San Bernardino, and from the Hyers had learned the whole sad story.

"I have been searching for you all this time," he whispered. "I am alone, dear. There is no one now but you to take care of me."

In Mexico, Felipe made a new home and there Ramona became his loving, loyal wife. But when the wood-doves called, she heard a voice saying, "Majella!" That was her only secret from her husband.

❧

THE RED AND THE BLACK*
by
STENDHAL

TRANSLATED FROM THE FRENCH BY C. K. SCOTT-MONCRIEFF
CONDENSATION BY MARGARET GILLETT

STENDHAL, pseudonym of Marie Henri Beyle (1783–1842), was a French littérateur who led an adventurous and diversified life as a soldier, businessman, and government

* From: *The Red and the Black* by Stendhal (Marie Henri Beyle). By permission of Liveright, Publishers, N. Y. Copyright © 1954, George Scott-Moncrieff.

official. He spent seven years (1814–1821) in Milan, where he met Byron and Mme. de Stael. In 1831 he was appointed consul at Trieste and Civitavecchia.

Although he contributed frequently to both English and French periodicals, he was generally not appreciated as a writer in his own day, except perhaps by his contemporary, Balzac. He achieved a kind of notoriety for his hectic love affairs, commemorated in his book, "De l'Amour" (1822), but it was not until 1880 with the appearance of his hitherto unpublished works that a literary revival gave him any real recognition. His reputation has increased in the last quarter of a century, particularly since the appearance of his "Journal" (1923–24), his complete works in French in seventy-nine volumes (1927–37), and the recent publication in English of his "Private Diaries" (1953).

The author of "The Red and the Black" (1830) always considered writing as simply an avocation, yet he devoted much of his energy to the production of literary pieces in various forms. His first book, written in Milan, was a biographical work, "Lives of Haydn, Mozart and Metastasio" (1814). Three years later his "History of Painting in Italy" was published in two volumes, along with his "Rome, Naples and Florence." "A Life of Rossini" (1824) was followed by his first novel, "Armance," in 1827. "Memoirs of a Tourist" (1838) and "La Chatreuse de Parme" (1839), usually considered his best novel, brought him to the high point of his literary career. Two more novels, "Laniel," and "Lucien Lenowen," were published posthumously.

M. de Rênal, owner of a thriving nail factory, became mayor of the prosperous town of Verrières in the Franche-Comté in 1815. He was of aristocratic birth, yet a shrewd business man, and considered the employment of a tutor for his three sons a good investment to increase his prestige and impress his social and political rivals, including M. Valenod, the Governor of the Poorhouse. Mme. de Rênal, who had never questioned her husband's judgment, agreed. But secretly she dreaded an unwashed, ill-dressed priest would come to whip her children. However, her fears were allayed when she saw the pale, gentle youth the Mayor had selected.

His name was Julien Sorel and he was of peasant stock, but he had learned Latin from the local curé. A slim young man with irregular but delicate features, large dark eyes and chestnut hair, he had a look that suggested a fiery spirit. He welcomed the idea of being in M. de Rênal's fine château—he hated his strong, ox-like brothers and their labor at his brutal father's sawmill—but he did not wish to be treated as a servant. He was determined to make his fortune and leave his life as a peasant behind him. He had devotedly admired Napoleon, but now times had changed, military distinction was no longer fashionable, priests were drawing huge stipends, and so he had decided to become a priest.

Mme. de Rênal's children soon adored Julien, but he did not care much for them. He felt only horror and contempt for the high society he now entered and on certain occasions could hardly conceal his loathing for the Mayor's wealthy friends who enlarged their fortunes at the expense of the poor. He admired Mme. de Rênal's looks but despised her for her aristocratic beauty and spoke to her as little as possible.

On the other hand, Mme. de Rênal, who had never loved her coarse husband, was charmed by Julien's gentleness and detachment and she soon forgave him his unpolished manners. She offered him money to buy clothes, but he was angry and thought it a trick of the rich to humiliate him. Although he did not realize she had fallen in love with him, he considered it a duty to himself and a way of appeasing his resentment toward the rich, to make advances to her.

So, one summer evening in the dark garden of the Mayor's country estate, while M. de Rênal talked heatedly of his political opponents, Julien seized Madame's hand and covered it with passionate kisses—or so they seemed to her. A few days later he boldly informed her that he would come to her room after midnight. As he spoke, he trembled lest his request be granted—the part of seducer was revolting to him—yet lest he be thought weak, he kept his tryst. Their first meeting was a conquest for him though it did not really give him pleasure. The second night he was less obsessed with the part he was playing, and soon he was madly in love. But his love was still founded on ambition: for him, a poor creature, so unfortunate and so despised, it was the joy of possessing so noble and beautiful a woman.

Such transports of delight did not go unnoticed. Mme. de Rênal's maid, whose affection had been spurned by Julien, told M. Valenod, the Mayor's arch political foe, about her lady's affair. Anonymous letters began arriving for M. de Rênal and soon the whole town was seething with the scandal. When the curé heard of it, he insisted that Julien leave Verrières at once for the seminary at Besançon or accept an offer of a business partnership with Fouqué, a timber merchant in a distant village. Julien, preferring the possibility of future greatness to assured comfort and mediocrity, chose the former.

However, he had no real vocation for the Church and thought of his life at the seminary as a purgatorial period from which there was no escape. He had considered himself a consummate hypocrite, but here he was surrounded by young men more hypocritical than himself—former peasants whose hearts were set on having good food to eat and fine clothes to wear. They despised Julien because he spoke well and because he was intelligent. Julien's only real friend was the stern Abbé Pirard, the director of the seminary, and when this worthy cleric accepted a handsome living in Paris from the Marquis de la Mole, he arranged for Julien to become secretary to the Marquis. The young seminarian gladly left for Paris, but he did not fail to break his journey at Verrières, where he spent two blissful nights with Mme. de Rênal.

The Marquis de la Mole found his new secretary extremely competent and, owing to his persistent hard work, reserve, and intelligence, gradually entrusted him with the most important business affairs. Mlle. Mathilde de la Mole, the Marquis' daughter, who was bored at the very sight of the polite gallants of Paris society, found this serious and intellectual young man from the provinces a fascinating novelty. She began to pay him flattering attentions, but the more she sought him out, the more he thought she was trying to make a fool of him and the more cold and respectful he became.

At last she invited him to come to her room. This was no plot to embarrass him, as he thought, but before he appeared Mlle. de la Mole had already regretted her rash invitation, fearing lest this peasant should come to dominate her. Nevertheless she allowed him to make love to her but then treated him coldly for many days. Julien was bewildered and miserable. More than once the idea of suicide occurred to him until, with a boldness born of desperation, he again climbed through her window. She welcomed him with joy, and later, she cut off half her hair and gave it to him as a pledge of her love. She even called him "My Master." But within two days remorse and pride made her withdraw her affections once more, and she told him cruelly, "I no longer love you, my wild imagination misled me."

Upon the advice of an old friend, Julien proceeded to pay attention to a certain lady who was a constant visitor to the Marquis' household. Mathilde's jealousy was aroused, she flew into a rage, flung herself at his feet and cried, "Despise me if you will, but love me"—and fainted.

Julien was delighted and, though now frantic with passion, tried to pretend indifference. At other moments frenzy swept aside all counsels of prudence, and in time Mathilde found she was pregnant.

The Marquis was furious and at first would not agree to the marriage of his daughter to a mere cleric. But eventually he made up his mind to give Julien a considerable sum of money and property, a commission in a cavalry regiment, a noble name, and to accept him as a son-in-law. Just at this moment, when the young man's ambitions all seemed about to be fulfilled, the Marquis received a letter from Mme. de Rênal bitterly denouncing her former lover. Bent on revenge, Julien set off for Verrières. There he found Mme. de Rênal in church, and he shot her.

Imprisoned and condemned to die, he was indifferent to his own fate, so filled was he with remorse for Mme. de Rênal's death. Great was his astonishment and gratitude, therefore, when he discovered that her wounds were not mortal. Meanwhile, bored by the devotion of Mathilde, he felt unworthy of the disgrace she risked in coming to the prison and bribing the officials. Nevertheless, thanks to her efforts, his acquittal seemed assured.

But Julien was his own undoing. No longer harboring ambitions, he spoke out freely against the hypocrisy and degeneracy of the times in a way that offended the court. He not only declared himself guilty of a premeditated attempt at murder, but said that, even if he were less guilty, the jury would condemn him as a peasant who sought to rise above his station—"That is my crime, gentlemen—," he said. He was promptly found guilty.

Julien accepted the verdict calmly and would not have appealed if Mme. de Rênal had not come and begged him to do so. The prisoner was in a transport of joy, for he knew at last it was she whom he really loved. Mathilde's jealousy rose to a pitch of insanity, but Julien was convinced that after his death she would soon forget him.

The appeal was unsuccessful and Julien went to the guillotine bravely and with dignity. Mathilde insisted on taking his head and burying it with her own hands. Mme. de Rênal did not seek to end her own life, but three days after Julien's execution she died while embracing her children.

THE RED BADGE OF COURAGE

by

STEPHEN CRANE

CONDENSATION BY MARGARET GILLETT

STEPHEN CRANE (1871–1900), whose fame rests almost entirely on his novel "The Red Badge of Courage" (1895), produced in his brief literary lifetime, some forty sketches and tales, five novels, three volumes of verse, and many journalistic essays, including a series of articles on narcotic addiction which shocked the complacent society of his era. More remarkable still is the fact that his stirring story of fighting and carnage was written with no war experience whatever; most of Crane's military knowledge was derived from a set of books entitled, "Battles and Leaders of the Civil War."

However, this was not the limit of the talents of this prolific and ingenious young man from New Jersey. Although slight of build, Stephen had always wanted to be a professional baseball player and had been captain of the team at Syracuse University while he worked part time as a newspaper correspondent. After his mother's death in 1891—his father, a clergyman, had died when Stephen was only eight—he lived in New York City, where he apparently gave up his ambition for a career in sports and deliberately set about being a writer. In 1892 he published his novelette, "Maggie: A Girl of the Streets," on money borrowed from his brother. This complete failure was followed three years later by "The Red Badge of Courage," which was just as complete a success.

The next year Crane went to Florida, as a correspondent, to cover a Cuban revolution, and sailed on a gun-smuggling ship which sank before it reached the island. Later he re-

*counted his experiences during his severe fifty-hour expo-
sure at sea in "The Open Boat" (1898). Next he made a
brief trip to Greece to cover the war and was supposedly
married on his return. (It seems clear that Cora Crane was
unable to get a divorce from her second husband and
hence was never legally married to Crane.) Subsequently
the couple went to England, where Crane became friends
with Joseph Conrad and Henry James. After another journey to Cuba to report the Battle of San Juan Hill for the
"World," he returned to England, broken in health, and
died on a visit to Germany the following year.*

Henry Fleming had yearned for a long time to enlist. He was
proud and exultant when at last he donned the blue uniform. He
had dreamed of battles all his life. He had believed that war was a
series of death struggles with small time in between for sleep and
meals; but since his regiment had come to the field, the army had
done little but sit still and try to keep warm. The old visions of
marches, sieges, conflicts, extravagant pictures, lurid with heroic
deeds of eagle-eyed prowess—all began to fade. He grew to regard
himself merely as a part of a vast blue demonstration in which he
was drilled and drilled and reviewed.

One morning, however, his regiment was ordered to be ready. The
men whispered speculations and recounted old rumors. In the gloom
before the break of day, their uniforms glowed a deep purple while
from across the river the red eyes of the rebel fires still peered. The
youth perceived that the time had come. He was about to be measured. He realized that against danger he was an unknown quantity.
He tried to prove to himself that he would not run from battle. As
he brooded, while the others laughed and joked and predicted victory, it seemed to him that he was not formed for a soldier.

Shots from the skirmishes in advance spoke to him of tragedies—
hidden, mysterious, solemn. Once on its march his line encountered
the body of a dead soldier. The youth looked keenly at the ashen
face. He vaguely desired to walk around the body and stare; the
impulse of the living to read in dead eyes the answer to the Question.

They were marched from place to place with apparent aimlessness,
but at last the brigade ahead went into action with a rendering
roar. It lay stretched in the distance behind a gray wall of smoke.
Of a sudden the youth felt a heavy hand laid upon his shoulder.

"It's my first and last battle, old boy," said Wilson, a soldier who had always been loud and cheerful. "Something tells me I'm a gone coon this first time and—I w-want you to take these here things—to—my—folks." With a sob he handed the astonished youth a little packet done up in a yellow envelope, gave him a glance as from the depths of a tomb, raised his limp hand in a prophetic manner, and turned away.

Across the smoke-infested fields came a gray swarm of running men. The enemy advanced, stooping and swinging their rifles at all angles. Perspiration streamed down the youth's face, which was soiled like that of a weeping urchin. He began to fire and suddenly lost concern for himself. He became not a man but a member. He felt a subtle brotherhood with his comrades in arms. A burning roar filled his ears. Following this came a red rage. He craved a power that would enable him to make a world-sweeping gesture and brush all back. Here and there men dropped like bundles. The captain was killed and a boy who had fled screaming was hit in the head. Another had his knee joint splintered by a ball.

At last an exultant yell went along the quivering line. "We've helt 'em back," was the cry. So it was over, and the supreme trial had been passed. The youth went into an ecstasy of self-satisfaction. He was a fine fellow!

But suddenly there were cries of "Here they come ag'in!" The youth stared. Surely it was a mistake. But through the smoke he saw the ground ahead covered with advancing men. The men groaned and complained as they watched the frantic approach of the yelling enemy. A man nearby dropped his rifle and ran howling. A soldier whose face had borne an expression of exalted courage threw down his gun and fled like a rabbit. Others began to scamper away. The youth watched them, and suddenly he too flung away his rifle and fled in terror.

After a time the sound of musketry grew faint and the cannon boomed in the distance. The sun, suddenly apparent, blazed among the trees. At length, he came to a place where the high arching boughs made a chapel. Near the threshold he stopped, horror-stricken at the sight of a thing.

He was being stared at by a dead man who was seated with his back against a tree. He was dressed in a uniform that had once been blue, but was now faded to a melancholy shade of green. The mouth was open. Its red had changed to an appalling yellow. Over the gray skin of the face ran little black ants. One was trundling something along the upper lip. The youth shrieked, and for some moments was turned to stone. Then he ran.

Presently he came upon a blood-stained crowd streaming to the rear. Wounded men were cursing, groaning, and wailing. Their torn bodies expressed the awful machinery in which they had been entangled. The youth joined them.

"Was pretty good fight, wa'n't it?" said a tattered, bloody figure beside him. "Where yeh hit, ol' boy?"

The youth felt instant panic and shame. His brow flushed. He turned away and slid through the crowd. He wished that he, too, had a wound, a red badge of courage.

He watched a tall soldier from his regiment, whose side looked as if it had been chewed by wolves, and who marched steadily forward, refusing aid, until he kept his rendezvous with death.

The youth wished that he too was dead. He conceded it to be impossible that he should ever become a hero. Those old pictures of glory were piteous things. He imagined his whole regiment saying,

"Where's Henry Fleming? He run, didn't 'e? Oh, my!"

These dismal thoughts were interrupted by waves of blue uniforms that suddenly came sweeping out of the woods. They, too, were fleeing and the youth was comforted by the sight. He clutched one of them by the sleeve. The man screamed "Let go me!" and adroitly and fiercely swung his rifle upon the youth's head. Henry fell, but finally struggled to his feet. He fought an intense battle with his own body, but somehow he kept going.

At last, through the mazes of the tangled forest, he saw the fires of his regiment. A nervous voice challenged him. It was Wilson, who had given him the packet before fighting began. Henry, who could hardly stand, told his friend how he had been in a violent skirmish, got separated from the regiment and had got shot in the head. "Yeh've been grazed by a ball," said the man who examined his wound.

In the morning Henry's self-pride was entirely restored. He had license to be veteranlike and call the generals "lunkheads." He remembered the terror-struck faces of the men who had run. They were weak mortals. As for himself, he had fled with discretion and dignity. When his friend with great embarrassment asked for his packet to be returned, the youth felt his heart grow even stronger.

The woods began to crackle with the enemy's renewed attack.

The youth felt a wild hate for the relentless foe. He was not conscious that he was on his feet. His rifle barrel grew too hot to touch, but he kept stuffing cartridges into it. He aimed through the smoke and pulled the trigger with fierce grunts. He was so engrossed he went on firing after the enemy had retreated. He became aware that his comrades were all staring at him. "By heavens," the lieutenant crowed, "if I had ten thousand wild cats like you I could tear th' stomach outa this war in less 'n a week!" Now he was suddenly, to his surprise, a hero.

In the welcome respite that followed, Henry overheard a general give orders for his regiment to charge. When the command came, the men made a frenzied rush. But soon they tired and began to falter and hesitate. The lieutenant, regardless of the vindictive threats of the bullets, went about coaxing, berating, bedamning. The youth, feeling a sudden indignation at the officer, challenged him to lead the way. With Wilson, they raced down the regimental front rallying the men, while the flag bearer and the men followed. In the fury the color sergeant flinched and fell. Henry tugged the flag from his grip and went on.

But the charge came to a halt. The men wavered on a little clearing, and then recoiled. Their retreat was a march of shame to the youth. Gaunt and bronzed veterans taunted them. The general exploded in reproaches, calling the men "mule drivers"—and "mud diggers." The colonel, too, was angry, yet he wanted to know who was the lad who had carried the flag at the head of the charge. Some of the men told Henry and his friend Wilson that the colonel said they deserved to be major generals.

When the battle was renewed, the exultant youth watched the wild and desperate rushes of men with serene self confidence. He saw a blue wave dash with thunderous force against a gray obstruction. When its time came, his own emaciated regiment bustled forth again with undiminished fierceness. Though it bled extravagantly, the regiment charged forward savagely, determined to redeem its reputation. The enemy were so close now, Henry could see their haggard faces. He saw the rival color-bearer bitten vitally by bullets. Wilson sprang at the flag and, with a mad cry, snatched it from the convulsing grip. Then, through the smoke, they saw the gray crowd retreating.

In a little while, the victorious men in blue received orders to return to camp. The youth nudged his friend.

"Well, it's all over," he said.

"B'Gawd, it is," he assented.

The youth smiled. He was a man, and he saw that the world was a world for him, though many discovered it to be made of oaths and walking sticks. He had rid himself of the red sickness of battle. The sultry nightmare was in the past. He turned now with a lover's thirst to images of tranquil skies, fresh meadows, cool brooks—an existence of soft and eternal peace.

ROBINSON CRUSOE

by

DANIEL DEFOE

CONDENSATION BY JAMES B. CONNOLLY

DANIEL DEFOE was born in London about 1600. After a life of varied and brilliant activity, he died, a homeless fugitive, in Ropemakers' Alley, Moorfields, on April 26, 1731. His father, a butcher, educated Daniel for the dissenting ministry, but the boy's unremitting energy led him to be a trader, a political intriguer, and an indefatigable journalist.

He rose to great intimacy with King William III, and abruptly fell to pillory and prison for his too perfect satire, "The Shortest Way with Dissenters." From Newgate he launched his remarkable "Review," a journal written entirely by himself. He advocated an income tax and higher education for women. He wrote two hundred and fifty distinct pamphlets and books, but his masterpiece, "Robinson Crusoe," was not published until 1719, when the author was nearly sixty years old. This, the first great English novel, has in some respects never been surpassed. Its immediate popularity incited Defoe to write a sequel and many thrilling tales of pirates and adventurers, of courtezans and

adventuresses. His vivid story of the plague appeared three
years after "Robinson Crusoe."

"Defoe was perhaps the greatest liar that ever lived. Yet
if we go deep into his rich and strangely mixed nature, we
come upon stubborn foundations of conscience." Whatever
the ultimate judgment of his honesty, "Robinson Crusoe"
lives immortally to attest his genius in invention.

My father designed me for the law, but I would be satisfied only
with going to sea, and being one day at Hull and one of my companions about to go by sea to London in his father's ship, nothing
would serve me but I must go with him—this on September 8, 1651,
and I being then nineteen years of age.

The ship was no sooner out of port than the wind began to blow
and the sea to rise in the most frightful manner, which made me
most terribly sick in body and frightened in mind. In my agony I
vowed that if God would spare me through this one voyage I would
go, immediately I set foot on land, directly home to my good parents
and be ever after guided in my conduct by their advice.

But next day the wind was abated and the sea calmer, and the
sun went down to a perfectly fine evening, and when to that was
added a bowl of punch made by a shipmate, I forgot my resolution
to return home after the voyage; and such has been my habit, to my
great misfortune, all my life—to disavow in the hour of peril the
headstrong actions which have brought me to peril, and when the
danger is past to forget all vows and plunge headlong once more
on my heedless courses.

Various were my adventures after that first tempestuous voyage.
Trading to Guinea in Africa, I was captured by a Turkish rover and
sold into slavery, from whence after many perils I escaped to the
Brazils, where I set myself up for a sugar-planter and was enjoying
a fine prosperity thereat, when I fell a victim to temptation. Help
being scarce in the Brazils and some planters there knowing that I
had traded with the slave coasts of Africa, they beguiled me into a
voyage to those parts with the intent to secure slave labor for our
plantations.

Only evil does ever come of evil counsel. Our ship was wrecked
on an unknown island off the northeast coast of South America, and
of all the ship's company I alone, by the blessing of God, was allowed
to escape through the high surf to the shore. All I possessed at the

time was a knife, a pipe, and a little tobacco in a box. Walking along the shore, when I had recovered sufficiently in strength so to walk, I found fresh water, a great joy. Having drunk and put a little tobacco against the hunger in my mouth, I took up by lodging in a tree and did there sleep, to my great refreshment, throughout the night.

Next morning the weather was clear and the sea mild, but what pleased me most was the sight of the ship, which, as the tide ebbed, lay so close to the shore that I found no trouble in swimming out to it. No living thing except a dog and two cats was left on the ship; but there was a store of necessities, and such I took, building a raft for the purpose of transporting them to an inlet in the island where was fresh water and a flat, high place for my habitation. Bread, rice, barley and corn, cheese and dried goat's flesh, some sugar, flour, planks, spars, rope—all these with muskets, two pistols, fowling-pieces, a store of lead and powder, two saws, an ax, a hammer and —which was the least use of all—thirty-six pounds sterling. All these I piloted from day to day between tides from ship to shore. On the night of the thirteenth day my work of transportation being done, I lay down in my usual fear of wild beasts, but also of thankfulness in the knowledge that I was prepared for some time to come against the barrenness of this island.

There were wild fruit trees on the island, but it was many days before I discovered them. There were also goats running wild, but without the firearms and ammunition I had brought from the ship, of what avail were they to me? So I had reason to be thankful for the good Providence which held the ship to the shore until I had taken off all that was of use to me.

There was much to be done if I were to secure my existence on this strange island. The needful things I did as best I could in turn, but not always with good fortune attending my efforts. In my first planting of barley and corn seed, the half of all my precious stock was wasted by reason of being planted in the very wrong time. I spent weary months in making earthware pots for holding fresh water; and forty-two days it took me to hew my first long plank from a tree trunk. I strove for weeks to fashion a stone mortar to stamp grain in, only to come at last to a block of hollowed-out wood. Five months I labored in felling a great cedar tree, hewing and shaping it to the hull of a splendid boat with which I was to escape from the island, only to be forced to abandon it for want of a means whereby to launch it into the sea. However, every failure taught me something I had not known before.

For the elements, there were great winds and rains and earthquakes. But I became used in time to all things. I planted and harvested my crops of barley and corn; I plucked my wild grapes and dried them into nourishing raisins; I raised and killed and smoked and salted my tame goats, being thus for variety of food not so badly served. And so through the twelve years during which I saw no sign of human existence on the island other than my own, until that eventful day on which I met with the print of a man's naked foot on the sand.

I was then like one thunderstruck. I listened, I looked, but I could hear nothing, see nothing. I went up the shore, down the shore; but there was only that single footprint! Terrified to the last degree, I ran to my habitation like one pursued; and for three days and nights thereafter I did not stir out.

What a commentary on the fear of man for man! After twelve years of pain and labor, twelve years of warring against the elements, to be thrown into terror by the imprint of a human foot! But so it was.

After observation I learned that it was the habit of cannibals from the main land to come to a part of the island which I seldom visited to feast upon the bodies of their captured enemies. One morning from my lookout I perceived thirty savages dancing around a fire. They had cooked one victim and had two more ready for the fire, when I descended upon them with two loaded muskets and my great sword, and was in time to save one which they had not yet eaten. The saved man I called Friday, in honor of the day of his rescue, and his was the first voice I heard in all my twenty-five years on the island. He was young, intelligent, of a superior race of savages, and became my trusted companion for all the time I remained on the island.

What Friday told me of the mainland, after I had taught him some English, decided me to leave my island. We built a boat, this time not too far from the sea for launching and were almost ready to set sail when twenty-one savages in three canoes landed on the island with three prisoners for a feast. One of the prisoners was a white man, which enraged me. I double-charged two fowling-pieces, four muskets, two pistols, and, giving Friday a hatchet and also a great dram of rum, and myself my great sword, we descended and killed all but four savages.

One of the prisoners was Friday's father. The white man was a Spaniard, a survivor from a ship of which I had seen the wrecked hull on my island some years before this, and from which I had taken some one thousand two hundred pieces of gold, but of which I made small account because of its being of less value to me than so much sand of the beach.

The Spaniard and Friday's father I sent with firearms and food in my new boat to bring back the wrecked crew of the Spanish ship. While waiting for their return an English ship with a mutinous crew put into my island. I helped the captain recover his ship and took passage with him for England, leaving on the island the most mutinous members, with two honest ones who wished also to remain. Later, my Spaniards returned and all settled together on the island, having their dissensions at first, but settling down finally into a flourishing colony, which some years later it was my happiness to visit.

After twenty-eight years two months and nineteen days I left my island. I anticipated much joy of my arrival in England, but I was like a stranger there. My mother and father were both dead, which was unfortunate, as I could have been of great service to them; for besides the one thousand two hundred pieces of gold from the Spanish ship, there was ten thousand pounds sterling awaiting me from an honest friend, a Portuguese captain to whom I had entrusted my estate in the Brazils before setting forth on the ill-fated errand which threw me for twenty-eight years on my island. So pleased was I with his honesty that I settled one hundred moidures a year on him and fifty moidures a year on his son, both for life.

I married and begot three children, and except for the one voyage to the old island, of which I have spoken, I roamed no more. So here I am, having lived a life of infinite variety for twenty-nine years, blessed with more than I deserve and resolved to prepare now for the longest journey of all. If I have learned anything, it is a knowledge of the value of retirement and the blessing of ending our days in peace.

ROMOLA

by

GEORGE ELIOT*

CONDENSATION BY PROF. WILLIAM FENWICK HARRIS

"Romola mia," said the blind scholar, "thou wilt reach the needful volumes—thou knowest them—on the fifth shelf of the cabinet."

Tito rose at the same moment with Romola, saying, "I will reach them, if you will point them out," and followed her hastily into the adjoining small room, where the walls were also covered with ranges of books in perfect order.

"There they are," said Romola, pointing upward; "every book is just where it was when my father ceased to see them."

Tito stood by her without hastening to reach the books. They had never been in this room together before.

"I hope," she continued, turning her eyes full on Tito with a look of grave confidence—"I hope he will not weary you; this work makes him so happy."

"And me, too, Romola—if you will only let me say, I love you—if you will only think me worth loving a little."

His speech was the softest murmur, and the dark, beautiful face, nearer to hers than it had ever been before, was looking at her with beseeching tenderness.

"I do love you," murmured Romola; she looked at him with the same simple majesty as ever, but her voice had never in her life before sunk to that murmur. It seemed to them both that they were looking at each other a long while before her lips moved again; yet it was but a moment till she said, "I know now what it is to be happy."

The faces just met, and the dark curls mingled for an instant with the rippling gold. Quick as lightning after that Tito set his foot on a projecting ledge of the bookshelves and reached down the needful volumes. They were both contented to be silent and separate, for that first blissful experience of mutual consciousness was all

* For biographical information see page 6.

the more exquisite for being unperturbed by immediate sensation.

It had all been as rapid as the irreversible mingling of waters, for even the eager and jealous Bardo had not become impatient.

When they told her father, he wanted time for reflection. "Be patient, my children; you are very young."

"No more could be said, and Romola's heart was perfectly satisfied. Not so Tito's. If the subtle mixture of good and evil prepares suffering for human truth and purity, there is also suffering prepared for the wrongdoer by the same mingled conditions. As Tito kissed Romola on their parting that evening the very strength of the thrill that moved his whole being at the sense that this woman, whose beauty it was hardly possible to think of as anything but the necessary consequence of her noble nature, loved him with all the tenderness that spoke in her clear eyes, brought a strong reaction of regret that he had not kept himself free from that first deceit which had dragged him into the danger of being disgraced before her. There was a sprig of bitterness mingled with that fountain of sweets."

George Eliot's magnificent study of character concerns itself with Florence at the time when Christopher Columbus was discovering America, when Savonarola was prior of Saint Mark's and ruled the city by his moral energy and his fanaticism, when his pious frenzies, his visions, and his predictions of heavenly wrath seemed to the majority of his fellow-citizens as coming from a more than mortal source; when Charles VIII of France invaded Italy; when the plague brought dire dismay; when the city was distraught by the struggles of the austere devotees of Savonarola and the gay partizans of pleasure; when the mighty ones of the land were united against poor distracted Florence; when Piero de' Medici was conspiring to regain the power once held by Lorenzo the Magnificent; when finally Florence turned against Savonarola, and he met his death in ignominy or martyrdom, as one viewed it as foe or partizan. Across the scene there flit the figures of Pico della Mirandola, of Fra Bartolommeo, of Domenico Ghirlandajo, of Cosimo di Piero, of Poliziano, of Bernardo del Nero, of Strozzis and Tornabuonis, of Niccolo Machiavelli, of a "promising youth named Michelangelo Buonarotti," and many others. All these make the setting for the lives of a woman and a man and the progress of their souls, the one upward and the other downward, as wonderfully drawn as ever human lives were portrayed by pen of man or woman.

Florence saw Tito Melema ever making his way upward from the

day when he found himself adrift after shipwreck, and was carried
to the market by the omnipresent Bratti, merchant and huckster,
and introduced to breakfast and a kiss from pretty little Tessa, and
passed under the deft hand of the wonder-working barber-philosopher
Nello. That shrewd craftsman with edged tools—razor or tongue—
introduced him to the bright and powerful folk who frequented his
shop as if it were a club, and brought him to the notice of the blind
scholar Bardo, who needed just such a clever young student as Tito
for a helper. From that his path was easy to the confidence of the
great; Latin secretary to the state, embassies to Rome, everything
was his, even to the envy of Niccolo Machiavelli. The world saw only
the dazzling success; there were a few who marked "the change that
came from the final departure of moral youthfulness," who saw the
perfidies and desertions of the dexterous and facile Greek, the base-
ness that smiles and triumphs; who knew how he had left to slavery
the adoptive father who had rescued him and made him what he was,
how he proved false to the memory of Romola's father, who set him
on his way to triumph in Florence, how he betrayed his great patrons, how he deceived poor Tessa, that "sweet, pouting, innocent,
round thing," how he threw away the great treasure of Romola's
love, and how his only bitter thought was that a timely, well-devised
falsehood might have saved him from every fatal consequence.

Over against the figure of the man she married stands Romola,
"fair as the Florentine lily before it got quarrelsome and turned
red," as the rhapsodic Nello described her. Her contempt of all injustice and meanness; the noble serenity with which she accepted,
though not without inward struggle, all that life and duty brought
her; the willing service she rendered her father, her husband, the
poor, the sufferers in the plague, Tito's abandoned father, even
Tessa, her rival to the title of wife, the mother of Tito's children; the
majestic self-possession which at the slightest touch on the fibers of
affection or pity could become passionate with tenderness—all this
justified her godfather, Bernardo del Nero, in his exhortation to her
father: "Remember, Bardo, thou hast a rare gem of thy own; take
care no man gets it who is not likely to pay a worthy price. That
pretty Greek has a lithe sleekness about him that seems marvelously
fitted for slipping easily into any nest he fixes his eyes upon."

But he that smiles and triumphs does not always triumph to the
end. He is sometimes found out. So it was with Tito. He had made

the last preparation for departure to a larger field of action. Pursued in the night by a crowd of angry men, he barely had time to leap from a bridge into the Arno. A long swim in the darkness—in the tumult of his blood he could only feel vaguely that he was safe and might land. But where? The current was having its way with him; he hardly knew where he was; exhaustion was bringing on the dreamy state that precedes unconsciousness.

But now there were eyes that discerned him—aged, strong for the distance. Baldassare—his father—looking up blankly from the search to which his poverty had led him, had seen a white object coming along the stream—could that be any fortunate chance for him? He looked and looked till the object gathered form; then he leaned forward with a start as he sat among the rank green stems, and his eyes seemed to be filled with a new light—yet he only watched—motionless. Something was being brought to him.

The next instant a man's body was cast violently on the grass two yards from him, and he started forward like a panther, clutching the velvet tunic as he fell forward on the body and flashed a look in the man's face.

Dead—was he dead? The eyes were rigid. But no, it could not be—justice had brought him. Men looked dead sometimes, and yet the life came back to them. Baldassare did not feel feeble in that moment. He knew just what he could do. He got his large fingers within the neck of the tunic and held them there, kneeling on one knee beside the body and watching the face. In his eyes there was only fierceness.

Rigid—rigid still. Those eyes with the half-fallen lids were locked against vengeance. Could it be that he was dead? Surely at last the eyelids were quivering; the eyes were no longer rigid. There was a vibrating light in them—they opened wide.

"Ah yes! You see me—you know me!"

Tito knew him; but he did not know whether it was life or death that had brought him into the presence of his injured father. It might be death—and death might mean this chill gloom with the face of the hideous past hanging over him forever.

But Baldassare's only dread was lest the young limbs should escape him. He pressed his knuckles against the round throat and knelt upon the chest with all the force of his aged frame. Let death come now!

THE SCARLET LETTER

by

NATHANIEL HAWTHORNE*

CONDENSATION BY GEORGE S. BARTON

One summer morning over two centuries ago the grass-plot before the jail in Prison Lane was occupied by many of the inhabitants of Boston. The door opened and the town beadle appeared, followed by a young woman carrying a baby about three months old. On the breast of her gown, in red cloth, appeared the letter A, and it was that scarlet letter which drew all eyes toward her.

The place appointed for her punishment was not far from the prison door, and in spite of the agony of her heart, Hester Prynne passed with almost a serene deportment to the scaffold where the pillory was set up, and under the weight of a thousand unrelenting eyes the unhappy prisoner sustained herself as best a woman might.

A small, intelligent appearing man on the outskirts of the crowd attracted Hester's attention, and he in turn eyed her till, seeing that she seemed to recognize him, he laid his finger on his lips.

Then, speaking to a townsman, he said, "I pray you, good sir, who is this woman, and wherefore is she here set up to public shame?"

"You must needs be a stranger, friend," said the townsman, "else you would have heard of Mistress Hester Prynne. She hath raised a great scandal in godly Master Dimmesdale's church. The penalty thereof is death, but the magistracy, in their mercy, have doomed her to stand a space of three hours on the platform of the pillory, and for the remainder of her life to wear a mask of shame in her bosom."

"A wise sentence!" remarked the stranger. "It irks me, never-theless, that the partner of her iniquity should not at least stand by her side. But he will be known—he will be known!"

The Rev. Mr. Dimmesdale, a young minister of high native gifts, who had already wide eminence in his profession, was urged to exhort Hester to repentance and confession. Addressing her, he advised

* For biographical information see page 153.

that she name her fellow-sinner even if he had to step from a high position to stand beside her, for it was better so than to hide a guilty heart through life.

Hester shook her head, keeping her place upon the pedestal of shame with an air of weary indifference.

That night her child writhered in convulsions, and a physician, Mr. Roger Chillingworth, none other than the stranger Hester had noticed in the crowd, was called. Having eased the baby's pain, he turned and said: "Hester, I ask not wherefore thou hast fallen into the pit. It was my folly and thy weakness. What had I—a man of thought—to do with youth and beauty like thine? I might have known that in my long absence this would happen."

"I have greatly wronged thee," murmured Hester.

"We have wronged each other," he answered. "But I shall seek this man whose name thou wilt not reveal, and sooner or later he must be mine. I shall contrive nothing against his life. Let him live. One thing, thou that wast my wife, I ask. Thou has kept his name secret. Keep likewise, mine. Let thy husband be to the world as one already dead, and breathe not the secret, above all, to the man thou wottest of."

"I will keep thy secret, as I have his."

Freed from prison, Hester did not flee, but established herself in a small cottage just outside the town, incurring no risk of want, for she possessed the art of needlework, which provided food for herself and child. She had named the little one "Pearl," as being of great price, and little Pearl grew up a lovely child. People wished to take her away, and the matter was discussed in the mother's presence by Governor Bellingham and his guests—Rev. John Wilson, Rev. Mr. Dimmesdale, and Doctor Chillingworth.

"God gave me the child!" cried Hester, and turning to the young clergyman, Mr. Dimmesdale, she exclaimed: "Speak thou for me. Thou wast my pastor. Thou knowest what is in my heart and what are a mother's rights, and how much the stronger they are when that mother has but her child and the scarlet letter! I will not lose the child! Look to it!"

"There is truth in what she says," began the minister. "There is a quality of awful sacredness between this mother and this child. It is good for this poor, sinful woman that she hath an infant confided to her care—to be trained by her to righteousness. Let us leave them as Providence hath seen fit to place them!"

"You speak, my friend, with a strange earnestness," said Roger Chillingworth, smiling at him.

"He hath adduced such arguments that we will even leave the matter as it now stands," said the governor. The affair being so satisfactorily concluded, Hester and Pearl departed.

Rev. Mr. Dimmesdale's health failing, he consulted Doctor Chillingworth. Taking him as a patient, the doctor decided to know the the man's inmost nature before trying to heal him. Arrangements were made for the two men to lodge together so that he might be constantly under the doctor's observation.

As Doctor Chillingworth proceeded with his investigation, begun, as he imagined, with the integrity of a judge desirous only of truth, a terrible fascination seized him and insisted that he do its bidding. He now dug into the poor clergyman's heart, like a miner seeking gold; and Mr. Dimmesdale grew to look at him with an unaccountable horror.

Often Mr. Dimmesdale tried to speak the truth of his past from the pulpit, but had cheated himself by confessing his sinfulness in general terms. Once, indulging in the mockery of repentance, he mounted the scaffold where Hester had stood. There was no danger of discovery, for every one was asleep. Even so he was surprised by Hester and Pearl, returning from a death-bed in the town, and presently by Roger Chillingworth.

"Who is that man?" gasped Mr. Dimmesdale, in terror. "I shiver at him, Hester. Canst thou do nothing for me? I have a nameless horror of the man."

Remembering her promise, Hester was silent.

"Worthy sir," said the doctor, advancing to the platform, "pious Master Dimmesdale! Can this be you? Come, good sir, I pray you, let me lead you home! You should study less, or these night-whimsies will grow upon you."

Hester now resolved to do what she could for the victim whom she saw in her former husband's grip. One day she met the old doctor in the woods, seeking herbs, and implored him to be merciful, saying that she must now reveal the secret of their former relationship, no matter what befell.

A week later Hester awaited the clergyman in the forest and told him about Roger Chillingworth and their relationship, bidding him hope for a new life beyond the sea in some rural village.

"Thou shalt not go alone," she whispered.

Arthur Dimmesdale attained the proudest eminence a New England clergyman could reach. He had preached the election sermon on the holiday celebrating the election of a new governor.

Hester had taken berths to England, and on the holiday the shipmaster informed her that Roger Chillingworth had booked passage on the same vessel; saying nothing, she turned and stood by the pillory with Pearl.

The minister, surrounded by leading townsmen, halted at the scaffold, and, calling Hester and Pearl to him, mounted the scaffold steps. Telling Hester he was a dying man and must hasten to assume his shame, he turned to the market-place and spoke with a voice that all could hear.

"People of New England! At last, at last I stand where seven years since I should have stood. Lo, the scarlet letter which Hester wears! Ye have all shuddered at it! But there stood one in the midst of you, at whose brand of sin ye have not shuddered."

With a convulsive motion he tore away the ministerial gown from before his breast. It was revealed! Then sinking down on the scaffold, he died, his head resting on Hester's bosom.

Afterward, conflicting accounts arose about the scene on the scaffold. Many testified to seeing a scarlet letter on the minister's bosom, while others denied it, saying that Dimmesdale's confession implied no part of Hester's guilt.

Roger Chillingworth died, bequeathing his property to Pearl.

Hester and Pearl lived in England for years, then, Pearl marrying, Hester returned alone to the little dwelling by the forest.

THE SEA WOLF*

by

JACK LONDON

CONDENSATION BY CLIFTON B. CARBERRY

JACK LONDON was born, with the love of adventure in his veins, at San Francisco, January 12, 1876. He began his education at the University of California, but did not finish it there, for the strenuous life was to be his school, and all humanity were to be his teachers, any strange place his school-room. Now he was in the Klondike; now at sea before the mast; then he was in Japan and seal-hunting in Bering Sea; again he was tramping through the United States and Canada, learning all he could of men and their ways; he was journalist and lecturer, war correspondent in the Russo-Japanese War, and ever and anon making those voyages which kept the eyes of the world upon him. How he broke into the realm of letters he has vividly described; his own great battle with John Barleycorn is told with unusual frankness. His own personality kept the great reading public as interested as did the creations of his imagination; his books came thick and fast, beginning with 1900, sometimes two and three a year. Naturally they were uneven, but through all his work glowed the genius of a born story-teller, a great heart, and a love for his fellows and their problems.

He was twice married, first to Bessie Maddern and second to Charmian Kittredge, who plays a large part in his later books. He died November 21, 1916.

The keen eyes of Wolf Larsen, master of the sealing-schooner *Ghost*, bound for Japanese poaching-grounds, spotted the bobbing head of Humphrey Van Weyden amid the waves of San Francisco

* Condensed from *The Sea Wolf* by Jack London. Copyright, 1904, by The Macmillan Company. Used by permission of author and publisher.

Bay, into whose waters Humphrey had been thrown as a result of a shipwreck. A few moments more and Humphrey was aboard the *Ghost*.

Rescued, he faced his rescuer with thanks and a request to be put ashore. The skipper eyed him curiously.

"What do you do for a living?" he asked.

"I—I am a gentleman," Humphrey stammered.

"Who feeds you?"

"I have an income."

Wolf Larsen's lips curled in a sneer.

"You stand on dead men's legs. You couldn't walk alone between two sunrises and hustle the meat for your belly for three meals. You stay here as cabin-boy for the good of your soul. I'll make a man of you."

Instant rebellion leaped into Humphrey's eyes. Before he could protest there came a sudden interruption—a clamor from the real cabin-boy, a great, husky youth who stood by. Wolf Larsen turned and crashed his fist into the boy's stomach. Crumpled like a wet rag around a stick, the lad collapsed into a heap on the deck.

"Well," said Wolf Larsen, meaningly, to Humphrey, "have you made up your mind?"

The spark of manhood in Humphrey died out.

"Yes," he replied, weakly.

"Say, 'Yes, sir!' "

"Yes, sir."

And thus Humphrey passed into the servitude of Wolf Larsen, the Sea Wolf. His blinking eyes, half revealing and half concealing his terror, surveyed his master and thus appraised him: "Massive of build, like a huge gorilla; with a strength savage and ferocious; features of no evil stamp; eyes of baffling protean gray, sometimes as chill as an Arctic landscape, sometimes all aglow with love-lights—intense, masculine, and compelling—which at the same time fascinate and dominate women until they surrender in a gladness of joy and of relief and sacrifice."

His creed, the mighty will which engined Wolf Larsen, was short.

"Life is a mess," he declared. "The big eat the little that they may continue to move; the strong eat the weak that they may retain their strength. The lucky eat the most and move the longest, that is all."

His company on shipboard: seamen sodden and sullen by drink, more animal than human; a group of seal-hunters, wild, reckless nomads, ignorant of an ordered world—all slaves in body and spirit to the Sea Wolf.

Yet there was a gentle side to Wolf Larsen. He was no ignorant cave-man. He could discuss literature with "Hump," roll over his lips the poetic glories of Shelley and Browning, argue the sciences with amazing fluency, and be disarmingly charming at times.

As the days rolled on and murderous quarrels made the hours hideous, Humphrey's backbone gradually stiffened. He dreamed of killing the Sea Wolf. But Larsen fascinated him and, like some splendid animal, some dangerous beast, held him in a spell. He knew the world should be rid of such a monster, yet Larsen's eyes compelled obedience.

Day by day, with not a gleam of graciousness to break the orgy of brutishness, this tragic drama went on. Humphrey despaired of even a gleam of sunshine. Suddenly fate intervened in the person of Maude Brewster.

Like Humphrey, she came to the *Ghost* from the sea, saved from a wrecked liner. Like Humphrey, she expected to be put aboard a passing vessel. But no! The Sea Wolf had other plans. She was added to the crew as Humphrey was, and likewise "for the good of her soul."

Maude received the news in wonderment. What kind of a man was this mocking master of the *Ghost?* She was soon to find out.

The cook had offended Larsen. A rope was coiled around the offender and he was cast overboard in the wake of the ship. A shark rushed for him and Larsen ordered him pulled in. Despite the maddened haste, the shark in the final rush tore away the foot of the victim.

"The shark was not in the reckoning, Miss Brewster," said the Sea Wolf, smilingly. "It was—shall we say—an act of Providence."

This scene convinced Humphrey that he must kill Wolf Larsen. His courage flared up so brightly that he actually threatened to murder him.

The Sea Wolf barked a whimsical guffaw: "Bravo, Hump! You do me proud. I like you the better for it."

Humphrey winced. He confided his resolution to Maude, with whom he had fallen in love. She counseled against it, protesting that moral courage always defeats brute force, but she failed to convince him. He knew the Sea Wolf too well.

The dancing lights in Wolf Larsen's eyes when he looked into Maude's warned Humphrey that some day the storm would break.

And it did. In the midst of the night he rushed into Maude's cabin to find her in the crushing embrace of Wolf Larsen.

Humphrey flung himself on the monster, to be tossed aside like a chip. He rushed again, drawing his knife, plunging the blade into the Sea Wolf's shoulder. Larsen staggered back and Maude seized Humphrey, begging him not to kill. Suddenly the Wolf collapsed, not from his wound, but as if from some uncanny spell that paralyzed him. The giant was helpless. Humphrey carried him to his berth and realized that opportunity for escape was at hand.

Maude and he put off in a small boat, hoping that they might make Japan, six hundred miles away. But the winds and creeping drift of the Pacific intervened and finally the grim adventure ended for a time on a little Arctic island. Here they prepared to remain for the winter.

Suddenly one morning, weeks after, Humphrey saw on the beach the wreck of a vessel, and it was strangely familiar. It could not be—yes it was—the *Ghost*. The blood chilled in his veins. Wild thoughts of flight or the sudden ending of both their lives entered his mind. Then a wondering cunning succeeded such fears. He would kill Wolf Larsen, kill him as he slept, for all on board were doubtless sleeping. With knife and gun he climbed to the deck. He saw no one. Was the ship deserted, after all?

But as he rounded the poop there burst on his gaze the Sea Wolf. Humphrey raised his gun; the trigger clicked sharply. Then silence.

"Why don't you shoot?" coolly remarked the Wolf.

Humphrey could not speak.

"Hump," said the Sea Wolf, slowly, "you can't do it. And after all I have taught you. You know that I would kill an unarmed man as readily as I would smoke a cigar. Bah! I had expected the better things of you, Hump."

Humphrey slowly lowered the gun.

The *Ghost's* presence was explained calmly by the Sea Wolf. He was caught in a net he had set for his hated brother, "Death" Larsen, his crew were taken away and he was left alone. Pacific storms did the rest.

A strange weariness in the Sea Wolf's bearing, a hesitant, pre-occupied air about him, puzzled Humphrey. A few days later he again summoned courage to put him out of the way. But this time he saw Wolf Larsen slowly making his way down the deck, his quivering finger-tips groping for the hand-rails.

Wolf Larsen was blind! No need to kill him.

Maude and Humphrey determined to escape by repairing the *Ghost,* but the Sea Wolf willed otherwise. Blind and helpless as he was, he craftily contrived to ruin Humphrey's work, determined they should all die together, so his grim revenge would be complete. Fiendish cunning and instinct to kill still remained.

A final reckoning was to come. Scorning precaution because he felt the Sea Wolf physically powerless from the suspected pressure of a tumor on the brain, Humphrey ventured too near one day. Suddenly the Sea Wolf's stupor passed. The steel-like fingers gripped Humphrey's throat. The trap had sprung.

Maude leaped into action, tearing at Larsen's hands. But for once the Sea Wolf's tremendous will could not spur his weakened body. His fingers twitched and then relapsed and Humphrey was released.

"That was the last play of the Wolf," said Larsen with his twisted smile. "I'd like to have done for you first, Hump. I thought I had that much left in me."

And so Wolf Larsen faded into unconsciousness, a pitiful ending for this grim sea murderer who pictured himself roaring to death in a blaze of tumult and evil splendor.

Soon the restored *Ghost* embraced the waves again, freighted with happiness. Then a trail of smoke on the horizon, a rescue, and the lovers' kiss as the cutter went dancing over the waves on the long road home.

A TALE OF TWO CITIES
by
CHARLES DICKENS*

CONDENSATION BY SARA A. HAMLIN

On a cold November night, in the year 1775, the English mail-coach, on its way from London to Dover, was carrying among its

* For biographical information see page 81.

passengers a Mr. Jarvis Lorry, a London banker of the well-known firm of Tellson & Co. As the coach stumbled along in the darkness, there arose before him the vision of an emaciated figure with hair prematurely white. All night between him and the specter the same words repeated themselves again and again:

"Buried how long?"

"Almost eighteen years."

"I hope you care to live?"

"I can't say."

About eighteen years before the story opens, Doctor Manette, a prominent young physician of Paris, had suddenly disappeared. Everything was done to discover some trace of him, but in vain. The loss of her husband caused his wife such anguish that she resolved to bring up her little daughter in ignorance of her father's fate; and when in two years she died she left little Lucie under the guardianship of Tellson & Co., to whose care Doctor Manette for many years had intrusted his financial affairs.

Strange tidings concerning the doctor had just come from Paris, and Mr. Lorry was on his way to meet his ward and explain to her the facts of her early life. This was a duty from which the kind-hearted banker shrank, and when he saw the slight, golden-haired girl who came to meet him his heart almost failed him; but his task was accomplished at last.

"And now," concluded Mr. Lorry, "your father has been found. He is alive, greatly changed, but alive. He has been taken to the house of a former servant in Paris, and we are going there. I, to identify him, you to restore him to life and love."

The servant that sheltered Doctor Manette was a man by the name of Defarge who, with his wife, kept a wine-shop in the obscure district of St.-Antoine. The banker and Lucie were taken to an attic, where a haggard, white-haired man sat on a low bench, making shoes, a wreck of a man oblivious of all around him.

Again was the Channel crossed, and again the old inquiry whispered in the ear of Jarvis Lorry:

"I hope you care to be recalled to life?"

"I can't say."

Five years later, in the court-room of the Old Bailey in London, a young Frenchman was on trial for his life. Near him sat an untidy looking individual by the name of Sydney Carton. With his eyes fixed on the ceiling, he was unobservant, apparently, of all that passed around him; but it was he, who first noticing the extraordinary resemblance between the prisoner and himself, rescued Charles Darnay from the web of deceit which had been spun around him.

Between these two young men the striking resemblance was in outward appearance only. Charles Darnay was of noble birth; but his ancestors had for many years so cruelly oppressed the French peasantry that the name of Evremonde was hated and despised. Wholly unlike them in character, this last descendant of his race had given up his name and estate and had come to England as a private gentleman, eager to begin life anew.

Sydney Carton was a young English lawyer, brilliant in intellect, but steadily deteriorating through his life of dissipation, able to advise others, but unable to guide himself, "conscious of the blight on him and resigning himself to let it eat him away."

He and Darnay soon became frequent visitors at the small house in Soho Square, the home of Doctor Manette and his daughter. Through Lucie's care and devotion, the doctor had almost wholly recovered from the effects of his long imprisonment, and it was only in times of strong excitement that any trace of his past insanity could be detected. The sweet face of Lucie Manette soon won the hearts of both the young men, but it was Darnay to whom she gave her love.

And so that interview between Lucie and Sydney Carton has a pathos that wrings our hearts. He knew that even if his love could have been returned, it would have added only to his bitterness and sorrow, for he felt it would have been powerless to lift him from the Slough of Selfishness and Sensuality that had engulfed him. But he could not resist this last sad confession of his love; and when she weeps at the sorrow of which she had been the innocent cause, he implores: "Do not weep, dear Miss Manette, the life I lead renders me unworthy of your pure love. My last supplication is this, think now and then that there is a man who would give his life to keep a life you love beside you."

But dark days were to come. In the year 1789 the downtrodden French peasantry turned upon their oppressors. The streets of Paris were filled with crowds of people whose eager cry was for "blood." Madame Defarge no longer sat behind the counter of her small wineshop, silently knitting into her work the names of her hated enemies, but, ax in hand and knife at her belt, headed a frenzied mob of women on to the Bastille. The French Revolution had actually begun.

Madame Defarge was one of the leading spirits of the Revolution. Early in life she had seen her family fall victims to the tyranny and lust of the cruel nobility, and from that time her life had been devoted to revenge.

Three years of crime and bloodshed passed, and in 1792 Mr. Jarvis Lorry and Charles Darnay landed in Paris, the former to protect the French branch of Tellson & Co. and the latter to befriend an old family servant who had besought his help. Not until they had set foot in Paris did they realize into what a caldron of fury they had plunged. Mr. Lorry, on account of his business relations, was allowed his freedom, but Darnay was hurried at once to the prison of La Force, there to await his trial. The reason given for this outrage was the new law for the arrest of all returning French emigrants, but the true cause was that he had been recognized as Charles Evremonde.

These tidings soon reached London, and Doctor Manette, with his daughter Lucie, hastened to Paris, for he felt sure that his long confinement in the Bastille would win for him the sympathy of the French people and thus enable him to save his son-in-law. Days and months passed; and although the doctor succeeded in gaining a promise that Darnay's life should be spared, the latter was not allowed to leave his prison.

At last came the dreadful year of the Reign of Terror. The sympathy which at first had been given to Doctor Manette had become weakened through the influence of the bloodthirsty Madame Defarge. Also, there had been found in the ruins of the Bastile a paper which contained Doctor Manette's account of his own abduction and imprisonment, and pronouncing a solemn curse upon the House of Evremonde and their descendants, who were declared to be the authors of his eighteen years of misery. Charles Darnay's doom was sealed. "Back to the Conciergerie and death within twenty-four hours."

To Sydney Carton, who had followed his friends to Paris, came an inspiration. Did he not promise Lucie that he would die to save a life she loved? By bribery he gains admittance to the prison; Darnay is removed unconscious from the cell, and Carton sits down to await his fate.

Along the Paris streets six tumbrels are carrying the day's wine to La Guillotine. In the third car sits a young man with his hands bound. As the cries from the street arise against him, they only move him to a quiet smile as he shakes more loosely his hair about his face.

Crash! A head is held up, and the knitting women who are ranged about the scaffold count "One."

The third cart comes up, and the supposed Evremonde descends. His lips move, forming the words, "a life you love."

The murmuring of many voices, the upturning of many faces, then all flashes away.

"Twenty-three!"

" 'I am the resurrection and the life,' saith the Lord; 'he that believeth in me, though he were dead, yet shall he live; and whosoever liveth and believeth in me shall never die.' "

⚬⚬⚬

TESS OF THE D'URBERVILLES*

by

THOMAS HARDY†

CONDENSATION BY RUTH MC CALL

"Good morning, Sir John." The bewilderment of a dusty, threadbare peddler thus addressed was speedily converted into a majestic pride upon learning that he, John Durbeyfield of Marlott, was actually a lineal descendant of the noble family of D'Urberville.

And no sooner had Joan, his handsome, shallow-minded wife, the easy-going mother of his many children, heard of her exalted estate than her romantic soul began secretly to devise a brilliant and fitting alliance for her beautiful young daughter. To which end Tess was artfully prevailed upon to seek work in a wealthy upstart family of the same illustrious name.

And so the innocent child, whose single-minded desire was to mend the broken fortunes of her family, became poultrykeeper for a blind old woman of spurious title and ultimate prey for her son, a dissolute wretch, young Alec D'Urberville. After a while back to

* Printed by permission of, and arrangement with, Harper & Bros., authorized publishers.

† For biographical information see page 111.

Marlott, came the disillusioned girl, where she lived in a gray seclusion until her wizened little baby's death.

But after several bitter years of heart-searching, Tess determined to leave home again—this time to be dairymaid at Talbothays, a large, fertile farm in the valley of the Great Dairies. And here, too, was a young man, the youngest son of a stern and zealous divine of the old school. Angel Clare had sadly disappointed his father, first by nonconformist views and then by sincere scruples against taking orders. So now, in process of becoming gentleman farmer, he was specializing at various farms. Cultured, idealistic, sympathetic, he seemed to Tess a demigod, and though she had sworn herself to celibacy, the enforced propinquity ripened into intimacy and drifted into love. Together they went afield in the wondrous dewy dawns and the warm summer afternoons found them making butter and cheese in the cool, white dairy-house. The birds sang for them and for them the stars shone, and the whole verdant valley, teeming with richness and increase, gave up its odorous vapors. Young, happy, pagan-hearted, the universe was theirs. Her quick mind grew in contact with his, and her warm, rich voice lost its country speech and unconsciously adopted his cultured accents.

Tess's specter loomed but vaguely now, until love's honest declaration brought her to poignant realization of her situation in this man-made world. But all withdrawals were overcome by Clare's gentle insistence; all attempts at revelation were lightly thwarted. Finally, within a week of the wedding-day which she had reluctantly set, her resolution takes shape in writing—a four-page confession is breathlessly thrust under his door. Ironically concealed under the carpet it lies until Tess, with a sudden late intuition on her wedding morn, discovers its hiding-place and tears it up. In a lumbering old relic of coach days (symbolic of an ancient D'Urberville legend of crime) Tess and Angel are carried to church, and upon their final departure a white cock crows thrice. "An afternoon crow," and the dairy folk shake their heads at the evil omen.

To an old farm-house—a derelict of an ancient D'Urberville mansion—in ready range of a model mill, Clare, with a sense of the practical and the romantic, takes his lovely bride. From the paneled wall outside her door two old D'Urberville portraits gleam evilly and Clare and Tess shiver as they trace a subtle likeness to her own in the malignant yet noble features. Before the glowing fire the adoring bridegroom, his wife's hand clasped in his, tells the story of his one aberration, of his forty-eight hours' dissipation with a Scarlet Woman, and confidently craves her pardon, which Tess is only too delighted to grant; and, with the first real gleam of hope, unfolds her own sad story. . . .

The wanton action of a man of maturity—the deceived innocence of an ignorant child! And yet, the man cannot forgive the woman! All the rigid rule of his forebears, all the domination of an unjust social order, grip him. Angel Clare, the prophet of emancipation, no longer exists. For several days they lead a formal, isolated existence. Tess, whose sole wish is to please her idol, acquiesces in his attitude, and, after a first wild outburst at the injustice, does nothing to exonerate herself, and her one chance for reinstatement is blighted by the mocking witness of the vindictive portraits. No chaste-minded, unsophisticated peasant maid she, but the last dregs of a decadent stock! A separation, temporary at least, is decided upon, and while Clare rages afar, Tess again creeps home. Joan, after the first bitter reproaches for the mad disobedience of her repeated injunctions of secrecy, treats the affair with her usual fatalistic light-heartedness; but the harsh words of the father in a drunken moment of excessive ancestral pride cause a dignified departure with the conciliatory donation of half her means of subsistence and the intimation that she is rejoining her husband.

Determined, however, to make no appeal to Clare's family, Tess easily finds summer employment among the farms; but with the coming of winter and too lavish contributions to her family's support, privation stares her in the face. Day after day she wanders on until at length on the high, chalky table-lands, in a great drab field of desolation, she finds the meanest, most arduous of tasks rendered tenfold difficult by a churlish boor of an employer in all the rancor of an ancient grudge against her. In the stinging rain and the chilling snow she toils unceasingly, uncomplainingly, living wholly in the hope of her husband's return. Songs that he loved she practices, the sweet, gay notes contrasting sadly with her tragic lips and great, sorrowing eyes. At length, distraught by the continued silence, she bravely decides to seek news of him from his parents, and walks the long, tremulous miles to Emminister Vicarage. Of rare spiritual as well as physical endowments, she would have undoubtedly received a welcome at the hands of the benevolent old clergyman and his wife, but an empty house reverberates to her knocking, and while she unobtrusively awaits their return from church she overhears a wayside conversation between Angel's two exemplary brothers that sends her homeward with rendered heart.

The voice of a "ranter" triumphantly consigning a barnful of rustics to eternal damnation caused Tess to pause a moment in a doorway, and there on a platform of corn-bags, in sanctimonious side-whiskers and semi-clerical blacks, stood Alec D'Urberville. Animalism had yielded to fanaticism and the bold, roving eye now gleamed with a ferocious righteousness. As she passed on down the lane he came after her, imploring forgiveness and offering redemption. Repulse after repulse failed to deter Alec, who persisted day by day, at first with a marriage license and holy words, and then, his former passion uncontrollably revived by Tess's compelling beauty, his new-found religion dropped from him like a cloak, the convert disappeared, and all the arts of man and devil were employed to ensnare the girl. And poor, hopeless Tess, grinding on under a benumbing strain, was in more danger than her scorn of the man could realize. Finally her father's death, resulting in the eviction of her family from their home, precipitates Tess's doom, and as a last desperate reparation to her helpless mother and sisters she yields, with a fatalistic calm, to the inevitable.

To Sandbourne, a gay watering-place, a melancholy specter of a man, wasted by illness and regret, comes in search of his lost bride, and in a fashionable boarding-house Clare finds Tess and learns the agonizing truth. Just beyond the town she overtook him, her eyes wild and trancelike, her whole body as if bereft of soul and will. "I have killed him . . . he taunted me . . . he called you by a foul name. . . . I owed it to you and I owed it to myself. . . . It came to me as a shining light that I should get you back that way."

With a final realization of the immensity of her love and the piteous plight it had brought upon her, Clare held out tender, protecting arms, and together they wandered through the untrodden ways like two children—the world and its retribution quite forgot.

For five days they continued in this idyllic state, and on the sixth night Tess half jestingly claimed sanctuary among the conspicuous ruins of the ancient pagan temple to the sun at Stonehenge. With the dawn came the guardians of the law, looming dark against the silvery horizon. In a grim, inexorable circle they waited until the sun's level rays, relentlessly reminiscent of a bygone sacrificial day, fell full upon another victim, and Tess, deserted by all the gods, awoke. Quietly she faced her captors. "I am ready," she said.

Eight metallic strokes shiver the morning air and from a near-by hill a stricken figure rivets involuntary eyes on the flag-staff of a sullen cage of a building. For Angel the prison where Tess is confined has at this fatal hour a deadly and significant fascination. Slowly, silently, a black square creeps up the pole and flutters chill against the morning sky.

Tess, more sinned against than sinning, has paid the great penalty.

THE THREE MUSKETEERS

by

ALEXANDRE DUMAS*

CONDENSATION BY CAPT. ANDRÉ MORIZE

"All for one; and one for all!"

This was the oath of the four comrades: of d'Artagnan, the young guardsman, and of Athos, Porthos, and Aramis, the three musketeers.

Only three months had d'Artagnan been in Paris, yet already he was the chosen companion of the noblest three in M. de Treville's picked company of Musketeers, in the service of Louis XIII. A true Gascon, fiercely proud, ready to fight at a word, the eighteen-year-old provincial lad had won the respect of the glorious three by challenging them, and their friendship by helping them to drive off the cardinal's guards who would have arrested them for dueling. Indeed, this latter exploit had won for d'Artagnan more than a glance from the king himself, who was not displeased to see Richelieu's men worsted by his own.

At Meung, even before reaching Paris, d'Artagnan had had an honorable encounter, his adversary being a tall, commanding stranger of olivine complexion and scarred on the cheek. A beautiful woman had accompanied this man. Both their faces were stamped on d'Artagnan's memory.

* For biographical information see page 57.

Before he could be admitted to the Musketeers d'Artagnan was to serve probation as a guardsman; but already he was a Musketeer in spirit and his comrades longed as keenly as he for the day when he would be allowed to join their company. Athos, Porthos, and Aramis were alike only in soldierly qualities. Athos was of noble bearing, and when he was drunk he would talk of a secret sorrow; Porthos was a great lover of ladies, and declared that his conquests would bring his downfall; Aramis, who had friends in the Church and a sweetheart at court, pretended that he was only temporarily a Musketeer, and would willingly change his plumed hat for a monk's cowl when the time came.

One day d'Artagnan's landlord, Bonancieux, burst into the room with news that Mme. Bonancieux, a pretty seamstress in the service of the queen, had just been abducted. From the landlord's description d'Artagnan recognized the abductor as his man of Meung and was anxious to help, the more so when he learned that the object of the abduction was to force the lady to tell what she knew of the love-affair between the queen and George Villiers, Duke of Buckingham, who was coming secretly to Paris.

It was in their resolve to protect Mme. Bonancieux, for whom the impressionable d'Artagnan had suddenly conceived an undying affection, that the four comrades came together in their oath.

"Remember," said Aramis, "henceforth we are at issue with the cardinal."

Aided by d'Artagnan, who fought off the cardinal's officers, the lady contrived to escape. He declared his love for her, but she would promise nothing. Next time he saw her she was conducting the Duke of Buckingham, disguised as a musketeer, toward the royal palace. If d'Artagnan had followed he would have learned that the queen did indeed love Buckingham, but was loyal to the king. As a token she gave Buckingham twelve diamond studs that the king had given her.

A spy reported this to Richelieu, who saw in it an opportunity to attack the king, the queen, and the duke all at once. First Richelieu asked the king to give a ballet for the queen and to ask her to wear the diamond studs, and then he sent a message to Lady de Winter in London, telling her to steal two of the studs from Buckingham. Learning of this plot through Mme. Bonancieux, d'Artagnan resolved to serve both his lady and his queen by recovering the jewels. For London the four comrades set out. Beset by the cardinal's men on the road, three were wounded, and only d'Artagnan reached London. There was just time to replace the stolen studs and return to Paris, which d'Artagnan reached on the night of the ballet, foiling Richelieu's plot.

He now set out to find his comrades. Porthos he found in bed at an inn, Aramis disputing with doctors of theology, and Athos drunk in a wine-cellar, airing his secret sorrow and defying the landlord to eject him. In his youth, Athos confessed, he had been tricked into marriage with a beautiful fiend, who, he later discovered, carried on her shoulder the executioner's brand, the fleur-de-lys. Horror-stricken, he had slain her.

In church next day d'Artagnan's eye was caught by a very beautiful lady whom he recognized as the one who had been with the stranger at Meung. Following her from the church, he saw her talking with an Englishman, and, drawing close, he heard her call this man her brother-in-law, Lord de Winter.

D'Artagnan fell deeply in love with Lady de Winter, but his ardor cooled when he learned that she was a cardinalist plotter. By a trick he obtained from her a sapphire ring, which he showed to Athos.

"Where did you get this?" cried Athos. "It was my mother's."

D'Artagnan told him.

"Renounce that woman," said Athos. "She is a fatal creature."

That night d'Artagnan accused Lady de Winter of treachery. She rushed upon him and, in avoiding her blow, he pulled her dress from her shoulder.

There was the executioner's brand—the fleur-de-lys.

At this time the war between England and France was at its height and the siege of La Rochelle was beginning. Richelieu, learning all that d'Artagnan had done, tried to buy him into his own service. D'Artagnan refused, knowing that refusal might cost him his life. The three musketeers set out now to discover the cardinal's next move. Eavesdropping, they heard Richelieu instruct Lady de Winter to go to London and there tell Buckingham to order that the English surrender, warning him that if the war continued Richelieu would expose the queen. If Buckingham refused, he was to be assassinated. For her part, the lady asked Richelieu for the death of d'Artagnan, who knew her secret, and of Mme. Bonancieux, who had thwarted her so often.

Half an hour later Athos was alone with the woman.

"The Count de la Fère!" she cried, deathly pale.

"Yes, my lady," said Athos. "You thought me dead, as I thought you dead, and the name of Athos concealed the Count de la Fère, as the name of Lady de Winter concealed Anne de Breuil."

Athos took from his false wife the carte-blanche passport Richelieu had given her and sent her to the coast, where a boat waited to take her to England. She could not disobey, knowing that Athos could expose her.

Back to the siege the four comrades then went, and, in order to be together to discuss their plans, they spent an hour in the Bastion of St. Gervais, withstanding all assaults. Between attacks they talked and as a result they sent messages to Lord de Winter exposing his false sister-in-law and heiress, and to an influential friend of Aramis, asking for the name of the convent where Mme. Bonancieux was confined.

Thus on her arrival in England Lady de Winter was seized and imprisoned in her brother-in-law's castle; but, exercising her wiles upon her young jailer, she contrived to escape, and so poisoned the jailer's ears against Buckingham that he was ready to do her deadly work. Sent by de Winter as a messenger to the duke, he plunged a dagger into Buckingham's side. De Winter arrived in London one minute too late to save the duke, but a messenger from Paris was just in time to deliver to Buckingham the queen's pledge of love. He died with the queen's name on his lips.

Now Mme. de Winter had fled to France—to the convent of Bethune, where Mme. Bonancieux was. By poison she accomplished her purpose, and when d'Artagnan and his comrades arrived at the convent they found the body of the pretty seamstress. They set out in pursuit of the murderess, and when they found her they held a formal trial and condemned her to death. An executioner was found —the very man who had put the brand upon her shoulder years before.

The next day d'Artagnan was arrested and taken before the cardinal, his captor being none other than his "man of Meung," who now called himself the Chevalier de Rochefort. D'Artagnan told the cardinal of the crimes of Lady de Winter, and finally produced the cardinal's own passport, absolving the bearer.

Admiration overcame anger in the cardinal. Instead of ordering d'Artagnan's imprisonment, he wrote out there and then a lieutenant's commission in the Musketeers. D'Artagnan offered the commission to his three friends in turn. All three refused it, protesting they did not deserve it. Besides, Aramis announced that he was about to enter the Church, and Porthos said he was about to be married. Athos thereupon wrote upon the blank commission the name of d'Artagnan.

As for Rochefort, d'Artagnan fought him many times, but at last they decided that they were both too good to die, and they became friends.

❧❀❧

THE TOILERS OF THE SEA

by

VICTOR HUGO*

CONDENSATION BY JAMES B. CONNOLLY

One Christmas morning, Deruchette, a charming young girl, wrote the name of a man, Gilliatt, in the snow. Gilliatt, seeing the name and knowing who wrote it, never forgot.

Gilliatt was a young man of doubtful birth and unpopular disposition who lived by himself in an old wreck of a house in St. Sampson in the Isle of Guernsey. He was a fisherman; also a carpenter, a wheelwright, a sort of engineer when need be. He was also a dreamer of dreams.

Deruchette lived with her uncle, Mess Lethierry, a man at once good-natured, intolerant, superstitious, and progressive. In his wandering days Lethierry had befriended Rantaine, an adventurer, who repaid his kindness by running off with 50,000 francs of Lethierry's, the savings of forty years and intended for Deruchette's dowry.

However, Deruchette had still his steamboat, the *Durande*. She at least would not fail him. Other steamboats failed, but not his *Durande*—this because of her wonderful engines. The master of the *Durande* was Sieur Clubin, who had built up a reputation for high respectability. He was a capable, prudent seaman and a wonderful swimmer. Also he was a man who knew how to bide his time.

* For biographical information see page 235.

In one of his trips to the mainland Clubin encountered the thief Rantaine as he was about to leave the country with a fortune of 75,000 francs. At the point of a revolver Clubin took from Rantaine the 75,000 francs, and at once, although it was foggy, set sail in the *Durande* for St. Sampson.

The *Durande* was wrecked on some rocks in the Channel. Clubin disembarked his passengers and crew in the long-boat. For himself, he would go down with his ship. The passengers and crew, arriving safely in St. Sampson, were loud in their praise of the heroic captain.

All Lethierry's hopes for Deruchette had lain in the *Durande*. He besought men to out to the wreck to see if there was hope for her or if Clubin remained alive. They went, Gilliatt first of all, and returned to report that no Clubin was there and that the *Durande* was hopelessly wrecked. Only her engines remained intact.

Her engines! The word roused Lethierry from his despair. Her engines! His engines, which he had designed himself! They were the real value of the ship! If he could but recover the engines! But how? What man could devise the means to save them? The superhuman being who could do that, why—he should marry Deruchette.

A man pushed his way through the crowd surrounding Mess Lethierry and his niece. "You would marry him to Deruchette?" said the man. It was Gilliatt.

Mess Lethierry raised a solemn hand. "I pledge myself to it in God's name!"

Next day Gilliatt set sail. With extraordinary skill he maneuvered to the one spot near the wreck where it might be possible to moor his sloop. This nook was four hundred yards from the wreck, too far for the sleeping-place of a man who had not a minute to waste. Yet he could not bunk on the hull of the *Durande*—a sea might come in the night and sweep him away.

He discovered a little plateau on the top of one of the Douvres pinnacles. He ascended the pinnacle by means of a knotted cord; every time he made his way up or down he risked his life, but there his bed must be, for time was everything. And for weeks he lived on the Douvres rocks at his work—work that demanded the knowledge of a sailor, a carpenter, an engineer, a blacksmith.

Incredible toil! To repair pulley-blocks and construct hoisting-tackle; to reshape broken joists and make old sails into twine; to cut iron bars into files and long spikes; to take apart and stow the paddle-wheels; to resharpen hatchets and renew saw teeth—these were but the beginning of his preparations.

And more than toil. Part of the food which he had brought with him was washed into the sea, and he dared not leave the wreck unguarded to sail to Guernsey for a fresh supply; so he gathered the tiny shell-fish from the rocks and hunted the crabs which ran in and out of crevices.

One day he pursued a crab into a cave. While peering about, up to his waist in water, he felt something rough, cold, slimy coil itself around his right arm. Its pressure was like a tightening cord, its steady persistence like that of a screw. A second cold coil wound itself around his body; a third, a fourth, a fifth lashed themselves around him. He could scarcely breathe.

Suddenly a round slimy mass darted toward him. It was the head of the devilfish.

Gilliatt had his knife; his left arm was still free. The monster stretched out a sixth tentacle for the free arm, which would mean Gilliatt's sure death; but with one superb circular stroke Gilliatt whipped off the slimy head. The tentacles relaxed, fell away; he was dead.

Gilliatt had still to get his crab. He looked into the deeper recesses of the cave and found the skeleton of a man. Around the ribs was a leather belt. On the belt was a name, Clubin. Attached to the belt was a flat, tightly sealed little iron box. Within the box were three sheets of paper, Bank of England notes of 1,000 each; in all, 75,000 francs.

But the engines were what he had come for. He toiled on, and one evening he sailed into St. Sampson and tied his sloop, weighted down with the *Durande's* engines, to Lethierry's wharf. He hummed a plaintive air which he had once heard Deruchette play on her piano.

It was five years since Gilliatt had first seen Deruchette. In all that time he had never spoken to her. He knew her as men know the morning star, at a distance. Once, seeing her with her uncle— he had dared to pass quite near. He fancied that she smiled.

He walked noiselessly now toward Lethierry's house. He saw above him the windows of Deruchette's room. In the garden he saw Deruchette herself. A nightingale was singing. The night was inexpressibly silent.

There was some one with Deruchette. It was a man, the young Episcopalian curate whose life, Gilliatt recalled, he had once saved from the high tide of the Gild-Holm-'Ur rock. The curate had offered him a sovereign, which Gilliatt had refused, saying it was no matter. The curate had then pressed upon him a Bible.

The curate had the beauty of a pale head and face of a pictured angel. He spoke a language which echoed the rhythm of the sacred Psalms. He spoke now. Deruchette spoke. Their speech was of love. They embraced. Gilliatt stole off in the night.

Lethierry was transported at the recovery of his wonderful engines. "I will build a hull around them," he said. "I shall have to borrow, but my credit is good. Only for that villain of a Clubin— see, here is a note from Rantaine. He gave Clubin for me, he says, seventy-five thousand francs, equal to what he stole from me with interest."

"Here," said Gilliatt, "are the seventy-five thousand francs." He handed Lethierry the little iron box with the three 1,000 notes.

Lethierry embraced him. "You more-than-man!" he exclaimed. "You shall marry Deruchette at once!"

"I shall not marry Deruchette."

Lethierry insisted. He stormed. Gilliatt was like iron. Lethierry grew redder, Gilliatt paler. Gilliatt had his way. Deruchette and the curate were married. They set sail for England on the packet *Cashmere*.

Gilliatt crossed at low tide on the stones which led to Gild-Holm-'Ur rock to see the *Cashmere* pass. The tide was coming in, but the *Cashmere* was coming out. She moved slowly in the light breeze. The tide crept up on Gild-Holm-'Ur, but Gilliatt's eyes were for the *Cashmere*. The tide crept higher—to Gilliatt's knees—but in a spot of sunlight on the *Cashmere* were Deruchette and the curate. Her head was on his shoulder, his arm around her waist. There was a silence like the calm of heaven on the sea.

The packet passed on. She was beyond the waters of the harbor. The tide was then to Gilliatt's shoulders, but the packet was still within sight. She became a spot in the haze. The spot dwindled, disappeared. As she vanished the head of Gilliatt was engulfed.

Nothing was visible but the sea.

TOM BROWN'S SCHOOL DAYS

by

THOMAS HUGHES

CONDENSATION BY PROF. WILLIAM FENWICK HARRIS

THOMAS HUGHES was born October 20, 1822, at Uffington, Berks. He died March 22, 1896. In 1834 his father sent Tom to Rugby to be under the charge of Doctor Arnold; the doctor and the father had been fellow-students at Oriel College, Oxford. Both school and master were made well-known by the book, "Tom Brown's School Days." Tom Hughes must have been very much the same sort of schoolboy as the hero of the story, but in fact, George, his brother, was the original of Tom, as Dean Stanley was the original of Arthur.

Thomas Hughes followed in his father's footsteps at Oriel; he was later called to the bar, and eventually was appointed a county court judge.

His life was one of true service to humanity; Frederick Maurice was the great influence that worked upon him, and he was of the group, along with Charles Kingsley, who devoted themselves to the cause of the Workingmen's College. He sat in Parliament, always a devoted friend of his friends, the workingmen; he tried his hand at an idealistic colony, called Rugby, in Tennessee; he was a frequent visitor to America, and was a great friend and admirer of James Russell Lowell, whose influence over him is shown in the frequent quotations in his books. His other volumes included a sequel to "Tom Brown's School Days," "Tom Brown at Oxford," "Religio Laici," and his "Memoir of a Brother." But he will always be remembered as the sane and greathearted author who has understood something of the soul of

*a schoolboy, and who has written the greatest book in Eng-
lish of the schoolboy's life.*

"Just as Tom was swallowing his last mouthful (three o'clock in
the morning), winding his comforter round his throat, and tucking
the ends into the breast of his coat, the horn sounds, Boots looks
in and says, 'Tally-ho, sir,' and they hear the ring and the rattle of
the four fast trotters and the townmade drag as it dashes up to the
Peacock.

" 'Anything for us, Bob?' says the burly guard, dropping down
from behind, and slapping himself across the chest.

" 'Young gen'l'm'n, Rugby,' answers a hostler.

" 'Tell young gent to look alive,' says the guard, opening the hind-
boots and shooting the parcels in after examining them by the lamps.
'Here, shove the portmanteau up atop—I'll fasten him presently.
Now there, sir, jump up behind.'

" 'Good-by, father—my love at home.' A last shake of the hand.
Up goes Tom, the guard catching his hatbox and holding on with one
hand, while with the other he claps the horn to his mouth. Toot,
toot, toot! the hostlers let go their heads, the four bays plunge at the
collar, and away goes the Tally-ho into the darkness, forty-five sec-
onds from the time they had pulled up."

So Tom Brown started to begin his school days at Rugby when
William the Fourth sat upon his throne. Squire Brown had meditated
something as follows the night before: "Shall I tell him to mind his
word and to make himself a good scholar? Well, but he isn't sent
to school for that—at any rate, not for that mainly. I don't care a
straw for Greek particles or the digamma; no more does his mother.
What is he sent to school for? Well, partly because he wanted so
to go. If he'll only turn out a brave, helpful, truth-telling Englishman, and a gentleman, and a Christian, that's all I want." Upon
this view of the case he framed his last words to Tom. "And now,
Tom, my boy, remember you are going at your own earnest request,
to be chucked into this great school, like a young bear with all your
troubles before you—earlier than we should have sent you perhaps."
(Tom was nine.) "If schools are what they were in my time, you'll
see a great many cruel blackguard things done and hear a deal of
foul bad talk. But never fear. You tell the truth, keep a brave and
kind heart, and never listen, or say anything you wouldn't have your

mother and sister hear, and you'll never feel ashamed to come home, or we to see you."

Tom's father was a great asset to the boy. For though he belonged to what is called the upper middle class, the opinion which the squire loved to propound above all others was the belief that a man is to be valued wholly and solely for that which he is in himself, for that which stands up in the four fleshy walls of him, apart from clothes, rank, fortune, and all externals whatsoever. He held, further, that it didn't matter a straw whether his son associated with lords' sons or plowmen's sons, provided they were brave and honest. So Tom had a merry and right democratic time with the boys of the village, and learned much that stood him in good stead when he got to Rugby, among other things to value man or boy wholly for what was in him, whether it was Harry Winburn, the quickest and best boy in the parish, who taught him the turns and holds which later carried him through his great fight with the bully of Rugby; or poor Jacob Doodle-calf (as the boys nicknamed him), in whose hands everything came to pieces and in whose head nothing would stick, or Job Rudkin, whose scandalized mother demanded, on the occasion of a visit from Madam Brown, "Job, Job, where's thy cap?"

"What! beant 'e on ma head, mother?" replied Job, slowly extricating one hand from a pocket and feeling for the article in question, which he found on his head and left there, to his mother's horror and Tom's great delight.

Rugby was a new world for Tom. He was a sturdy and combative urchin, able to fend for himself on his own heath; yet it was a great boon for him that he fell into the hands of a boy of his own age, but a bit ahead of him at Rugby. The first sight he encountered on his arrival was a lordly crowd of youngsters who looked quite as if they owned the place. One of these young heroes ran out from the rest and accosted Tom. "I say, you fellow, is your name Brown?"

"Yes," said Tom, in considerable astonishment, glad, however, to have lighted on some one already who seemed to know him.

"Ah, I thought so; you know my old aunt, Miss East; she lives somewhere down your way in Berkshire. She wrote to me that you were coming to-day, and asked me to give you a lift. You see," said his friend, as they strolled up toward the school gates, "a great deal depends on how a fellow cuts up at first. If he's got nothing odd about him, and answers straightforward and holds his head up, he gets on. You see, I'm doing the handsome thing by you because my father knows yours; besides, I want to please the old lady. She gave me half a sov this half, and perhaps 'll double it next if I keep in her good books."

Thus began a friendship which lasted through all their school days and meant much to both of them. Friendship and loyalty and good sportsmanship are great features in this book, which shows an insight into the brain and heart of a boy which is just as wise in the year of our Lord 1920 as it was in the days of William the Fourth. Tom and East were together in games, in mischief, in fights, in good deeds, or in deviltry, as they were in ingenious syndicating methods of working out the mysteries of the Greek and Latin languages. And years later, when the wise "Doctor," Arnold of Rugby, decided that Tom was headed toward destruction, it was by means of friendship for a weaker boy who needed his protection that he rescued him. What was the marvel of the Doctor's power over boys? "We couldn't enter into half that we heard; we hadn't the knowledge of our own hearts or the knowledge of one another; and little enough of the faith, hope, and love needed to that end. But we listened, as all boys in their better moods will listen (aye, and men, too, for the matter of that), to a man whom we felt to be, with all his heart and soul and strength, striving against whatever was mean and unmanly and unrighteous in our little world. It was not the cold clear voice of one giving advice and warning from serene heights to those who were struggling and sinning below, but the warm, living voice of one who was fighting for us and by our sides, and calling on us to help him and ourselves and one another. And so, wearily and little by little, was brought home to the young boy, for the first time, the meaning of his life: that it was no fool's or sluggard's paradise into which he had wandered by chance, but a battle-field ordained from of old, where there are no spectators, but the youngest must take his side, and the stakes are life and death. And he who roused this consciousness in them showed them at the same time, by every word he spoke and by his whole daily life, how that battle was to be fought; and stood there before them their fellow-soldier and the captain of their guard. The true sort of captain, too, for a boy's army, one who had no misgivings and gave no uncertain word of command, and, let who would yield or make a truce, would fight the fight out (so every boy felt) to the last gasp and the last drop of blood.

And so Tom lived his life from the first green days to the last memorable night, when he was "chaired" round the quadrangle by the eleven, shouting in chorus, "For he's a jolly good fellow," himself as great a boy as all the rest, despite the passage of the years and his dignity of captain. It is a story of humanness, with all its good points and its frailties, but especially of loyalty and of friendship; of games, so much like our own in spirit, and yet so different in details; of East and Arthur, of the brutalities of the old fagging system, the school bully and Tom's classic fight with him, of the final war of independence against what was mean and sordid.

" 'I want to leave behind me,' said Tom, speaking low, 'the name of a fellow who never bullied a little boy nor turned his back on a big one.' And then, 'I would sooner have the Doctor's good opinion of me as I really am than any man's in the world.' "

TOM JONES
by
HENRY FIELDING

CONDENSATION BY MARGARET GILLETT

HENRY FIELDING (1707–1754), often called the father of the modern novel, was born near Glastonbury, England, attended Eton for a time, and studied law at the University of Leyden. When he returned to England he began to write light comedies and farces of which "The Tragedy of Tragedies, or Tom Thumb" (1731), a burlesque of contemporary playwrights, and "The Miser," from Molière, are among his best.

In 1735 he married a girl who became the prototype for his heroines, Sophia and Amelia, but her dowry was meagre and soon spent, so that, in 1736, Fielding became for a time the manager of a small theater in Haymarket. However, after another period of study in which he completed his legal training, he was called to the bar. In 1743 his wife died and four years later he married her maid. Then in 1748 he was appointed Justice of the Peace for Middlesex and Westminster with a pension.

"Joseph Andrews" (1742), his first novel, started as a parody of Richardson's "Pamela," but turned into a polemic on domestic manners. "Jonathan Wild" (1743) is a biting social satire. "Tom Jones" (1749), his masterpiece and one of the great novels of all time, introduced the technique of the interpolated essay. "Amelia" (1751) is a heavily moral tale.

During this period of prose fiction (1739–1752), Fielding was also editing several periodicals and writing social reform pamphlets based on his experiences as a magistrate. In 1753 he went to Lisbon for his health but died there the next year and was buried in the English cemetery. His "Journal of a Voyage to Lisbon" (1755) was his valedictory.

In his writing, Fielding was sometimes vulgar but always vigorous. Although on occasion not very well structured in plot, his stories have a picaresque quality which makes their rambling indirection part of their total effectiveness, while their robust humor and objective method guarantee a fresh and realistic approach.

Dear Sir,

I declare that to recommend goodness and innocence hath been my sincere endeavour in this history.

> Your most obliged,
> Obedient, humble servant,
> *Henry Fielding*

*   *   *   *   *

In Somersetshire there lived a widower, Allworthy by name, who had been greatly favoured by both Nature and Fortune. Generous and pious in his person, he resided in the country with his amiable and discreet sister, Bridget, with whom he shared the amenities of a fine house, garden, and loyal retainers.

One night just after returning from London, where he had been on business a full quarter of a year, Mr. Allworthy was about to retire when he noted something in his bed. Upon lifting the covers he discovered a tiny infant in a deep sleep. When the astonishment which this event inevitably caused in the normally undisturbed and well-regulated household had died down, Mr. Allworthy decided to keep the baby boy, but not without giving proper and lengthy admonitions to the suspected mother, a young domestic, Jenny Jones.

Not long after this amazing discovery, Miss Bridget was finally married to a Captain Blifil and promptly became the mother of a son destined to inherit Mr. Allworthy's estate. She was almost as promptly widowed, when her husband suffered an attack of apoplexy, and the rearing of the two children became her responsibility.

Although of nearly the same age and brought up in the same establishment, the two boys developed very different dispositions: the foundling's gay and carefree, Bridget's son's grave, prudent, and sober. This contrast was the more apparent as they approached manhood and Tom Jones grew robust, merry, and handsome while Master Blifil became increasingly reserved and sagacious. Because of his more staid deportment, Mr. Allworthy's nephew was preferred by the tutors, Mr. Thwackum and Mr. Square, who undertook all of the boys' training after Bridget's untimely death.

However, as might be expected, Tom drew great sighs of longing from the young ladies of the shire and, indeed, he found considerable interest in their company, although his contact with the fair sex was somewhat restricted by virtue of the thinness of the population in those parts as well as by his lack of opportunity to travel abroad. Nevertheless, two local young women of very different stations engaged his full attention at almost the same time.

One of these, Molly, the daughter of a gamekeeper, a buxom, forward sort of lass, first captivated his fancy and his senses; while the other, Sophia, a young lady of great beauty and delicacy, captured his esteem, his admiration, and his deepest devotion. Sophia was the daughter of the neighbouring Squire Western, in whose company young Jones spent many an hour riding to hounds. The older man's passions were his horses, his dogs, and his daughter—in that order. He was also addicted to the bottle, kept a good table, and frequently invited Tom to stay to supper. Thus the handsome Mr. Jones spent more and more time on the Squire's estate where he saw a great deal of the lovely Miss Western and consequently had less time for the gamekeeper's daughter.

Partly as the result of the latter's importunities and partly because of the dilemma of his position, young Jones was torn in twain by his feelings and fell into a distracted melancholy. To add to his distress, his kindly foster father was taken seriously ill. Though Mr. Allworthy recovered, Tom's joy in this event was marred by the jealous Blifil who led his uncle to believe that during his illness Tom had been concerned only with drinking and wenching, and that such an ungrateful reprobate deserved to be banished. Ordered to leave and in deep disgrace, Tom Jones left his home, determined to go to sea.

Directly upon learning of her lover's departure, and in spite of her great fondness for her father, Sophia also fled from her home and from the marriage Squire Western had contracted for her with Blifil. Having little alternative, she decided to make her way to London where there lived a distant relative, a great and noble lady, who the distraught girl felt certain would be her friend and protector.

After many minor adventures of the kind which befall all travellers, and a few narrow escapes of a more serious nature which are likely to afflict ladies unaccustomed to the public highways, the strangest coincidence occurred: the lovers' paths crossed. Although they spent the night at the same inn, they did not see each other. In fact Tom was quite unaware of Sophia's presence under the same roof until the next morning when, to his great astonishment, he found a muff that she had purposely left behind. And soon as he learned her destination, he set out in hot pursuit. On the way he suddenly realized how much Sophia meant to him and he vowed to dedicate himself to *her* service alone.

Meanwhile, Squire Western had also joined the chase but he was soon dissuaded from what seemed a fruitless search and Sophia continued her journey to London uninterrupted.

When our hero arrived in the great city, he made strenuous efforts to locate his ladylove and through devious means at last discovered her whereabouts. But this availed him little, since the relative with whom Sophia had sought refuge made it very difficult for Tom to see her. This worldly woman was not the benevolent guardian Sophia had hoped but, rather, had an eye on Tom for herself and designs for a marriage for her ward that were even more repugnant to Sophia than her father's plans concerning Blifil.

But Sophia's loyalty was severely strained at this point by the reports of her lover's affairs with other women, as well as by her father's passionate hostility to Tom as the cause of his daughter's defection and disappearance. Even before she left home—indeed, as soon as he learned of their attachment—the Squire had sworn to dis-inherit her and see her dead before he would consent to her union with such a penniless scoundrel.

As for Tom, many temptations were cast in his way to wean him from his single-minded devotion to Sophia, but through them all he never lost sight of his goal which was her happiness. Even against such odds, the couple remained steadfast, and their constancy was finally rewarded by a most surprising disclosure made by a Mrs. Waters, formerly Jenny Jones. She revealed that Tom was not her child at all but the first son of Bridget Allworthy. Furthermore, her claim was supported by a letter, written by Mr. Allworthy's sister on her death bed—a letter which had been concealed all these years by Blifil.

Thus the real scoundrel was unmasked and Tom took his rightful place as the heir to the Allworthy fortune. With his changed circum-stances he, of course, had no trouble in securing the approbation of his father-in-law to-be and readmission to Sophia's lodging as well as to her heart. Impatient after so long a delay, he pled with her to set an early wedding date.

"Yet permit me at least once more to beg you would fix the period. Oh, consider the impatience of love," cries he.

"A twelvemonth, perhaps," said she.

"Oh! my Sophia," cries he, "you have named an eternity."

"Perhaps it may be something sooner," says she.

"Oh! my dear, my divine angel," cried he, "these words have made me mad with joy." He then caught her in his arms, and kissed her with an ardour he had never ventured before.

TREASURE ISLAND
by
ROBERT LOUIS STEVENSON*

CONDENSATION BY ALICE G. GROZIER

Squire Trelawney, Doctor Livesey, and the others have bidden me tell the story of our search for old Buccaneer Flint's hidden treasure, and so I go back to the time when my father kept the Admiral Benbow inn. Then it was that the seaman, Bill Bones, came to us for lodging, his sea-chest following after in a handbarrow.

At his request we called him "Captain"; he settled down, always on the watch for a "seaman with one leg," and constantly singing an old sea-song:

> Fifteen men on the dead man's chest—
> Yo-ho-ho, and a bottle of rum!
> Drink and the devil had done for the rest—
> Yo-ho-ho, and a bottle of rum!

Then one day an old blind man left him the pirate's "summons" or "black spot," which so excited him that, combined with the effect of his rum-drinking, it brought on a stroke and we found him dead upon the floor.

Mother and I opened his sea-chest, where I discovered a packet done up in oil-silk; this I took with me, and as soon as I could went to the doctor's house, where I found him with the squire.

To them I told the story of the happenings at the inn and gave them the packet.

"You have heard of Flint, I suppose?" laughed the doctor, as he handled the packet.

"Heard of him!" said the squire. "Heard of him you say! He was the bloodthirstiest buccaneer that ever sailed! If we have here the clue to old Flint's treasure, as you seem to think, then I'll fit on a ship in Bristol, take you and Hawkins here along, and I'll have that treasure if I search a year!"

When they opened the packet there fell out the map of an island,

* For biographical information see page 90.

with every particular needed to bring a ship to safe anchorage on its shore, and full directions for finding the treasure.

"To-morrow," said the squire, "I start for Bristol; in two weeks —yes in ten days, we'll have the best ship, sir, and the choicest crew in England. You shall be ship's doctor, Livesey, Jim cabin-boy, and I am admiral."

But it was longer than the squire expected ere we were ready for sea. In the mean time I went to Bristol also, and while looking over the ship and around the dock I discovered that our cook was a seaman with one leg. He was very domineering with the crew, but servile and smiling to the rest.

I began to have my suspicions, but he was so deep and clever that my doubts of "Long John Silver" were soon quieted.

We settled aboard our ship the *Hispaniola,* with Captain Smollet in command; then one morning, a little before dawn, the boatswain sounded his pipe and the crew began to man the capstan bars.

"Now Barbecue, tip us a stave," cried a voice.

"The old one," cried another.

"Ay, ay, mates," said Long John, who was standing by with his crutch under his arm, and at once broke into the air and words I knew so well: "Fifteen men on the dead man's chest"—the crew coming in on the chorus; and then we were off on our cruise for the treasure.

At sundown one evening, I went to the apple-barrel for an apple, and, finding them low, I got into the barrel bodily and, being rather sleepy, sat there awhile in the dark; soon a heavy man sat down with a crash near by. I was about to jump out when I heard John Silver's voice and kept very still. Before he had said a dozen words I knew that all honest men aboard were in great danger.

Well, I made the discovery that Long John and most of the crew were old shipmates of Bill Bones and John Flint; they knew the object of our voyage and were planning to do away with our party and get the treasure for themselves.

A moment more and the lookout shouted "Land ho!" and we anchored at "Captain Kidd's anchorage," according to the chart. I told the doctor and the squire what I had heard, and they had the captain send the crew ashore, so that we might have an opportunity to talk matters over.

It was decided that we must go on, and we counted those we could trust, only to find that we were but six against nineteen.

The next morning it was plain that mutiny hung over us like a thunder-cloud. Captain Smollet thought it best to give the crew shore leave, and a party was made up, including Silver. Some of the men, however, remained aboard. I suddenly took it into my head to go ashore, too, and slipped unseen over the side and into the forward sheets of the nearest boat: as soon as the bow struck among the shore-side trees, I caught a branch and swung ashore, making off into the near-by thicket.

I cannot tell all the details of the voyage; they were many and exciting, but one or two happenings I must tell.

While wandering about in the thicket I came upon a wild-looking man who said he was a seaman, Ben Gunn, marooned on the island three years before. I got his story and he ours; he was a great help to us, as you shall see.

In the mean time our party had abandoned the ship and taken up the fight ashore. I had a notion to get out to the ship, cut her adrift, and let her go ashore where she would, and so prevent the mutineers from sailing away in her; and remembering Ben Gunn's mention of a coracle which he had made and put in hiding, I set out to find it. Being successful, I made my way to the ship and, laying hold of her hawser, was about to finish cutting her loose when I heard voices from the cabin; one I recognized as that of the coxswain, Israel Hands, the other was a sailor whose name I did not know. Both were drunk, and when I got a look at them through the cabin window I saw that they were in a death's grip.

The strong current had by this time parted the last strand of the hawser which I had left, and both coracle and ship were adrift; with a leap I caught at the jib-boom, and clung, panting, left without retreat on the *Hispaniola*.

When I got aft I found the sailor dead, and Hands in a sad condition. He was friendly enough while helpless, but as he grew stronger he asserted himself and issued orders, which I obeyed until the ship was round in a low wooded north inlet.

The excitement of the last maneuvers had interfered with my watch upon the coxswain, but something caused me to turn my head, when I saw the fellow half-way toward me, his dirk in his hand; he chased me around the deck, trying to corner me; quick as thought I sprang into the mizzen shrouds and rattled up hand over hand into the cross-trees; none too soon, the dirk had struck not a foot below me as I climbed.

Now I primed my pistols and reloaded, and Hands, seeing this, knew that the dice were against him; in spite of this he started up after me. "One more step, Mr. Hands," said I, "and I'll blow your brains out!" I saw his right hand go up over his shoulder, something sang like an arrow through the air, and I was pinned to the mast; both my pistols went off and escaped from my hands, but they did not fall alone; with a choking cry the coxswain loosed his grasp and plunged down head first, and I saw him through the clear water lying on the sand beneath.

I found that I was held simply by the skin of my arm, and, pulling myself free, I finally got ashore and with difficulty reached my friends. They had had some fierce battling with the mutineers, but in the end a flag of truce appeared and Silver came forward to bargain. The doctor, much to the surprise of all, gave him the chart; but this was explained later, for when they dug for the treasure and reached the bottom of the cache, nothing was found but a broken pick and a board with the word "Walrus" burnt into it—the name of Flint's ship!

Ben Gunn was the real hero. Early in his stay on the island he had come upon the treasure, and with great difficulty transported it to a cave and hidden it; seven hundred thousand pounds in minted money of all nations, besides heavy bars of gold.

The doctor had wormed the secret out of Ben Gunn and then arranged to give the chart to Silver, knowing that the cache was empty.

We piled the treasure aboard the ship, set sail, and finally reached a port on the Mexican coast, where we added to our crew.

After a good voyage we reached home just as friends of the Squire were about starting out in search of the *Hispaniola*.

TRILBY*

by

GEORGE DU MAURIER

CONDENSATION BY ALICE G. GROZIER

*GEORGE LOUIS PALMELLA BUSSON DU MAURIER
was born in Paris in 1834, and died in England in 1896. His
father, a naturalized British subject, was the son of emigrés
who had left France during the Reign of Terror and settled
in London.*

*In "Peter Ibbetson," the first of the three books which
won du Maurier, late in life, a reputation as novelist, almost
as great as he enjoyed as artist and humorist for more than
a generation, the author depicts his own singularly happy
childhood.*

*He was brought to London when three or four years old,
but vague memories of this period were suddenly exchanged,
one beautiful day in June, for the charming realities of a
French garden, and an "old yellow house with green shut-
ters and mansard roofs of slate." Here at Passy, with his
"gay and jovial father and his young English mother," the
boy spent seven years of sweet, priceless home life.*

*The year 1856 found him in Paris, in the Latin Quarter,
a student at "the core of the art world" of which in "Trilby"
he produced a fascinating idealistic picture, with both pen
and pencil.*

*For many years he was connected with "Punch," "The
Cornhill Magazine," and "Once a Week." He spent some
years in Antwerp, and it was there, while working in the
studio of van Lerius, that the great misfortune of his life
came upon him—the gradual loss of sight in his left eye,
accompanied by alarming symptoms in the right eye, which,
it was thought, might also become affected—but this did not*

* Printed by permission of, and arrangement with, Harper & Bros.,
authorized publishers.

happen; he went on with his work, although his weak sight made it difficult for him to sketch in the open air. Du Maurier's three novels, "Trilby," the story of a tone-deaf artist's model who became a prima donna; "Peter Ibbetson," the story of the dream existence of Peter and the Duchess of Towers; and "The Martian," which tells of Barty Josslin and his guardian angel from Mars—are all equally preposterous, yet plausible and fascinating.

A charming studio, in the Latin Quarter of Paris, sheltered "Three Musketeers of the Brush"; Talbot Wynne, or Taffy, a big, fair, blue-eyed young Yorkshireman, who had been a soldier, but was at last following his wish to be an artist; then Sandy McAllister, or the Laird, as his friends called him, intended by his parents for a solicitor, but who was in Paris painting toreadors and singing French ballads with a decided Scotch accent.

"The third he was Little Billie," or William Bagot, a pleasing young Englishman from London. To live and work in Paris had been Billie's dream, and at last it was a reality, he and his two friends having taken the studio together. He often looked at these friends, and wondered if any one, living or dead, ever had two such glorious chums. His absolute belief in all they said and did touched them exceedingly, and they in turn loved him for his affectionate disposition and lively ways; and recognizing his quickness, keenness, and delicacy in all matters of form and color, they had also a great admiration for him.

On a showery April day the three friends were in the studio, each occupied to his taste, Taffy vigorously swinging a pair of Indian clubs, the Laird sitting before his easel, painting; and Billie, kneeling on the broad divan before the great studio window, was gazing out over the roofs of Paris, speculating upon the future of himself and his friends.

These speculations were rudely interrupted by a loud knocking at the door, and two men entered; first a tall, bony individual of any age between thirty and forty-five, of Jewish aspect, well-featured, but sinister. He had bold, brilliant black eyes, with long, heavy lids. He went by the name of Svengali, spoke fluent French, but with a German accent. His companion was a little, swarthy young man, possibly a gipsy; under his arm he carried a fiddle and bow.

Svengali at once suggested that they have some music, and, seating himself at the piano, ran his fingers up and down the keys with the easy power of a master. Then he fell to playing Chopin's Impromptu in A flat so beautifully that Little Billie's heart was nigh to bursting with emotion and delight. He never forgot that Impromptu, which he was destined to hear again one day in very strange circumstances.

Then the two, Svengali and his companion, Gecko, made music together so divinely, indeed, that even Taffy and the Laird were almost as wild in their enthusiasm as Billie, but with an enthusiasm too deep for words.

Suddenly there came another interruption, a loud knuckle-rapping at the outer door, and a voice of great volume, that might belong to any sex, or even an angel, uttered the British milkman's yodel, "Milk below," and before any one could say, *"Entrez,"* a strange figure appeared framed in the gloom of the antechamber; the figure of a very tall and fully developed young girl, clad in the gray overcoat of a French infantry soldier; below this there showed a short striped petticoat, and beneath it were visible her bare white ankles, the toes losing themselves in a huge pair of men's list slippers.

While not strictly beautiful, the girl had great charm; she was really much like a healthy young English boy. Closing the door behind her, she said, wistfully: "Ye're all English, now, aren't ye? I heard the music and thought I'd just come in for a bit and pass the time of day; you don't mind? Trilby, that's my name, Trilby O'Ferrall."

Yes this was Trilby of the studios, artists' model, taking her noonday rest. She sat down upon the model-throne to eat her luncheon and listen to the music.

When Svengali had brought the music to a close, Trilby remarked it was not very gay, and offered to sing a song which she knew, and in English, whereat she sang "Ben Bolt," and finished amid an embarrassing silence, for her hearers did not know whether it was intended seriously or in fun; such a volume of sound ensued that it flooded the studio, but without melody or music of any kind, in fact as if the singer were tone-deaf, as indeed she was.

With her charm and good-fellowship Trilby won the hearts of the Three Musketeers, Billie's most of all, and it was Billie for whom she felt the deepest affection. She cooked for them at times, mended their clothing, listened to their music and the wonderful talks of "the glory that was Greece and the grandeur that was Rome." At other times she criticized their work, in fact was quite "one of them."

A climax came one day when Billie, visiting another studio, discovered Trilby posing for the "altogether." He was so shocked that he was awakened to the fact of his great love for Trilby, and, rushing home to his friends, declared that he was going to Barbizon to paint the forest and that he wanted to be alone.

Trilby, too, saw matters in a different light, and, after much self-examination and struggle, decided that she would pose no more, but would earn her living as a fine laundress, with an old friend who had a laundry and was doing well. Poor Trilby was certainly one of the frail ones, but through ignorance, rather than wrong intent; now she saw her mistake, and with her love for Billie there came a strange new feeling, a dawning self-respect.

Nineteen times Billy asked Trilby to marry him, but she always refused, feeling herself unworthy. Then one Christmas night he asked her the twentieth time: *"Will* you marry me? If not I leave Paris in the morning never to return"; and Trilby, fearing to lose him out of her life, finally answered, "Yes."

Billie's mother, hearing of the intended marriage, journeyed to Paris to make inquiries about Trilby, finally deciding that she was not the wife for her son, all of which she said to Trilby, who in her great love for Billie, and thinking it best for him, promised to go away and not see him again.

Trilby kept her promise and Billie became very ill; when he had sufficiently recovered he went back to England with his mother, his heart, as it seemed, quite dead.

This was a sorrowful time for Taffy and the Laird, as they missed both Trilby and Billie. Nothing was heard of the former for a long time.

Years went by and Billie became a famous painter, with a beautiful home in London and many friends.

Then the Three Musketeers were together again in Paris, where they visited the scenes of former times, at last going to the old studio, now rented to other tenants, but having still upon its wall Billie's famous drawing of Trilby's foot, protected by a covering of glass; and beneath it some stanzas to *"Pauvre Trilby, la belle et bonne et chère!"*

One night they attended a concert in a large hall on the Rue

St.-Honore. The first violin had scarcely taken his seat before they recognized their old friend Gecko. Just as the clock struck, Svengali appeared—the conductor. Then a moment of silence, and two little page-boys each drew a silken rope, the curtains parted, and a tall figure walked slowly down to the front of the stage. The house rose to meet her as she advanced, bowing to right and left—"It was Trilby."

Her eyes on Svengali, at a signal from him she sang without accompaniment, in a voice so immense in its softness, richness, and freshness that it seemed to be pouring itself from all around; and then her dove-like eyes looked past Svengali, straight at Billie, and all his long-lost power of loving came back with a rush.

At last—the final performance of the evening. Trilby vocalized, without words, Chopin's Impromptu in A flat; astounding, no piano had ever given out such notes as these! Amid the wild applause and enthusiasm of an immense audience, Trilby had made her début in Paris.

Her début in London was a different matter; Svengali, ill, and unable to conduct, had taken his place in a box exactly opposite Trilby, but his presence had no effect upon her. When it came time for her to sing she started "Ben Bolt," but sang only a few bars, when the house was in an uproar of laughter, hoots, and hisses. Trilby had lost the power of "singing true."

She seemed to be awakening from sleep, not knowing where she was. Her old-time friends rescued her and took her home to Billie's mother. Svengali collapsed from shock and died very suddenly.

The friends learned from Gecko that "there were two Trilbys," Svengali had but to say "Dor" and she suddenly became an unconscious Trilby of marble, to do his bidding. So they traveled, giving concerts, Svengali, Gecko, Trilby, attended by Marta, an old servant of Svengali.

The long strain had its effect upon poor Trilby, and she drooped and died, surrounded by the old-time friends and Billie's mother. Not long after, Little Billie, broken-hearted, followed her.

TWENTY THOUSAND LEAGUES
UNDER THE SEA

by

JULES VERNE

CONDENSATION BY JAMES B. CONNOLLY

*JULES VERNE was born at Nantes, February 8, 1828.
Though he had gone to Paris to study for the bar, he followed in the footsteps of the legion who have found the idle
moments of the law a pleasant occasion for the wandering
imagination. The opera and the stage attracted him, but it
was not long before he discovered a field which he made his
own, that of imaginary voyages to any impossible place to
which his whimsy might direct him, for which, however, he
had prepared a timetable and made all sorts of scientific preparation in the most minute way. Such imaginary trips have
been made by writers from Homer's days to those of H. G.
Wells, and the guides have included such personages as
Virgil, Dante, Cyrano de Bergerac, Dean Swift, and Daniel
Defoe. But none have been more matter of fact or more
brilliant in carrying off the matter.*

*Perhaps the most famous trips were those to the "Center
of the Earth," "From the Earth to the Moon," "Twenty
Thousand Leagues Under the Sea," and "Around the World
in Eighty Days." All the languages of the world know the
tales, and most theaters know the last named, as well as
"Michael Strogoff."*

He died at Amiens, March 24, 1905.

I was leaning forward on the starboard bulwark, my servant Conseil beside me, when the voice of Ned Land, the big harpooner,
broke the silence. "Look! There is the thing we are looking for!" he
cried.

We all saw the sea monster, or whatever it was, which we had been hunting for months. It made off as we charged. We gave chase. Throughout all that night and next day we pursued. We stopped. It stopped. Once it allowed us to creep close to it; and as we crept it rammed us.

The shock of the collision threw me into the sea. I would have drowned but for my faithful Conseil. He supported me to the hard metallic back of the monster. Here we were joined by Ned Land. As we were resting there, eight masked men came through a hatch and drew us down into the bowels of what we now saw was not a monster, but a strange kind of sea-craft. Thus began the strange voyage with that remarkable character who called himself Captain Nemo, and in that strange wonderful ship which he called the *Nautilus*.

The *Nautilus* was a cigar-shaped steel ship of 232 feet in length, 26 feet beam, and 1,500 tons dead weight. There were two hulls, one inside the other, joined by T-shaped irons, which rendered them of almost uncrushable strength. She was driven by electric engines of tremendous power. Tanks which could be filled or emptied at will enabled her to cruise on the surface or under the water as she pleased.

She was fitted with all kinds of working and lounging quarters. In a library were books on the sciences, morals, and literature of almost every language. There was a drawing-room with a luminous ceiling which served also as a museum and into which an intelligent hand had gathered submarine treasures of the world—the rarest shells, pearls of all colors and beyond price, every variety of under-sea vegetation; also paintings of the masters, admirable statues in marble and bronze, a great organ piano.

From the inside of her a staircase led to a platform or deck from which rose two cages, partly inclosed by thick glasses. One cage was for the helmsman, the other contained an electric search-light to light the course of the ship in dark waters. On this platform also was a place wherein was stored a long-boat.

Captain Nemo was tall and robustly built, with pale skin, lofty brow, and the fine taper hands of a highly nervous temperament. He spoke French, English, German, Latin, all equally well. He may have been thirty-five, he may have been fifty years of age.

It was on November 6, 1866, with the coast of Japan in view, that this strange captain told us we were prisoners for him to do with as he pleased. "And now," he added, "our course is E.N.E.

and our cruising depth twenty-six fathoms. I leave you to the resources of these quarters and your own reflections."

We remained mute, not knowing what surprise awaited us. Suddenly a dazzling light broke in on us. We saw that only glass panels separated us from a sea which was illuminated far to either side by the powerful electric gleams from the ship. What a spectacle! An army of undersea creatures escorted us. They were various and beautiful in the clear water, many known, but hundreds unknown, to us.

We heard and saw nothing of the captain for several days; then came a note inviting us to a hunt on the bottom of the sea. We donned diving-suits, then fastened on a sort of knapsack which furnished us not only with air to breathe, but with the light to see our way. We carried air-guns which fired glass bullets heavily charged with electricity, which had only to touch the most powerful animal to kill him. A connecting compartment filled with water let us into the sea. And thus equipped, wading on the bottom of the clear ocean, we killed our game with ease and without danger.

That hunt was but the first of the wonders of the cruise. Onward we rushed, sometimes on the surface, sometimes under the sea. There was our fight with the immense devilfish which once in a huge school enmeshed the *Nautilus*. There was the visit to a wonderful pearl-fishery, where Captain Nemo showed us a mollusc within whose jaws was a pearl weighing perhaps 500 pounds. Some day he would return and pluck that treasure, but not yet—every year was adding to its value. We visited the skeletons of long-sunken ships, the corpses of the drowned crew still clinging to the hulls of some. We hunted in the Papuan Islands, where the *Nautilus* was attacked by the native savages. An electric current turned them back shocked and howling ere they could climb aboard.

When one of the crew died Captain Nemo had him buried in a coral glade in the South Pacific, where was a cross of red coral that looked like petrified blood. It was a wonderful, solemn sight to see the pall-bearers with the dead body on their shoulders, and all treading so reverentially the way from the ship to the coral cemetery, where at the foot of the cross the body was interred and covered up. All knelt in prayer. Captain Nemo was the last to leave.

"Your dead sleep quietly out of the reach of sharks," I said, when we were back on the *Nautilus*.

"Of sharks and men," he replied.

We voyaged under colossal icebergs to the South Pole and all but perished there, escaping from an icy tomb only as our last breath of storage air was exhausted. Wonderful was our passage from the Red Sea into the Mediterranean by means of a subterranean tunnel under the isthmus. (This was before the digging of the Suez Canal.) There we witnessed the transfer of a million dollars' worth of gold ingots from the *Nautilus* to the vessel of a Greek diver.

Whence came this store of gold? Later we learned.

In Vigo Bay on the Spanish coast the *Nautilus* came to rest on bottom. Here in 1702 a fleet of Spanish galleons were sunk, and here from this sunken treasure more than a century and a half later this ruler of the underseas came and helped himself whenever it pleased him. "Five hundred millions were there," said Captain Nemo, "but not now. Do you see now how with these and the other treasures of my domain I could pay the national debt of France and not feel it?"

We had now been six months aboard the *Nautilus*. For me, the scientist, it was a voyage of ceaseless interest; but not so for Conseil and Ned Land. At their request I pleaded with Captain Nemo for our liberty.

"You came to my ship without invitation. You will now remain here," was his grim answer.

We had left the southern hemisphere and were in the waters off France and the British Islands when we were pursued by an armed war-ship. Flying no colors, she attacked at once. Her cannon shot rebounded from our iron hull.

Captain Nemo, pointing to her, said: "I am the oppressed, and there is my oppressor. Through him I have lost country, wife, children, father and mother. Why should I withhold my vengeance?"

He called out his orders. The *Nautilus* sank below the sea. We felt her rushing forward, felt the shock of her steel ram piercing the hull of the enemy. Through the glass panels we saw her doomed crew crowding the ratlines, clinging to the rails, struggling in the sea. The *Nautilus* passed on.

I saw Captain Nemo go to his room and kneel before the portrait of a woman and two little children. "How long, O Lord, how long!" he cried out.

We steamed north, to that part of the Norwegian coast where lies that dreaded maelstrom which draws into itself all floating things. The *Nautilus*—was it an accident?—was drawn into the whirlpool.

Around and around she whirled. Even her steel hull felt the strain; we could hear bolts being pulled out from her girders. The long-boat was torn from its place on deck and hurled like a stone into the whirlpool. I lost consciousness.

When I came to myself I was in a Loffoden fisherman's hut, and Conseil and Ned Land were chafing my hands.

So ended our voyage of 20,000 leagues under the sea. What became of Captain Nemo and his strange craft I do not know. I hope his powerful ship conquered the maelstrom, even as I hope, if he lived, that his philosophy and powerful will finally conquered his desire for vengeance.

UNCLE TOM'S CABIN

by

HARRIET BEECHER STOWE

CONDENSATION BY JOHN KENDRICK BANGS

HARRIET BEECHER was born at Litchfield, Connecticut, in 1811. She died at Hartford, Conn., July 1, 1896. She came of a family which achieved large reputation. Her father was Lyman Beecher, a militant clergyman, and her best-known brother, Henry Ward Beecher, was one of the preacher-orators of his time. In 1836 she married another clergyman, Calvin Stowe.

Her inheritance and her sympathies were all toward the cause of anti-slavery. Her life in Cincinnati, on the borderland of free and slave territory, gave her an insight into the peculiar institution such as few Northerners possessed. The wife of a poor minister, occupied with the care of a large family, with little literary training, she seemed the last person to electrify the world and achieve a lasting historical importance. Yet probably none of the great names associated with the cause of anti-slavery did more to force the issue than the minister's wife. In 1852 there issued from Brunswick, Maine, where her husband had become a professor at Bowdoin College, the famous "Uncle Tom's Cabin"; within five years over half a million copies had been sold. How many million people have since read the book or seen the vast variety of plays based on it, no man can tell.

Mrs. Stowe wrote, later, "Dred," "The Minister's Wooing," "The Pearl of Orr's Island," "Old Town Folks," and other books, but "Uncle Tom's Cabin" was her great work. It was written with knowledge of the subject and with a noble purpose; the sincerity of the author and a spark of native genius created an effect that few other books have ever attained; the scene is true to life; the characters have remained alive long years after the circumstances which gave them birth have passed away. "Uncle Tom's Cabin" is part of the world's history of the struggle toward freedom.

It was in the days when African slavery flourished under the free skies of America. Evil times had befallen the house of Shelby, and pressing debt required the sacrifice of a portion of the holdings of the Kentucky planter in human chattels. Uncle Tom, instead of the freedom that had been promised him as the reward of a lifetime of devoted service, found himself torn from wife, home, and children, transferred to the hands of an unscrupulous trader, and consigned to the terror-ridden slave-markets of the lower Mississippi. So trusted had the black man been that numerous avenues of escape lay open to him. Of one of these, in the dead of winter, over the ice-bound waters of the Ohio River, by the "underground" to Sandusky, and thence to freedom in Canada, the mulatto-girl Eliza and her son, who had been sold at the same time, had availed themselves. But Tom's fidelity to his master was too strong, and, fearing to involve him in further difficulties, he bravely faced the miseries of the future.

"I am in the Lord's hands," said he to those who tried to persuade him to escape, "and there'll be the same God there that there is here."

"Well, it's a nasty mean shame, Tom!" sobbed his master's son George, as he bade the old slave farewell. "But remember—some day I'll come down and buy you back."

The voyage down the Mississippi with the slave-gang to which Tom was attached was filled with scenes and episodes of woe and tragedy, but Tom found relief from sorrow in the companionship of a fellow-passenger, a fairy-like little girl, full of the smiling spirit of play, who, fascinated by Tom's unusual dexterity in the making of strange toys dear to the hearts of children, clung to him as to an old and beloved friend.

"Where are you going, Tom?" she asked one day.

"I dunno, missy," said Tom. "Reckon I'm gwine to be sold to somebody—but I dunno who."

"Well, my father can buy you," said she, "and I'll ask him to this very day."

"Thank you, my little lady," smiled Tom, gratefully.

And his "little lady" she soon became, for the brave black won little Eva's life back from the swirling waters of the Mississippi into which she had fallen, and in sheer gratitude for her deliverance the child's father, Augustine St. Clare, bought him from the trader.

The scene now changes to New Orleans, where in a beautiful home, in daily comradeship with his little mistress, Tom for a time was happy. St. Clare, his new master, was kindly and sympathetic, and while of an easy-going disposition, a dawning consciousness of the iniquity of slavery had come into his soul, a consciousness confirmed and accentuated by his daily contemplation of the nobility of heart of the faithful Tom. Two years of this unlooked-for happiness passed away, and once more Tom was face to face with misfortune. His flower-like little companion, growing daily more and more fragile, herself in spite of her years envisaging and depressed by the wickedness of the system of slavery which not only destroyed the souls of the oppressed, but debased the character of the oppressors, finally died. Heartbroken over his loss, St. Clare found comfort only in the companionship of the equally heartbroken Tom, and one day in a sudden surge of gratitude he promised the old man his freedom, but the light of joy that shone in Tom's face when he heard the promise disconcerted him.

"You haven't had such a bad time here that you should be glad to leave me," he said, sadly.

" 'Tain't leavin' ye, Marse St. Clare," said Tom, "it's bein' free that I'm a-joyin' in."

But it was not to be. The easy-going nature of St. Clare caused him to delay Tom's emancipation papers, and one night, trying to separate two drunken brawlers intent upon killing each other, St. Clare was himself stabbed to death; and in the settlement of his estate Tom once more found himself at the auction-block, to be knocked down to the highest bidder.

Enter now one Simon Legree, a master of far different type from Shelby and St. Clare. A brute and a drunkard. A beast whose glance was an insult to womanhood. A fiend who prided himself upon his inflexible brutality, and with brutish satisfaction showed, to all who would look, his knuckles calloused with the blows he had inflicted upon the helpless. To him by virtue of length of purse fell Tom, who now tasted the tragic dregs of the cup of slavery. The manifest contrast between his own crass brutality and the high-minded character of his chattel aroused the envious wrath of his new owner, who endeavored by every wicked expedient possible to break Tom's spirit and his unalterable faith in divine guidance and protection. Furtively he watched him at work, hoping to find a flaw, but in vain; but one day he found the way. He ordered Tom to flog a woman-slave who was guiltless of the short-coming attributed to her, and for the first time in his career Legree was denied. Tom refused. Legree's answer was a blow upon Tom's cheek.

"What?" he roared in his rage. "Ye dare tell me ye won't, ye blasted black beast?"

"I'll die first," Tom replied, simply.

"Well, here's a pious dog—a saint—a gentleman!" sneered Legree. "Didn't ye never read in your Bible, *'Servants obey your masters'?* And ain't I your master? Didn't I pay twelve hundred dollars cash for ye, and ain't ye mine, body and soul?"

"No, Marse Legree," replied Tom, through the tears and blood that coursed down his cheeks. *"My soul ain't yours! It's been bought and paid for by One that is able to keep it.* Ye may kill my body, but ye can't harm my soul."

Now, according to the nature of his kind, Legree was superstitious, and while his hatred increased, he began to fear in the presence of his fearless possession. In Tom's presence what passed for a conscience was aroused in him. Some of the unspeakable crimes of which in his lustful gratifications, and through his murderous instincts, he had been guilty began to prey upon him. Dark things had happened in the decayed old mansion in which Legree dwelt, and in common with the ignorant blacks by whom he was surrounded Legree began to have fears, accentuated by the delirium of drink, of impending visitations by ghosts. Taking advantage of these fears, his one-time mistress, Cassie, a woman of subtle powers, herself a slave, conspired with Emmaline, an attractive mulatto whom Legree was endeavoring to install in her place, to destroy his peace of mind, and ultimately himself by means of wraithful apperances and weird sounds in the garret of the old mansion. Pretending to escape through the swamps, eluding their pursuers, they returned to the house and lay hid there for days, working their soul-stirring stratagem upon the worried Legree. Legree at the head of a pursuing party made up of negroes and bloodhounds sought the missing women in the swamps and forests by which his isolated plantation was surrounded, but in vain; and in the rage of failure, believing him to have been party to the escape, he turned upon Tom.

"Well, ye black beast," he roared, in a paroxysm of baffled rage, "I've made up my mind to kill ye."

"Very likely, Marse Legree," replied Tom, calmly.

"Unless ye tell me what ye know about these yer gals," said Legree.

"I hain't got nothin' to tell, Marse," said Tom.

"Don't you dare tell me that ye don't know, ye old black Christian," cried Legree in angry contempt, striking him furiously.

"Yes—I *know*, Marse," said Tom, "but I can't tell anything. *I can die.*"

"Hark ye, Tom," roared Legree, in a terrible voice, "this time I mean what I say, "I'll conquer ye or I'll kill ye! I'll count every drop of blood in your body till ye give up."

"Marse," said Tom, "if you was sick, or in trouble, or dyin' and it would save ye, I'd give ye my heart's blood, and if takin' every drop of blood in this poor old body of mine would save your precious soul, I'd give 'em freely as the Lord gave His for me. Do the worst ye can. My troubles will soon be over, but if ye don't repent, *yours won't never end!*"

For a moment Legree stood aghast, awed into silence by Tom's absolutely fearless reliance upon his faith, but only for a moment. There was one hesitating pause, and the spirit of evil within him, defied, rose with sevenfold vehemence. Foaming with rage, he struck his victim to the ground and gave him over to be flogged to ribbons.

"Pay away until he gives up!" shouted Legree, as the floggers led him away.

Two days later George Shelby, Tom's boy-friend from Kentucky, now grown to manhood, appeared to fulfil his promise of redemption, but he came too late. Tom lay dying of his wounds.

"I've come to take you home," said George, tears falling from his eyes as he bent over his old friend.

"Bless the Lord—it's Marse George!" cried Tom, as he opened his eyes, bewildered. *"They haven't forgot me! They haven't forgot me!* Now, I shall die content."

At this moment Legree sauntered in and looked on carelessly.

"The old Satan!" cried George, in his indignation. "It's a comfort to think the devil will pay him for this some of these days."

"Hush, Marse George!" said Uncle Tom. "Don't feel so. He 'ain't done me no real harm—*only opened the gates of heaven for me—that's all.*"

The sudden flush of strength died away. A sense of sinking came over him and he closed his eyes. His broad chest rose and fell heavily. The expression of his face was that of a conqueror.

"Who—who shall separate us from the love of Christ?" he whispered in a voice that contended with mortal weakness, and with a smile on his lips he fell asleep.

"Witness, Eternal God," said George Shelby, as he knelt beside the body of his departed friend, "oh, witness from this hour, *I will do what one man can do to drive out this curse of slavery from my land.*"

U.S.A.*

by

JOHN DOS PASSOS

CONDENSATION BY MARGARET GILLETT

JOHN DOS PASSOS was born in Chicago in 1896. His father, a lawyer of Portuguese extraction, took him as a child to Mexico and Europe but later sent him to school in Washington, D. C. He also spent some time on a farm in Virginia before going to Harvard where he was gradu-

* By permission of the author. Copyright 1930, 1932, 1933, 1934, 1935, 1936, 1937.

*ated in 1916. He was married soon afterwards. In the First
World War he served as a medical corps private.*

*His first book, "One Man's Initiation—1917" (1920),
was a war novel of the debunking type and his second,
"Three Soldiers" (1921), written while he was in Spain as
a correspondent, likewise drew on his military experience. It
was with his next novel, "Manhattan Transfer" (1925),
that he began his documentation of the American big city
scene and forecast his trilogy, "U.S.A. (42nd Parallel"
[1930], "1919" [1932], and "The Big Money [1936],)
which really made him famous.*

*The author's particular style of punctuation, his ramming
of words together, distinctive cadences, crackling realism
of dialogue, and cinematically shuttling episodes—have had
a wide influence on lesser writers, who followed him.*

*Dos Passos tried to repeat his success in "U.S.A." with
another trilogy, "District of Columbia" (1949–1952), but
it lacked the technical virtuosity of his previous work and
the preacher approach was too obvious. In addition to his
novels, he has written poetry, "A Pushcart at the Curb"
(1922), travel books, plays, personal narrative, and what
might be called essays in social philosophy. His most recent effort, "Midcentury" (1961), containing all his favorite devices of interstitial biographies, newsreels, etc., has
been described as "vintage Dos Passos" and a "book of
wormwood and gall."*

*At present the novelist lives on a farm in Westmoreland
County, Virginia, with his second wife (his first died in
1947) and daughter.*

U.S.A. is both a social study of America from 1900 to 1935 and a
literary production in the form of a trilogy composed of the separately
published novels: *The 42nd Parallel, Nineteen Nineteen,* and *The Big
Money.* These three novels, in which the interlocking lives of the characters depict the levels and indicate the mobility of the social stratification
in America, also present a panorama of the political, economic, and moral
relations of Americans.

The technical devices, used as interpolations between chapters (but not
appearing in this condensation), are the *Newsreel,* a collage of headlines
and brief excerpts from the press of the day; the *Camera Eye,* a series
of impressionistic episodes related by the author from his own experience;

and brief *Biographies* of contemporary figures done in stream-of-consciousness style, among them the following: Eugene V. Debs, Luther Burbank, William Jennings Bryan, Andrew Carnegie, Thomas Edison, Charles Steinmetz, Robert LaFollette, Theodore Roosevelt, Woodrow Wilson, J. P. Morgan, Paul Bunyan (every lumberman), the Unknown Soldier, Henry Ford, Thorstein Veblen, Isadora Duncan, Rudolph Valentino, Frank Lloyd Wright, William Randolph Hearst, Samuel Insull.

* * * * *

U.S.A. is the slice of a continent, a chain of movie theatres, a public library full of old newspapers. U.S.A. is the speech of the people.

MAC

Fainy McCreary was brought up in Chicago and learned his trade by working for his uncle, a socialist job printer, until the poor man was run out of business by the master printers. After that Mac got interested in labor problems and worked his way out to the Coast where he met Maisie Spencer, a clerk in the Emporium, and because he was sick of whoring around, he married her. But Mac wasn't satisfied with humdrum married life and finally, after a big row with Maisie, who had no use for Mac's radical ideas, he took off for Mexico where the Revolution was brewing.

There he bummed around for awhile, sightseeing, until he got a job as an English-language printer on the *Mexican Herald*. At first he was fired with enthusiasm for the workers' cause, but after he settled in with a girl named Concha who was a good cook, his attendance at labor meetings fell off and he took to staying home at night and entertaining a couple of Norte Americanos, now and then. One of these knew a big hombre from New York, J. Ward Moorehouse, who was coming down on government business and asked Mac if he would show him the town.

JANEY

Janey Williams had been a public stenographer in Washington and she had a brother, Joe, in the Navy. After she got a steady job with J. W. Moorehouse, the big public relations counselor, she was a bit worried that Joe might come around. He had not tried to improve himself since he left school and had grown almost uncouth since he went to sea. In a way it was a relief when she had to go to Mexico with Mr. Moorehouse as his private secretary. Although she was scared at first, Mr. Moorehouse was friendly but businesslike and there wasn't any funnystuff at all.

J. W.

J. Ward had come up the hardway with a few breaks here and there. He started out as a book salesman, then had a better chance in real estate, where he met Annabelle whose father owned a lot of resort property. He married her even though she was older than he was and treated him like a kid half the time. Her father sent them to Europe on their honeymoon but Ward got sick of running around after his wife and jumping like a goddam poodle every time she whistled. Through her family connections he wangled a sort of public relations post on the Paris edition of the *NYHerald* and he was rarely home. Annabelle, who was a bit of a nympho, had young men hangerson all the time until Ward got sick of it. When they got back to the States, he divorced her.

After that he became a reporter on the Pittsburgh *Times Dispatch*, but he hated every minute of it. Luckily he ran into one of the big wheels he had met abroad and got a line on a much better job in advertising and promotion. He was good at persuading people, smiling boyishly at them with his frank, blue eyes. He was so successful, in fact, that it was not long before another millionaire's daughter, Gertrude Staple, fell for him. But J. Ward didn't worry much about Gertrude; he was too busy with his own advancement at the office where his exceptional diligence soon put him in the $10,000 a year bracket. The first thing he did was complete his payments on the Stutz roadster he'd been buying on time.

ELEANOR

After their marriage, the Moorehouses began building a mansion near Great Neck and they gave the decoration of it to Eleanor Stoddard, who had to spend a great deal of time in consultation with J. W. Soon Mrs. Moorehouse decided that her husband was in love with the attractive interior decorator but Eleanor, no mean salesman herself, was able to convince Gertrude that it was only a platonic affair. However, she had made herself so indispensable to J. W. that, when he was sent abroad during the war to handle publicity for the Red Cross, he arranged for Eleanor to be taken on for an important job in Paris. Later, after the war, she really did become engaged to a Russian nobleman who proved a great asset to her both socially and in her business. Of course that was after J. W. had his stroke and Dick took over management of the firm.

JOE

Joe Williams, AWOL in Buenos Aires, changed to civies and dropped his naval uniform, weighted with a cobblestone, off the end of the dock. Now he had to find Paquito and get a forged certificate so when the MPs stopped him he could show Merchant Marine papers. But, even so, when the *Argyle* got to England, the bobbies stuck him in jail for a spy because he didn't have a passport. He had to stay there until somebody from the American Consulate bailed him out and got him a berth on an American ship.

Back in Norfolk he met Della but she didn't want to marry a seaman and spend half her life alone, she said. So he went off again on another ship and didn't see Del for several months but when he returned, he persuaded her to marry him. He tried to stay ashore for a while but he couldn't hold a job and was worried about being picked up as a deserter. He had to ship out again pronto or he'd go crazy. The next trip was a lousy one. On the way back they were torpedoed and the crew never was paid off. Then he got dengue fever and was sick for months, stuck in some dump in the Caribbean until he was able to bum a passage back to New York City. He tried to find his sister, Janey, but she'd gone off somewhere on her job and he had to hit for home in Norfolk even though he was broke.

Del was changed and didn't seem to care what he thought about her running around with shavetails. Finally he just got fed up hanging around the house, and took off on a tramp steamer bound for Genoa, where he caught another dose that steadied him down for awhile. When be got back to Brooklyn the next time, he actually went to shoreschool and got his second mate's license. He wrote to tell Janey about it and even changed his ways for a few months, but the war fever finally caught up with him and on Armistice night he got his skull crushed in a drunkenbrawl in St. Nazaire.

DICK

Dick was a bright boy and, since he had no father, the rector took an interest in him and got him a scholarship to a private school. When he finished high school, Dick worked in a lawyer's office and made such a good impression that his employer advanced him the money to go to Harvard, where he made a name for himself in stuᴅent literary activities. About the time of his graduation war broke out, and before he could be drafted, he signed up for duty overseas with the volunteer ambulance corps.

From Italy he wrote a great many letters home, most of them quite literary and critical of the war. As a result it was only a short time before he received orders to return to the U.S., his loyalty in question. Fortunately, his former employer, now a major, helped Dick get things straightened out so that he ended up with a plushy army job and the rank of captain. Back in Paris his commanding officer took a shine to Dick, too, and invited him to dinner one night with a famous New York publicity man, J. W. Moorehouse, who was handling the Peace Conference. Shortly after that Dick had orders to go to Rome.

ANNE

On the train he met a girl from Texas who was working for the Near East Relief and very earnest about helping the underprivileged. Anne Elizabeth was her name and she was traveling with someone attached to the American delegation. Dick saw a lot of them in Rome where everything was so hectic and Anne promised to sleep with him. To his surprise she was a virgin. When she announced she was pregnant Dick told her he couldn't marry yet and take on family responsibility with his career hardly begun. He explained that Moorehouse had offered him a job in Paris after the Armistice and, if she would wait until then when things were more settled, it would be easier. Anne was panicky, especially when the NER fired her without notice, suspecting probably. One night in a cabaret, after a few drinks, she talked a French ace into taking her up for a loop-the-loop. The plane disintegrated.

BENNY

Benny Compton was a good student at City College where he picked up some 'liberal' ideas. But before his second year he went off to live with an older woman who worked at Wanamakers and was allwrappedup in 'the movement.' She explained to Benny about the evils of the capitalist system and got him all excited about the rights of the underdog. After he worked his way out to Seattle, so he'd know labor problems at first hand, he managed to get mixed up in a riot and spent three weeks in a hospital recovering from the beating the sheriff's deputies gave him.

All that winter he lived at home, back in Brooklyn, and tried to get some legal training working as a clerk for a labor lawyer on lower Broadway. In the evenings he gave speeches before radical groups. He was only twenty-three when he was sent down to Atlanta for ten years for subversive activity.

CHARLEY

At the outbreak of the war, Charley Anderson, an automechanic from Fargo, North Dakota, signed up as a grease monkey in the ambulance service. By the time the war ended he was a pilot, a lieutenant in the air-force and a hero. With a small inheritance from his mother's estate he planned to go into the manufacture of plane parts after he got home. But the deal didn't panout as he hoped and he signed a contract as consulting engineer with an aviation firm in Detroit. Although he was financially very successful over the years, both as an engineer and as a private investor, his marriage to a wealthy girl was a failure and his affairs were in such a mess that he decided he needed a vacation. He went down to Miami where he met Margo and learned her story.

MARGO

Margo's foster-parents had been theatre people who had boarded her in a convent, off and on, while she was growing up. When she was still a teenager, she had married Tony, a Cuban guitarist, and run away to Havana just for kicks. After weeks of nightmare among strange people she couldn't even talk to, Margo found out that Tony was a homosexual and filthy with disease. Her baby was born blind but luckily died when it was only a few days old. By hocking her wedding ring, Margo was able to raise her fare back to New York and, after sitting around the casting offices for more than a month, she landed a backrow job in the Ziegfeld Follies.

When Charley heard all her hard luck, he wanted to set her up in a Park Ave. apartment, but nothing doing. What did he think she was, anyway—just because she had been in the Follies? No siree! But she accepted a few things, jewels and a fur coat, like that. She got herself work as a model in a gown shop, but the outfit was on its last legs and soon folded. After that, things went from bad to worse. Charley's drinking increased and he and Margo went on a continuous wild binge. After a crazy party one night, he wrecked his car at a grade crossing and died of complications. While he was still conscious, Margo managed to get a check signed but his affairs were so tangled that there weren't any funds to cover it. Then, to make things even more desperate, Tony turned up. He wheedled and threatened Margo until she finally agreed to try to crack Hollywood with him. After all he *might* turn out to be a smaller Valentino.

Tony was a success on the movie lots but not the way Margo hoped. He was very popular with 'the boys' and was able to support himself, or rather get someone to support him. Meanwhile Margo worked as an extra for three years before she was 'discovered' and married to her director. From then on she was a star in her own orbit.

Eveline Johnson, nee Hutchins and a girlhood friend of Eleanor's was giving one of her fabulous parties—reds and everything. Mary French, who had been to Vassar and worked at Hull House, said she would go because important labor people would be there and Margo, the new screen personality.

"They say she came from the gutter."

"Not at all. Her people were Spaniards of noble birth who lived in Cuba."

The young man, symbolizing all the unemployed of the Great Depression, waits hungryandtired by the side of the road for a hitch while the rich ride above him on the transcontinental airline or whiz past him in their Cadillacs. A hundred miles down the road lie the promises.

VANITY FAIR
by
WILLIAM MAKEPEACE THACKERAY*

CONDENSATION BY CAROLYN WELLS

After six years at Miss Pinkerton's school, Amelia Sedley went home, guaranteed a polished and refined young lady. Amelia was a

* For biographical information see page 143.

dear little creature, all rosy health and bright good humor, though the silly thing would cry over a dead canary-bird or a mouse the cat had seized upon. She was accompanied by her dear friend, Becky Sharp, who was to make a short visit at the Sedley home before beginning her career of self-support as a governess.

Becky was small, pale, and sandy-haired, with eyes habitually cast down; when they looked up they were large, odd, and attractive. As Miss Sharp's father had been an artist and a drunkard, and her French mother an opera girl, it is not surprising that Rebecca asserted she had never been a girl—she had been a woman since she was eight years old.

At the Sedley home, Becky met Amelia's brother Joseph, a stout, puffy man, who wore buckskins and Hessian boots, several immense neckcloths, a red striped waistcoat, and an apple-green coat. He was lazy, peevish, a glutton, and a hard drinker, but Rebecca decided instantly to set her cap for him and began by whispering to Amelia, rather loud, "He's very handsome!" Rebecca's plans, however, were foiled by George Osborne, an admirer of Amelia, and Miss Sharp took her departure from the Sedley house.

She went to be governess in the home of Sir Pitt Crawley, which place, in her letters to Amelia, she dubbed Humdrum Hall. There were many Crawleys, the most important being Sir Pitt's spinster sister, and his second son, Rawdon Crawley. The old lady possessed seventy thousand pounds, and had almost adopted Rawdon, who was her favorite nephew, while several members of the family fought to supplant him in her favor. Captain Rawdon Crawley was a large young dandy, who spoke with a great voice and swore a good deal. He remarked of the demure Rebecca, "By Jove, she's a neat little filly!" and both he and his aunt took a decided fancy to the clever and fascinating little governess, though, indeed, she made conquest of pretty much whomsoever she chose.

Now we must flit back to London to see what has become of Miss Amelia. Far less interesting than Becky, and with nothing but her wax-doll face to recommend her, yet all the young men clustered round her chair and battled for a dance with her. She was now engaged to George Osborne, albeit his sisters wondered, "What *could* George find in that creature?" So much did they wonder this, that it affected George, and he concluded he *was* throwing himself away on the chit. But poor little Amelia adored him, and Captain Dobbin, who favored Amelia himself, kept Osborne up to the mark in his attentions. The infatuated girl cared nothing about the Napoleonic war that was raging, the fate of Europe was to her only Lieutenant George Osborne; while he, often away with his regiment, the Horse Guards, read her letters hastily, murmuring, "Poor little Emmy—how fond she is of me! and gad! what a headache that mixed punch has given me!"

About this time Miss Crawley returned from visiting her brother and brought back with her to her house in Park Lane no less a personage than Miss Rebecca Sharp, who, so well had she played her cards, was now Miss Crawley's much cherished companion. Whereupon Captain Rawdon Crawley became a frequent visitor at his aunt's home. Incidentally, Lady Crawley died—so incidentally that Miss Crawley merely said, pettishly, "I suppose I must put off my party for the third!" Immediately upon the death of his wife, Sir Pitt came to his sister's house and endeavored to retrieve his lost Becky as governess.

"I daren't. I don't think it would be right to be alone—with—you, sir," she replied, seemingly in great agitation.

"Come as Lady Crawley, then! There, will that satisfy you?" and the vulgar, ill-bred old M. P. fell down on his knees and leered at her like a satyr.

Rebecca, in real consternation at her lost chance, wept genuine tears, as she exclaimed, "Oh, Sir Pitt—oh, sir—I—I'm married already!"

When it further transpired that the bridegroom of Becky's secret marriage was the brass-spurred and long-mustachioed Captain Rawdon Crawley, there were two cataclysms, one in which Miss Crawley went from one fit of hysterics into another, and one where the frenzied old Sir Pitt went wild with hatred and insane with baffled desire. But the bridegroom captain remarked to his wife: "You're sure to get us out of the scrape, Beck. I never saw your equal, and I've met with some clippers in my time, too!"

George Osborne, though dependent on his mercenary, low-bred father, despised him, and when the elder Osborne forbade George to marry our little Amelia the young man broke over the traces and married her out of hand. The marriage was egged on and managed by the faithful Dobbin; and, radiant in her straw bonnet with pink ribbons and a white-lace veil, little Emmy went off with her husband to Brighton for the honeymoon.

Here they fell in with the Rawdon Crawleys. Becky, mistress of a fine establishment and surrounded by respectful admirers, was so adroit at wheedling tradesmen and standing off creditors, that she made it possible for them to maintain a fine social position on nothing a year.

Soon after this, among the brilliant train of camp-followers that hung around the Duke of Wellington's army, our friends were all in Brussels. George, now desperately infatuated with Becky, and neglecting his six weeks' wife shamefully, slipped a note in a bouquet at a ball, begging Becky to elope with him. But before the note was answered came the call to arms, and Lieutenant Osborne, forgetting all love and intrigue, kissed his Amelia and marched away—marched, alas! to his death on the field of Waterloo.

Colonel Rawdon Crawley, promoted for gallantry, returned in triumph, and he and his wife passed the winter of 1815 in Paris in much splendor and gaiety. Becky's *salon* became famous, and great people hobnobbed there. Colonel Crawley's dexterity at cards and billiards became so marked that he constantly won from his guests, and under Becky's tutelage he became a clever and successful gambler, and thus aided in their fortune of nothing a year.

Amelia, now the widow of Osborne, and with a small son, Georgy, was in sad penury, her father-in-law refusing to see her at all, and her own father and mother dependent upon her. Becky, too, was the mother of a son, but she cared nothing for her child, nor for her husband; indeed, she so far forgot her wifely duty as to be guilty of an intrigue with the rich old Lord Steyne. Colonel Crawley discovered this, thrashed the nobleman, and left his wife. Then Becky, following her own devious ways, became an undisguised adventuress and neglected to care for her reputation. She bobbed about from one city to another, now hounded by creditors; now cared for by some rich admirer.

At last, when poor Becky had fallen very low in funds and in repute, she was found by Joseph Sedley and his sister Amelia. The old acquaintance was renewed, and gentle, generous Amelia took her one-time bosom friend into her heart and home. Major Dobbin strongly disapproved, and denounced Becky for what she was in her very presence. Amelia resented this, and Dobbin then begged Amelia, once again, to marry him—a plea he had often before made. On her refusal, Dobbin went off, vowing never to return, leaving Amelia alone with her fealty to her dead George. Whereupon, Becky, learning the state of things, told Amelia of George's note to her asking her to elope with him, and contrasting the faithless George most unfavorably with the patient and long-suffering Dobbin. So Amelia recalled Dobbin, married him, and they lived happy ever after.

Mrs. Rawdon Crawley then attached herself to Joseph Sedley, though not by any legal bonds. He was her utter slave and insured his life heavily for her benefit—and benefit she did, for he died soon after.

Rawdon Crawley died, too, and the son Rawdon refused ever to see his mother again.

Rebecca lived at Bath or Cheltenham, where some excellent people considered her a most injured woman. She devoted her life to works of piety and charity, and though when she met Amelia and her husband once they turned quickly away, Becky only cast down her eyes demurely and smiled.

Vanitas vanitatum! Which of us is happy in this world? Let us shut up the box and the puppets—our play is played out.

~⦿~

THE VICAR
OF WAKEFIELD

by

OLIVER GOLDSMITH

CONDENSATION BY PROF. WILLIAM FENWICK HARRIS

OLIVER GOLDSMITH, poet, playwright, novelist, and man of letters, was born in 1728. There has been some question as to the place of his birth, but recent investigators have claimed that it was at Smith-Hill House, Elphin, Roscommon, Ireland. While Oliver was still a child the family moved to the county of West Meath. He was sent to the village school when only seven, where the master, while teaching reading, writing, and arithmetic, man-

aged to also fill the minds of his pupils with stories of fairies, ghosts, banshees.

Goldsmith left this school at the age of nine, and went to several grammar-schools, and acquired some knowledge of the ancient languages. He was not a brilliant scholar; in fact was considered rather backward. He was small of stature, with features harsh to ugliness, and was the butt of the other boys and the masters.

After many and varied attempts to fit himself for a profession, and repeated failures, he took to writing. As his name gradually became known, his circle of acquaintances widened. He was introduced to Johnson, then considered the first of English writers, to Sir Joshua Reynolds, the famous English painter, and others.

Before the "Vicar of Wakefield" appeared in 1766, came the great crisis of Goldsmith's life. In Christmas week, 1764, he published a poem entitled "The Traveller." It was the first work to which he had put his name, and it raised him at once to the rank of a legitimate English classic.

After "The Traveller" appeared "The Vicar of Wakefield," and it rapidly obtained a popularity which has lasted down to our own times. "The earlier chapters show all the sweetness of pastoral poetry, together with all the vivacity of comedy." It is claimed that the latter part of the tale is not worthy of the beginning.

The success which he won with this story encouraged Goldsmith to try his hand as a dramatist, and he wrote the "Good Natur'd Man." The play, however, which is best known to later times is "She Stoops to Conquer." It was brought out at the Covent Garden Theater, and "pit, boxes, and galleries were in a constant roar of laughter."

Goldsmith died on April 4, 1774, in his forty-sixth year. He was laid in the churchyard of the Temple, but the spot was not marked by any inscription and is now forgotten.

I chose my wife for such qualities as would wear well. She could read any English book without much spelling; but for pickling, preserving, and cookery, none could excel her. We were ever unstinting of our hospitality, and our gooseberry wine had great reputation, so that our cousins, even to the fortieth remove, remembered their affinity without any help from the heralds' office, and came very frequently to see us.

My children were well formed and healthy. Two daughters, who, to conceal nothing, were certainly very handsome: Olivia, of luxuriant beauty, and Sophia, soft, modest, and alluring. My eldest son, George, was bred at Oxford while Moses, my second boy received a sort of miscellaneous education at home.

But alas! by a sudden stroke of ill-luck, my entire fortune was swept away, and out of fourteen thousand pounds I had but four hundred remaining. This caused my neighbor, Mr. Wilmot, to break off the engagement existing between my son George and his daughter Arabella. Mr. Wilmot had one virtue in perfection, which was prudence, too often the only one that is left us at seventy-two.

We were now poor, and wisdom bade me conform to our humble situation. I gave George five pounds and sent him to London to do the best he might for himself and for us. I found a small cure of fifteen pounds a year in a distant neighborhood, and thither we at once repaired.

On our journey we fell in with one Mr. Burchell, a pleasing and instructive companion, who told me much of Squire Thornhill, our new landlord, who, it seemed, was the pleasure-loving nephew of the great and worthy Sir William Thornhill. Mr. Burchell had the great kindness to rescue my daughter Sophia, who had the mischance to fall into a rapid stream, and who, but for his timely assistance, must have been drowned. On this, my wife immediately built a future romance for the two young people. I could not but smile, to hear her, but I am never displeased with those harmless delusions that tend to make us more happy.

Our landlord, Squire Thornhill, became a frequent visitor at our little habitation, lured, perhaps, by my wife's venison pasty—or perhaps by the charms of my pretty daughters. Mr. Burchell, too, came often, so we were not at loss for merry company. My wife, ambitious to hold our heads a little higher in the world, desired that I sell our colt at a neighboring fair, and buy, instead, a horse that would make better appearance at church or upon a visit.

She sent Moses, who was a most discreet bargainer, and whom his sisters fitted out bravely for the fair. They trimmed his locks, brushed his buckles, and cocked his hat with pins. He wore a thunder-and-lightning coat and a gosling-green waistcoat; but, alas! at the fair he was imposed upon by a prowling sharper, who, after

Moses had well bargained away the colt, managed to get the purchase money from him in return for a gross of green spectacles in shagreen cases! and so, as usual, unforeseen disaster frustrated our attempts to be fine.

My daughters planned a pleasure expedition to town, and this Mr. Burchell so strongly disapproved of that a quarrel ensued between him and my wife, and the gentleman left our house in a fit of anger, nor could Sophia's pleading looks stay him.

The town trip being still in prospect, my wife decreed that I go to the fair myself and sell our one remaining horse. But when one would-be purchaser examined the animal and declared him blind of one eye, another observed he had a spavin, a third perceived he had a windgall, a fourth said he had the botts, and so on, I began to have a most hearty contempt for the poor beast myself, for I reflected that the number of witnesses was a strong presumption they were right, and St. Gregory himself is of the same opinion. However, I at last sold my horse, but had the misfortune to receive in payment a forged and worthless draft, the same being, indeed, the wicked work of the very man who had sold Moses the spectacles.

Mr. Burchell being absent from our fireside, only Sophia missed him, for the rest of us were greatly pleased by the visits of our landlord, who now came often. It must be owned that my wife laid a thousand schemes to entrap him as a husband for Olivia, and used every art to magnify the merits of her daughter. The results, however, being small, my wife sought to rouse Mr. Thornhill's jealousy by hinting of Olivia's marriage with Farmer Williams, a most worthy though humble neighbor. This failing to egg on the backward Thornhill, the wedding-day was set for Olivia and Farmer Williams. But four days before the day I learned to my distraction that my Olivia had gone off secretly in a post chaise with a gentleman who, as I was told by an onlooker, kissed her and said he would die for her. Well did I know the villain who had thus robbed me of my sweet, innocent child; it was none other than the wicked Thornhill. My wife fell to loud berating of him, and Olivia as well, but I declared my house and heart should ever be open to the returning repentant sinner. I set out to find her—but my first efforts persuaded me that it was Mr. Burchell, and not Squire Thornhill, who had seduced my darling. This, though, was not the truth. 'Twas but part of the villain's plan. After long search I found my darling girl, in a hiding-place whither she had fled from the dreadful Thornhill who, under pretense of marriage, had ruined her. It seems they were married by a black scoundrel who had before married the squire to six or eight other wives!

I took my poor darling home, only to be met with the astounding news that my little home was utterly destroyed by fire. With what cheerfulness we might, we made shift to live in one of our farm out-buildings, and endeavored to enjoy our former serenity.

But this was not to be. The despicable Thornhill, about to marry Miss Wilmot—yes, the same to whom my son George was once be-trothed—made proposal that we marry my Olivia to another, yet let her still be a friend of his own. My righteous denunciation of this re-sulted in the squire's threats of retribution, and this came in the form of a demand for my annual rent, the which I was all unable to pay. I was thereupon thrown into a debtor's prison, but even here I endeavored to preserve my calm, and after my usual meditations, and having praised my Heavenly Corrector, I slept with the utmost tranquility.

Man frequently calls in the consolations of philosophy, which, I have found, are amusing, but often fallacious. In the prison, though I attempted a much-needed reform movement, and though I lectured and advised with all my powers, I suffered many and various sor-rows and disappointments. I was informed of the death of my daugh-ter, Olivia—an untrue report, thank Heaven! I was told of the for-cible abduction of Sophia by desperate villains.

From this danger, however, dear Sophia was rescued by Mr. Burchell, to whom I willingly gave my treasure for a wife. And, we then learned that our friend Mr. Burchell was in reality the great Sir William Thornhill, and my daughter would be a fine lady. And, another joy, I learned that my daughter Olivia was the lawful wife of Squire Thornhill, his previous marriages all having been so performed by the wicked clergyman that they were not legal.

Whereupon, my son George having reappeared, Miss Wilmot, his one-time love, accepted anew his offers, and those two were happy together. As a cap-sheaf to my harvest of good fortune, the rascal who did me out of my fortune so long ago was arrested and forced to give up his effects. My wrongs being set right, I, of course, was freed of the prison, and it now remained only that my gratitude in good fortune should exceed my former submission in adversity.

VIVIAN GREY

by

BENJAMIN DISRAELI

CONDENSATION BY ALICE G. GROZIER

BENJAMIN DISRAELI (Lord Beaconsfield), eldest son of Isaac D'Israeli, was born in London in 1804. Although all the children were born into the Jewish communion, the father, with all his household, withdrew from the faith when the son Benjamin was but twelve years old.

"None of the family was akin to Benjamin for genius and character, except Sarah, the eldest child, to whom he was indebted for a wise, unswerving, and sympathetic devotion, when, in his earlier days, he needed it most."

At fifteen Disraeli was sent to a Unitarian school at Walthamstow. He soon, however, left there and went to school no more. With his father's guidance and the help of his fine library, Benjamin started out to educate himself.

The vivid imagination and wonderful perceptive quality of Disraeli was much helped by his association with persons of distinction in literary pursuits; and his keen powers of observation and wide range of reading helped him in the writing of his novels, as well as in the political career which he chose.

In 1837 Disraeli won the election to Parliament, being returned from Maidstone. Many years later he became Prime Minister, but for a brief period only, resigning in 1868 in favor of Mr. Gladstone. He was Prime Minister again from 1874 to 1880.

His greatest gift was not the romantic imagination which he possessed so abundantly, but the perceptive, interpretative, judicial, or divining imagination, "without which there can be no man of great affairs." His novels contain many character portraits of the men and women of his time. "Vivian Grey" is said to be a pen-picture of the author.

Disraeli died at his home in Curzon Street on the 19th of April, 1881. Then the greatness of his popularity and its warmth were first declared. "No such demonstration of grief was expected, even by those who grieved the most." He lies in the Hughen Churchyard, but within the church is a marble tablet to his memory, placed there by Queen Victoria. The anniversary of his death has ever since been honored and is called "Primrose Day."

Among Disraeli's works are: "Vivian Grey," "Coningsby," "Endymion," "Sibyl," "Lothair," "The Young Duke," "Venetia," "Tancred," "Contarini Fleming," and other novels, besides many political articles and like literature.

Disraeli's story of Vivian Grey, like others of his novels, deals largely with politics, and contains character portraits of well-known persons of the period.

When Vivian Grey reached the age of five years it was discovered that the treatment of a doting mamma and over-attentive nurses had spoiled the child, and it was decided that he had better be sent away to school; when, however, the subject was under discussion, there was a strenuous protest from Vivian against curls and going to school.

"I won't have my hair curl, mamma; the boys will laugh at me," bawled the spoiled youngster. "Charles Appleyard told me so; his hair curled, and the boys called him girl. Papa! give me some more claret. I won't go to school!"

But in spite of these protests he was sent to school, where he stayed some four years, when it was decided that he should remain at home for a time and do his studying there; but he was later sent off again, this time to the school of Mr. Dallas at Burnsley Vicarage.

The rumor of the arrival of "a new fellow" circulated rapidly through the inmates of the Vicarage, and the fifty young rascals were preparing to quiz the newcomer when the school-room door opened and Mr. Dallas, accompanied by Vivian Grey, entered.

"A dandy, by Jove!" whispered one. "What a knowing set-out," squeaked a second; "Mummy sick," growled a third; this last exclamation was, however, a scandalous libel, for certainly no being ever stood in a pedagogue's presence with more perfect sang-froid and with a bolder front than did, at this moment, Vivian Grey.

The young savages at Burnsley Vicarage had caught a Tartar;

in a very few days Vivian was decidedly the most popular fellow in the school; "he was so dashing! so devilish good-tempered, so completely up to everything!"

Vivian developed talents of a literary nature which inspired great admiration among his fellow-pupils and also in the mind of Mr. Dallas.

But there are other attributes which will win the admiration of a school of real boys; and this proved to be the case at Burnsley Vicarage, when, as so often happens, some of the boys, jealous of Vivian's popularity, found, as they thought, an opportunity to triumph over him. There was trouble between the followers of Vivian and those of Mallet, the head usher; one of the latter made an insulting remark to Vivian which he promptly resented and the battle was on, and Vivian Grey showed that he could fight as well as write.

Vivian's chief characteristic was a burning ambition; with this he had a great amount of courage and self-assurance, and besides these attributes, tact combined with a pleasing personal presence and manners.

At a dinner in his father's home, when Vivian was still a very young man, he made the acquaintance of the Marquess of Carabas. He came to the rescue of the marquess and his opinions in an after-dinner discussion, during which he quoted a whole passage from Bolingbroke in support of the marquess; this was challenged by Vivian's father, who knew his son's habit of quoting the opinions of others, which were more often his own opinions put into the mouth of some one else; so Mr. Grey, looking smilingly at his son, remarked, "Vivian, my dear, can you tell me in what work of Bolingbroke I can find the eloquent passage you have just quoted?"

"Ask Mr. Hargrave, sir," replied the son, with perfect coolness; then turning to Mr. Hargrave he said, "You know you are reputed to be the most profound political student in the House, and more intimately acquainted than any other with the works of Bolingbroke."

Mr. Hargrave knew no such thing, but he was a weak man, and, seduced by the compliment, he was afraid to prove himself unworthy of it by confessing his ignorance of the passage.

Vivian carried this same self-assurance into politics and won many triumphs by tactics of the kind. He attached himself to the marquess, and was responsible for his entering politics, spending much time at the estate of the marquess, "Château Désir," with large house parties of famous persons, some interesting to him and some otherwise.

Among the guests at one time was a relative of the marquess, a young matron, Mrs. Felix Lorraine, who was much impressed with Vivian and tried her charms upon him, but to no avail; then in pique she attempted intrigue to make trouble between the marquess and Vivian, which she came very near to accomplishing.

Meantime Vivian kept his eyes and thoughts for the pawns upon the political chessboard, among which was a Mr. Frederick Cleveland, who attracted his attention, and when the marquess's party was looking for a leader, Vivian suggested the name of Mr. Cleveland. Now it happened that these two, the marquess and Cleveland, had been at odds, which Vivian did not at first realize; when he was alone he said to himself: "What have I done? I am sure that Lucifer may know, for I do not. This Cleveland is, I suppose, but a man; I saw the feeble fools were wavering, and to save all made a leap in the dark. Well, is my skull cracked? We shall see."

Again was Vivian's assurance to the fore; he was certainly "all things to all men." He had the power, with his silver tongue, of conciliating many persons, but not so Mr. Cleveland.

The first great trouble came to Vivian when, after many attempts at diplomacy and the political game, he estranged both the marquess and Mr. Cleveland; the latter, while under the influence of wine, met Vivian at their club and in a fit of anger struck him, and a duel was the result. Vivian fired into the air, hoping that the affair would end safely, but Cleveland insisted upon another shot; Vivian shot at random but his bullet pierced Cleveland's heart.

A great remorse seized Vivian and for many weeks he was ill with fever at his father's home, under the loving care of his mother. "But the human mind can master many sorrows," and after a desperate relapse and another miraculous rally Vivian Grey arose from his bed. He left England and traveled in Germany, visiting, among other places, Frankfort during the time of the fair.

On a bright sunshiny afternoon, while crossing the square, Vivian was attracted by an excited crowd of people around a conjurer, whose appearance was of the oddest kind and held Vivian's attention; he was called Essper George. Later he became serving-man to Vivian, who had offered to protect the fellow against the crowd he had in some way angered.

Vivian and Essper George had many lively adventures during their travels, all of which experiences, whether of politics or romance, gave Vivian new ideas of the world, and proved to be a most interesting school for him. He one day rescued a German nobleman from a wild boar, and was invited to visit at his castle; while there a romantic attachment between him and a young German lady of title engaged Vivian's attention for a time, but his thoughts, in spite of himself, constantly returned to two of his English friends.

Like many a knight and his serving-man of olden times, Vivian and Essper George found themselves on several occasions in very dangerous situations; sometimes it was Vivian to the rescue, and at others Essper.

On leaving that part of Germany where he had been entertained as honored guest of his titled acquaintances, Vivian passed through a small settlement where there were going on preparations for a wedding, and Vivian discovered that the bridegroom was an old friend from Heidelberg, Eugene von Konongstein, and he was persuaded to stop and assist at the wedding. All was so quiet and peaceful there that it set Vivian to speculating about his own future.

In the morning the travelers were on their way again; the day being intensely hot and sultry, they withdrew to the shade of the woods, and while resting there Vivian asked Essper about his history. For a time they sat in quiet conversation, then were rudely interrupted by the approach of a terrific storm during which a lake on the top of the mountain burst and became a falling ocean, carrying all before it.

Essper's horse being swept from him, he climbed into a tree, but the lightning struck, felling the tree and killing Essper—then "Vivian's horse, with a maddened snort, dashed down the hill, his master clinging to his neck; finally, standing upright in the air, he flung his rider and fell dead."

THE WAR OF THE WORLDS*

by

H. G. WELLS

CONDENSATION BY ALFRED S. CLARK

HERBERT GEORGE WELLS was born at Bromley, Kent, September 21, 1866, the son of a famous professional cricket-player. His mother was an innkeeper's daughter who had been a lady's maid before her marriage. The boy had an irregular education, but he was quick to learn, and at the age of sixteen, after working as an attendant in a store, he secured a position as assistant in a grammar-school. He obtained a scholarship at London University, was graduated with high honors, and taught science in a private school.

In 1893 he began to write, doing articles for, and later becoming dramatic critic of, the "Pall Mall Gazette." He was already interested in social conditions and an untiring student of science. These two interests he combined in the series of romances that opened with "The Time Machine." In novels and short stories he created startling fantasies of the future, displaying his most abundant invention in "The War of the Worlds." He oftentimes discussed future wars in these stories and his forecasts were amazingly like what was seen on the battle-fields of Europe.

In the meantime he had been writing stories about contemporary life and books about social conditions. These he turned to more and more with the years. Of his later novels, bristling with wit and ideas, those that have been most widely read and discussed include "Kipps," "Tono-Bungay," "Ann Veronica," "The New Machiavelli," "Marriage," and "Joan and Peter." Most popular of all was "Mr. Britling Sees It Through," regarded by many as the best war novel written in English.

He died in London, August 13, 1946.

* Printed by permission of, and arrangement with, Harper & Bros., authorized publishers.

What I marvel at now, when I recall the days when the Martians were speeding earthward, is our unconcern. The skies were peopled with incredible evil, with unimaginably repulsive monsters armed with superhuman weapons. The catastrophic Things were hurtling on, covetous of our greener and warmer planet, and lovers wandered through English lanes, with no thought of the swift and scorching death above their heads.

Through a telescope, I had watched one of the colossal squirts of flame on the rim of the tiny red planet. It did not occur to me that these gaseous jets accompanied the firing of a mighty gun and had launched ten huge cylinders into space. Learning to ride a bicycle interested me more than eruptions on Mars. The planet seemed so remote. Forty million miles away!

Ogilvy, the astronomer, found the first messenger. He had seen it falling and supposed it a wandering meteorite, but its shape surprised him. It was cylindrical, fully thirty yards across the exposed face. It was so hot that he could not get near it. Then, to his utter amazement, the top began to unscrew. There was something in it, something alive! Not until then did he link it with the flashes on Mars.

Late that afternoon I saw the Martian. I was one of a curious crowd in front of the cylinder when the lid fell off. I peered into the black interior and fancied I saw shadows stirring. Then something like a snake wriggled into sight. I stood stricken with terror. A round body, about four feet across, pulled itself painfully to the opening.

I had expected to see something like a man, fantastic, perhaps, but two-legged. This thing was just an oily, leathery body, legless and armless, with a chinless and noseless face. About the quivering mouth wavered sixteen long tentacles. Two great eyes, dark and luminous, were mirrors for an extraordinary brain. The creature panted and heaved, weighed down by the greater pull of gravity on earth. An intense loathing came over me. Suddenly the monster toppled over into the pit. Then I ran, madly.

From a distance I watched the deputation that went out under a white flag. I saw three flashes of greenish light, and darts of fire leaped from one to another of the little figures. Even as I saw them touched with death, I did not realize what was happening. Suddenly I knew and again I ran.

People near by slept unconcernedly that night, although the heat rays had set half a dozen villas aflame and pine-trees were red torches. We were sure that these dangerous invaders were fatally sluggish. A well-aimed shell would finish them. And while we slept, the Martians were methodically rearing those mighty machines that were so soon to shatter our neat theories about their helplessness. That night another cylinder fell and eight more were driving on.

It was the next night that I saw the striding Martians. "Boilers on stilts," I heard them called later. I saw them by flashes of lightning and the glow of countless fires, clanking machines one hundred feet high, moving upon three gigantic legs like an exaggerated tripod, driving on with an express train's speed, smashing everything in their path. At the tops, crouched in metal hoods, lay the Martians.

Looking out from my windows at dawn, I beheld an abominable desolation, a blackened world that had been green and fair. I struck out for London and for miles saw not a living being. I had reached the Thames when I saw the Things coming, five of them. I ran for the water. Straight toward me sped one, but I might have been an ant in a man's path. It strode through the river and towered above Shepperton. Then six hidden guns belched together. One shell struck the hood and there was a horrible confusion of flesh and blood and metal. Something drove the uncontrolled machine on, crashing through the village, topping over the church tower, collapsing in the river. The others rushed to the spot and the air was filled with hissing of heat rays and crackling of flames. Shepperton leaped into flame. I staggered to the shore and when I looked up, the Things were bearing away the smashed machine.

I stumbled on, panic-stricken, dazed. The world was doomed. These monsters could slay with heat rays beyond the range of our biggest guns. Not again could we kill one of them by surprise. Terror stalked through London. To the horror of heat rays had been added the black smoke, a cloud of poison that blighted all living things. So London streamed in flight, 6,000,000 people roaring out along the highways until they were like rivers in flood.

I fell into a doze under a hedge and there the curate joined me. He was half mad with fright and clung to me. We plodded on to a suburb where we sought refuge in a deserted house. At midnight came a blinding flash. When day broke, we peered through a peep-hole and in the garden was a Martian. Embedded in the earth was another glowing cylinder.

For fifteen days I was penned there, so I saw more of the monsters than any other man now living. I watched their intricate machines—

the automatic digger, the sensitive handling-machine like a metallic spider—so flexible and so swiftly sure that they seemed centuries in advance of our rigid machinery. I could study, too, the Martian habits. I learned that evolution had made them all brain, cold, remorseless intelligences unswayed by emotion. They neither slept nor ate; they were sexless and their young were budded off, like the young of corals. Most horrible to me was the fact that they injected men's blood into their veins for nourishment.

It was this that drove me to act as I did when the curate went raving mad. I knew that his shouts would warn the Martians of our presence and I tried to silence him. He broke away and I caught him in the kitchen; where I felled _im with a meat-chopper. He dropped, stunned, and then I saw two dark eyes at the window. I fled to the coal-cellar and above me I heard a tapping, tapping, and then the noise of a heavy body being dragged across the floor.

I piled wood and coal over me when I heard that tapping at the cellar door. Through crevices I could see the terrible arm of a handling-machine, waving, feeling, examining. Once it ran across the heel of my boot and I nearly screamed. Then it went away.

A week passed before I dared look out. About the peep-hole was massed quantities of the red weed that the Martians had brought —evidently vegetation on Mars is red. I pushed it aside and gazed out. The garden was deserted.

I crept into a desolate world. About me was a smashed village. I struggled on through the outskirts of London, and not until I reached Wimbledon Common did I meet a man. He had food and drink and plans for the future, visions of a people living in the great drains until they had science enough to conquer their conquerors. I stayed with him until I had regained my strength and then walked into dead London.

The metropolis was stilled of all its humming life. Here and there were heaps of dead, withered by black smoke; here and there were signs of destruction, but it was little changed except for the horrible quiet. I was near South Kensington when I heard the mournful howling, "Ulla, ulla!" Not until the next day did I see the hood of the giant that was making this sobbing wail. He did not move, nor did three others that I saw, standing strangely still. Driven by fear, I resolved to end it all. I walked toward the Thing nearest me and saw birds circling about the hood, tearing at something within.

I scrambled hastily up a great rampart and below me was the

Martian camp. They were all dead, nearly fifty of them, some in their machines and others prone upon the ground. They could conquer man, but they had fallen before man's most relentless foe, the disease bacteria of earth.

Whatever destruction was done, the hand of the destroyer was stayed. All the gaunt wrecks, the blackened skeletons of houses that stared so dismally at the sunlit grass of the hill, would presently be echoing with the hammers of the restorers and ringing with the tapping of the trowels. At the thought I extended by hands toward the sky and began thanking God. In a year, thought I—in a year. . . .

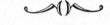

WAVERLEY

by

SIR WALTER SCOTT*

CONDENSATION BY HENRY T. SCHNITTKIND, PH. D.

Let us for a few thrilling minutes transport ourselves to Scotland in 1745, when its Highland forests teemed with the caves of robbers and its moors resounded with the shouting of the chieftains as they battled to restore the exiled House of Stuart to the throne, then occupied by King George II.

Are you ready? Then let us join the handsome young English officer, Edward Waverley. He is about to visit the cavern of the Highland robber, Donald Bean Lean, little dreaming of the maze of adventures into which this visit will lead him. Waverley is enjoying a furlough at the Scottish Lowland mansion of the eccentric, garrulous, and lovable Baron of Bradwardine. The baron's seventeen-year-old daughter, Rose Bradwardine, "with a profusion of hair of paly gold, and a skin like the snow of her own mountains in whiteness," has fallen in love with Waverley, who, however, finds her tender attentions too tame for his poetic imagination. It is his

* For biographical information see page 138.

ambition to explore the wild regions of romance, and fortunately an opportunity presents itself. The baron's cattle, having been stolen by the robber, Donald Bean Lean, are restored through the interposition of the baron's friends, the powerful Highland chieftain, Fergus MacIvor. The chieftain's lieutenant, Evan Dhu Maccombich, invites Waverley to visit Donald Bean Lean's den. After a journey through Lowland glen and brae, over Highland lake and forest, they arrived at the cavern, where Waverly spends an interesting night in the presence of Donald Bean Lean and his company of robbers, who come singly or in groups, each cutting with his dirk a slice of flesh from a carcass suspended in the cave, broiling the steak and washing it down with draughts of undiluted whisky. A buxom Highland lass, the robber's daughter, takes care of this romantic den.

The next morning Evan Dhu Maccombich induces Waverley to visit the Highland Mansion of his master, Fergus MacIvor, whose handsome face "resembles a smiling summer's day in which, however, one can detect signs that it may thunder and lighten before evening." His love for his beautiful and accomplished sister, Flora MacIvor, is equaled only by his ambition to restore the exiled Stuart family to the throne.

Fergus entertains Waverley at a picturesque banquet attended by hundreds of the clansmen of MacIvor. After the banquet Flora asks Waverley to meet her in her favorite haunt near a cascade. As Edward approached the waterfall "the sun, now stooping in the west, seemed to add more than human brilliancy to the full expressive darkness of Flora's eyes. Edward thought he had never, even in his wildest dreams, imagined a picture of such exquisite loveliness."

Conscious of her charms in this "Eden in the wilderness," Flora sings to him a stirring martial song which she accompanies on a small Scottish harp, the melody blending harmoniously with the sound of the waters of the cataract. Waverley, bewitched by her loveliness, proposes to Flora, who promptly rejects him.

Disappointed, but not discouraged, Waverley gladly accepts an invitation to remain at Fergus MacIvor's mansion for a few days. While attending a stag-hunt he sustains an injury which keeps him in bed for some time. On his recovery he is both astonished and incensed to learn that the colonel of his regiment has reduced him to the ranks for "absence without leave." His anger is aggravated by a letter from his father, who, through a political blunder, has lost a high position in the court of King George. At the same time, too,

Rose Bradwardine writes to him that her father, the baron, has been obliged to flee in order to escape arrest for his adherence to the cause of the exiled Stuarts.

Despite these apparent acts of injustice Waverley remains loyal to King George and decides to return home. On the way to England, however, he is arrested and charged with desertion and treason. Knowing himself to be innocent, he is mystified at this turn of affairs. What plot has been hatched against him, and by whom? His stupefaction increases when he is rescued by a band of Highlanders. Who are these Highlanders? And why do they interest themselves in him? These and similar questions perplex his bewildered senses.

Wounded during the rescue, he is nursed back to health in a peasant's hut by a young girl who always manages to make her escape whenever he tries to catch a glimpse of her. When his health is restored the Highlanders take him to Edinburgh, where he meets his friends, Fergus MacIvor and the Baron of Bradwardine, among the insurgents who are making an attempt to recover the throne for their gallant leader, the exiled Prince Charles Edward. Waverley now feels compelled to join this army.

Just before enlisting Waverley tries once more to win Flora's love, but is again repulsed. He therefore throws himself heart and soul into the cause of the young prince.

The army is about to engage in its first battle. The sun has just risen. The rocks, and the very sky itself, "resound with the clang of the bagpipes." The mountaineers rouse themselves with the hum and bustle of a multitude of bees, arming and ready to swarm out of their hives.

The insurgents win the battle and Waverley captures a brave English officer who remains alone beside his cannon after the others have fled. The officer turns out to be a certain Colonel Talbot, an old friend of the house of Waverley whom Edward has never met before. Colonel Talbot has left an invalid wife in order to find Waverley and to induce him to return home, since his conduct has put the entire Waverley family into danger.

When Edward learns that Colonel Talbot's imprisonment is likely to cost the life of his sick wife, he obtains the colonel's release. In return for this kindness Colonel Talbot promises to intercede with the English king in Waverley's behalf. The way for such a plea has fortunately been paved by the revelation of some of the mysteries attending the arrest of Waverley for desertion and treason. By means of a packet of letters, which Donald Bean Lean's daughter has slipped into Edward's baggage, he learns that her father, the Highland robber, being in the service of Prince Charles Edward, and wishing to gain favor in his eyes, has concocted a plot whereby the British government was led to believe that Waverley was a traitor, thereby forcing him into the army of the insurgent prince. Only one question now remains unexplained. Who was the girl that nursed him during his fever in the peasant's hut?

Before the solution is found to this question the insurgent army is totally defeated, Fergus MacIvor is captured, the prince escapes, and Waverley, who is now also a fugitive, pays a secret visit to the mansion of the Baron of Bradwardine, for he is anxious to learn about the fate of some of his friends. He finds the baron in hiding in that selfsame hut where he had been nursed during his fever. Here he learns that it was Rose Bradwardine who nursed him. It was Rose, also, who had paid Donald Bean Lean with her mother's jewelry in order to induce him to rescue Waverley after his arrest for treason. Overcome with gratitude for such devotion, Edward asks the Baron of Bradwardine for his daughter's hand. He can now marry her in security; for, thanks to the kindness of Colonel Talbot and other influential Englishmen, both he and the baron have been pardoned.

It takes the loquacious baron an hour to tell Rose of Edward's love for her. It takes Edward just five minutes to convince her of it.

Their happiness would now be complete but for the sad fate of Fergus MacIvor, who has been condemned to death. He faces the executioner unflinchingly, expressing no regret for his fate, but only the hope that "they will set my head on the Scotch gate, that I may look, even after death, to the blue hills of my own country, which I love so dearly."

With this shadow to mar the sunshine of their happiness, Edward and Rose are married.

Thus we come to the end of the romantic tale, and we must again return to the drab reality of our every-day existence. But before so doing, let us, together with Flora MacIvor, who has joined the Scottish Benedictine nuns in Paris, bid the happy couple good luck and adieu!

WESTWARD HO!

by

CHARLES KINGSLEY

CONDENSATION BY JAMES B. CONNOLLY

CHARLES KINGSLEY was born on the 12th of June, 1819, at Holne Vicarage, under the brow of Dartmoor, in Devonshire, England. He left Holne when six weeks old, and never saw his birthplace until he was a man of thirty; yet Devonshire scenes and associations had always a mysterious charm for him.

Kingsley was said to have been an instance of the truth of Darwin's theory, "that genius which implies a wonderfully complex combination of high faculties tends to be inherited." His love of art, his sporting tastes, his fighting blood, he inherited from his father's side, the men of whose family were soldiers for generations.

From his mother's side came not only his love of travel, science, and literature, but the romance of his nature and his sense of humor.

When Charles was still a young child his father, the Rev. Charles Kingsley, moved to Barnock Rectory. It was at Barnock that the boy's earliest sporting tastes and love of natural history developed; as soon as he was old enough he was mounted on his father's horse in front of the keeper, to bring back the game-bag.

The glorious sunsets over the Fens had great charm for him all his life; the pictures of the Fens and the life there were stamped on his mind and inspired him, in after years, in writing the story of "Hereward the Wake."

Later his father moved to Clovelly; the new elements in life here, the unique scenery and the impressionable character of the people, their courage and the wild life of the men, threw a charm of romance about the place, which colored his life. This is shown in "Westward Ho!" and in the song of "Three Fishers," which was not an imaginary picture, but a true delineation of what he saw again and again at Clovelly.

As a preacher, Kingsley was vivid, eager, and earnest. He was keenly interested in the movement known as Christian Socialism.

As a novelist, his chief power lay in his descriptive faculties. Besides sermons, poems, and addresses, he wrote the "Saint's Tragedy," a drama, and among others the following novels: "Alton Locke," "Yeast," "Westward Ho!" and "Hypatia." Many of his writings in "The Christian Socialist" and "Politics for the People" were signed by the pseudonym "Parson Lot."

He died at Eversley, January 23, 1875.

> With a hey bonny-boat and a ho bonny-boat
> Sail westward-ho and away!

With wonderful speech of Spanish gold and the vast, rich countries lying to the west, Capt. John Oxenham was home again; and not a promise he made but was increased tenfold by his swearing henchman, Salvation Yeo.

Amyas Leigh, a stout Devon youth, was afire to take the sea with Captain John as he listened; but his godfather, Sir Richard Grenvil, said he was yet too young. Later, it might be. And later he went, his first voyage being with the famous Sir Francis Drake around the world.

Following that voyage came fighting in Ireland in the company of Sir Walter Raleigh and the poet Spenser; and then an expedition with Sir Humphrey Gilbert wherein, because of mutinies, disease, ill-found ships, and great storms, Sir Humphrey met his death; and Amyas came home in sadness.

At this time Amyas, with a score of other Devon gallants, was in love with Mistress Rose Salterne; but she was for no Devon cavalier. A Spanish captain of bravery and charm was dwelling in Devon till his ransom should be coming, and it was he who captured the fancy of the lovely but capricious Rose, and carried her off to Caracas, whereof he had been appointed governor.

Whether Rose went as Don Guzman's wife or leman, no one could say. Mr. Salterne, father to Rose, and rich merchant of the port, gave a ship and five hundred pounds toward the fitting out, the same to be commanded by Amyas, by now experienced in seamanship and the handling of rough men; and so he sailed on his first venture on the good ship *Rose,* of two hundred tons burthen and one hundred men, with beef, pork, and good ale in abundance, and culverins, swivels, muskets, calivers, long-bows, pikes, and cutlasses aplenty. He was to discover the whereabouts and condition of Rose if he could but surely to damage to his utmost what Spaniards he should fall afoul of. A commission to his liking for it was an article of faith with Amyas as with most young English rovers of that day, that all Spaniards were cruel and cowardly, even as his own great Queen Elizabeth was all white purity. With Amyas went Frank his brother scholar and courtier, and mad likewise for love of Rose Salterne; also Salvation Yeo, his own Captain Oxenham being long dead.

Westward they sailed to tropic shores; to low wooded hills, spangled by fireflies; westward through wondrous seas where islands and capes hung suspended in air. In a wooden bight they spied a caravel, which they captured, and in her they found a store of brown pearls; also a cargo of salt hides, which smelt evilly as they burned.

Amyas sailed on to La Guayra in Caracas, finding Don Guzman not at home, but having sight of Rose Salterne, she being truly Don Guzman's wife, in a garden of the governor's palace. In the fight with Don Guzman's men Frank Leigh was wounded and captured. Amyas was knocked unconscious, but taken safely away by his men.

Leaving fatal La Guayra far behind, the *Rose* thrashed through rolling seas and overhauled a long caravel, too long indeed to maneuver with the nimble *Rose.* Two galleys were also with her. Victory fell to Amyas, but a victory which left his ship so battered and his crew so decimated that he ran into a little bay for repairs and recuperation. Here, with their culverins and swivels behind a stockade, Don Guzman came upon them, in force too strong for their shattered numbers; so, first burning the *Rose,* they turned their backs to the sea and marched inland.

And now came hope of glory for their Queen and for themselves great treasure in quest of the Golden City in the Kingdom of Manoa, whereof friendly Indians told them. Through untrodden hills and forests they marched, past the falls of the Orinoco and the upper waters of the great Amazon, from low swamps to high plateaus, wherefrom they viewed the eternal snows of Chimborazo towering above the thunder-cloud and the fiery cone of Cotopaxi flaming against the stars; a region eight hundred miles in length by four hundred miles in width they traversed. Three years of fever and cold and famine they spent on that trail, and once a gold pack-train loosely guarded fell to their hands; but of the Golden City never a trace.

They came upon a white maiden, Ayanacora, golden-haired, tall, and beautiful, treated as a princess by the Indians with whom she dwelt. Amyas was for leaving her, having witnessed on former voyages the evil influence of women among lonely men; but she by signs made it clear she would not be left. He packed her off. She came back, and, she being by then far from her habitation, he had not the heart to cast her adrift in the vast wilderness. So every man solemnly pledged to treat her with honor. She came to be with them in the adventure where Amyas, his crew much worn and wasted and he desirous of heartening them up, set upon a great galleon in the harbor of Cartagena. Silently, in two canoes, they made the harbor, and, it being night, boarded the galleon secretly by her stern gallery; and after a short, fierce fight the galleon, with much treasure aboard, fell into their hands. It was here in this fight that Amyas would have been run through by the Spanish captain but for Ayanacora, who came leaping from behind and knifed the Spaniard ere he could drive home the long blade.

But forty of their one hundred remained; notwithstanding which they sailed with much content in the great galleon to England. Ayanacora, sailing with them, did one day burst into singing of sea-songs which only English sailors knew; which caused Salvation Yeo to ask questions, to which, as she acquired the English tongue, she made answer; which answers recalled to Yeo that fair Spanish lady of Panama who had run off with Captain Oxenham, and to whom was born the baby girl which was later made off with. Captain Oxenham had suffered death at the hands of the Spanish husband and Yeo himself had escaped only with many cruel scars, but the scarred old rover had spent days enough with the lovely little girl to know now, as in a dozen ways he proved, that this was the daughter of Captain Oxenham and his Spanish lady, the little girl to whom he had taught the English sea-songs before she was taken from them.

Homeward the great galleon ran before the southwest breeze, and proudly into Plymouth Sound she sailed one day without veiling topsails or lowering the flag of Spain, for which they had like to get a solid shot from the admiral of the port.

And so Amyas came home in honor and glory, but with the lovely and loving Ayanacora he would have nothing to do, she having in her too much of that Spanish blood which he hated. However, his gentle mother, understanding better the worth of loyal virtue, took the girl to her bosom.

Once more Amyas took the sea, now as an admiral under Lord Howard, who had gathered all of England's stout ships and seamen to fight Spain's Armada. Amyas won his share of glory in that fight, and he might have come home in safety; but there was Don Guzman, who had left Rose to be put to death, even as he had his brother Frank, the one for a traitor and the other for a heretic.

Amyas must have his vengeance of Don Guzman, who was commanding a ship of the Armada, and so he strove to hold close to him; but the tempest, which seemed to bear hate for the Spanish fleet, now cast Don Guzman's tall caravel to her death on the sands of Flanders. The vengeance of Amyas was sated, as was Yeo's; but almost on the instant, from the heart of the tempest flew a white bolt of lightning to strike down both him and Yeo, Yeo to his death and Amyas to the blindness of both eyes.

So Amyas came home from his last cruise, a great, helpless hulk, as he bitterly said; but so mayhap only as such could one of his nature have ever come to understand the heart of a lovely, virtuous woman.

It was the patience of Ayanacora, the wisdom of his mother, which taught him. "Fear not, Amyas," he heard his mother's voice saying—"fear not to take that dear girl to your heart; for it is your mother who lays her there."

And so at last Amyas came to understand.

THE WHITE COMPANY

by

SIR ARTHUR CONAN DOYLE

CONDENSATION BY A. J. STAFFORD

SIR ARTHUR CONAN DOYLE was born on May 22, 1859, in Edinburgh, and died July 8, 1930. His father, Charles Doyle, was an artist of fantastic imagination. The boy went to Stonyhurst College, studied in Germany, and returned to take his degree at Edinburgh University in 1885. He signed as ship's doctor for a two years' whaling trip in the Arctic, traveled in West Africa, and finally settled as a doctor in Southsea. His restless imagination found constant expression in short stories. Sherlock Holmes made first appearance in "A Study in Scarlet" (1887) but won his immense popularity in "The Adventures of Sherlock Holmes." The original of the genius-detective was Doctor Bell of Edinburgh University. The popular hero lived again in "The Memoirs of Sherlock Holmes," "The Hound of the Baskervilles," and "The Return of Sherlock Holmes."

The numerous Sherlock Holmes tales and the historical romances show but two sides to the author's unusual versatility. He always kept up his keen interest in medicine, his first profession. In "The Crime of the Congo" he wrote about the cruelties of King Leopold's administration of the Congo rubber traffic. In South Africa, and more recently in France, he studied and wrote about modern war. Long before the great war overwhelmed Europe he saw the storm-cloud gathering and in short stories he forecast some of the terrors and marvels of war as it might be and as it proved to be. In "Great Britain and the Next War," in 1913, he exposed the specious arguments of General Bernhardi.

For many years he was investigating spiritualism, starting as a convinced unbeliever. More and more he was won over to complete faith in communications from the spirit world, and in numerous articles and "The New Revelation" (1918) he set down the story of his progress from skepticism to belief.

The Abbot of Beaulieu sat in a lofty room, before him his thirty monks. All were labor-stained and weary, for the abbot was a hard man. A big, red-haired youth, the black sheep of the fold, stood awaiting punishment. His sins were many, the worst being that he had "conversed with a maiden . . . and did carry her across a stream, to the infinite relish of the devil."

The abbot rose in wrath. "John of Hordle!" he thundered, "thou shalt be cast into the outer world! Seize him and scourge him from the precincts!"

But the culprit had different plans. Lifting the big oaken desk, he hurled it at his accusers, sprang through the open door, and escaped.

"He is possessed of a devil!" they shouted.

Far different was the leave-taking of Alleyne Edricson, a slender, yellow-haired youth, favorite of all.

"Twenty years ago," said the abbot, "your father, the Franklin of Minstead, died, leaving to the abbey three hides of land, and you, his infant son, for us to rear until you reached man's estate; and now you must return into the world."

Alleyne was a learned clerk, skilled in music, writing, painting, and other attainments. His reading was scant and he had only a vague idea of Europe, beyond which were "Jerusalem, the Holy Land, and the great river which hath its source in the Garden of Eden." The abbot now told him of strange nations, including that of the fair but evil women who slay with beholding, like the basilisk. After many prayers, blessings, and warnings from the abbot against sin and the snares of women, Alleyne left the peaceful abbey and went out into the world. And he found it a fearful place.

His only relative was a brother, now Socman of Minstead, who had earned an evil name. Alleyne decided to go to his brother and try to reform him. On the way he was set upon by robbers and would have been killed had not the bailiff appeared. He was then made sick by seeing one robber shot and the other decapitated. Night found him with a boisterous crowd at the Pied Merlin, kept by Dame Eliza. His clerkly ways got him into trouble, but big Hordle John protected him. Samkin Alyward, a bowman of the White Company, came in with rich booty from France. He induced John to enlist for the wars, and in the morning they started for Castle Twynham, held by the famous knight, Sir Nigel Loring, who was to command the White Company.

Alleyne set out to find his brother. In a forest he came upon the most beautiful creature he had ever beheld. Such he had pictured the angels. She was being held against her will by a big yellow-haired man. Alleyne came to the girl's assistance and found that the man was his brother.

"Young cub of Beaulieu! My dogs shall be set upon you!" cried the Socman. But he was unarmed, and Alleyne, raising his iron-shod staff, compelled him to free the girl. He ran for weapons and dogs, but the other two escaped through the woods. The girl's page came with horses, and when the young clerk told her that he intended to join two friends at Castle Twynham she laughed and rode away without telling her name. Long he stood, hoping she might return. Then he turned away, no longer a light-hearted boy.

At Twynham Castle Alleyne met his angel again. She was the Lorings' only child. He became squire to Sir Nigel, while Lady Loring engaged him to teach the wayward Maude and two other girls. Maude was no easy pupil, given to strange moods. In spite of the abbot's warnings, teaching three girls was to Alleyne a joyous experience.

Time came for him to follow Sir Nigel to the wars. Maude was far above him in station, yet he told her of his love and begged her for some word of hope.

"Win my father's love and all may follow," she told him.

Sir Nigel was a small man with a lisping voice, but when he said, "let us debate the matter further," it meant a fight. He spoke of his "small deeds," and he called a deadly hand-to-hand fight a "small bickering." With Alleyne, John Aylward, and one hundred and fifty archers and men-at-arms he set sail for France. They fought a bloody battle with two pirate craft. Alleyne had his first taste of war and fought bravely. Sir Nigel's sword flashed everywhere at once. Aylward led the archers and John took the big Norman captain prisoner by sheer strength. They lost nearly all their men, but captured both pirate ships. In a fast-sinking ship they landed at Bordeaux, where King Edward was mustering his forces to carry the war into Spain. Here Alleyne fought a duel and came out a hero. Five English knights held the list against all comers. The English won two bouts, their opponents two, and Sir Nigel won the fifth. Then an unknown knight came forth from the East and challenged the victors. Four knights went down before him in short order, but Sir Nigel broke even.

The White Company was at Dax and he set out to take command. With him were Aylward and John and his two squires, Alleyne and Ford. In the brushwood they saw many strange lean people who fled before them. Some were too weak with hunger to move. Their feudal lord had taken the last fruits of their toil. At a hotel they found the strange champion of the tournament. He was Du Guesclin, a French knight, known to Sir Nigel. His wife, Lady Tiphaine, was with him. They all went for the night to a château. Here they found several other knights and squires. They had a great feast and made merry, unmindful of the starving peasants.

Lady Tiphaine went into a trance, which she called the blessed hour of sight. She saw the English driven out of France, but the power of England spread to many lands. She saw Sir Nigel's castle beseiged by a mob led by a big yellow-haired man. Lady Loring and Maude stood on the wall, directing the defenders. The big leader was slain and his followers dispersed. She told her husband that he also was in great danger, but he laughed at the idea.

When all were asleep the enraged peasants stole into the château and murdered all but eight. Sir Nigel, Alleyne, Aylward, John, Du Guesclin and his wife, and two others fought their way to the keep. In a narrow passage at the head of the stairs they held the mob off. The peasants set fire to the buildings. The stairs fell away and they were about to be enveloped in flames when the White Company arrived and rescued them.

Sir Nigel and the White Company, four hundred strong, joined Edward's army and marched into Spain. Sent ahead to reconnoiter, they stole up near a Spanish camp and did some small deeds. Hordle John captured a Spanish knight by the foot and held him for a ransom. Later they were surprised by a large force of cavalry. On a rocky hill they made their last stand.

"To your arms, men!" roared Sir Nigel. "Shoot while you may, and then out swords and let us live or die together."

Sir Nigel sent Alleyne for help. Sorely wounded, he lashed himself to his horse, broke through the Spanish lines, and, nearly dead, reached the English. When the rescue party arrived and drove away the Spaniards the flag still waved, with only John and six archers around it. All the rest were either killed or taken prisoner.

The fame of the White Company traveled far. Alleyne was knighted, John got five thousand crowns ransom, and the two hurried back to England. Maude Loring, hearing that every one of the company had been killed, had entered a nunnery, but Alleyne took her home and they were married.

Sir Nigel and Aylward were taken prisoners, but escaped, seized a small coaster, and came home with a rich cargo. Aylward wed the dame Eliza, John became Alleyne's squire, and they all lived many years filled with honor and happiness and laden with every blessing.

Sir Nigel rode no more to the wars, but he found his way to every jousting within thirty miles. Twice again Sir Alleyne Edricson fought in France, and came back each time laden with honors.

<hr/>

THE WOMAN IN WHITE

by

WILKIE COLLINS*

CONDENSATION BY ALICE FOX PITTS

It was a close and sultry night early in August, and I, Walter Hartright, master of drawing, aged twenty-eight, was walking from Hampstead to London. In one moment every drop of blood in my body was brought to a stop by the touch of a hand laid gently on my shoulder. There, in the middle of the highroad, stood a woman dressed from head to foot in white garments. She asked me the way to London. I told her, and we parted.

Ten minutes later a carriage passed me and a few yards beyond stopped near a policeman. A man put his head from the window and asked: "Have you seen a woman pass this way—a woman in white? She has escaped from my asylum." At a shake of the policeman's head the carriage drove rapidly on.

* For biographical information see page 251.

The next day I was at Limmeridge House, Cumberland, in the service of Frederick Fairlie, Esquire. I was there to instruct his two young nieces in the art of painting. I found Marian Halcombe to be dark and ugly, but intelligent. Laura Fairlie, her half-sister, was light, pretty, and dependent. They were devoted to each other, and before my engagement was up I admired the one and loved the other.

My feelings were the cause of my leaving Limmeridge House. Marian Halcombe brought to me a realization of my own heart. "You must leave," she said, "not because you are only a teacher of drawing, but because Laura Fairlie is engaged to be married."

A few days before I left Cumberland, while walking alone in the evening, I was confronted by the same face which had first looked into mine on the London highroad by night. But I was startled less by its sudden reappearance than by my immediate recognition of an ominous likeness between this fugitive from the asylum and my fair pupil at Limmeridge House. Still greater was my consternation when the woman admitted having come to the neighborhood for the sole purpose of thwarting the proposed marriage of Laura Fairlie.

I left Limmeridge House, and soon after embarked on an expedition to Central America. The same year Laura Fairlie became the bride of Sir Percival Glyde, Bart., and with her sister went to live at Blackwater Park, her husband's country estate. Count Fosco, an audacious and domineering Italian, and his wife were guests of the household. But all was not as harmonious as an English country party should be. Lady Glyde and her sister, as inseparable and confiding as ever, felt a perceptible coolness rising between them and the two gentlemen. Coolness turned to suspicion and soon to fear.

Then it was that Lady Glyde met the Woman in White. The mysterious person stole noiselessly up to her in the twilight one evening and whispered: "If you knew your husband's secret, he would be afraid of you. He would not dare use you as he has used me. I ought to have saved you before it was too late." But before the secret was told there were footsteps in the distance and the woman moved stealthily away.

Sir Percival learned of that brief interview, and *was* afraid of his wife. He demanded, begged, threatened her to tell him all she knew. What had been a battle of wits between the two sisters and the two men became a struggle of strategy, and the women lost the fight. Lady Glyde was decoyed into leaving Blackwater Park for Count Fosco's London home. Less than two weeks later a tombstone in

Cumberland bore this inscription, "Sacred to the memory of Laura, Lady Glyde."

On my return from Central America the same year I heard of the death, and immediately visited the grave. As I approached it, two women came toward me. One was Marian Halcombe; the other was veiled, but when she raised this covering from her face, there, looking at me, was Laura, Lady Glyde. She was pale, nervous, and depressed—more perfect than ever in her resemblance to the Woman in White.

Marian Halcombe told me what she knew. She had found her sister in an asylum and in the grave at our feet was her mysterious double. Sir Percival's boldness and Count Fosco's cleverness had succeeded in exchanging the destinies of the two women. The circumstance had netted these two gentlemen some thirty thousand pounds, derived from the estate of Lady Glyde.

The fortune was gone beyond recall, but Lady Glyde's true identity might yet be established in the face of such evidence as her death certificate and tombstone, and the incredulity of her friends and relatives. This I determined to do. Cast upon the world alone, the sisters readily agreed to allow me to take up their fight, and I determined that Laura should one day re-enter her father's estate recognized by all.

It soon was apparent that Sir Percival and Count Fosco were the persons I must fight. I worked secretly but directly, for I had no funds with which to carry on a fight through the courts. The secret with which the Woman in White had threatened Sir Percival seemed to me to be the key to the whole situation. Through a series of inquiries, working always under the watch of spies, I found it opportune to look up the marriage registration of Sir Percival's parents. I found it in a little country church—and it was forged. I was no sooner in possession of the knowledge of his illegitimate birth than Sir Percival, in furious desperation to destroy the evidence, entered the little church by night, set fire to the structure, and through the agency of his own stupidity and an old-fashioned wooden lock trapped himself into an awful death.

Laura was free of her husband, but she remained an outcast—a woman dead to her friends and relatives. I was still determined this should not be. My only hope of success lay in Count Fosco, who alone had the evidence which could establish her legal existence. But to acknowledge Lady Glyde's identity would be to admit his guilt of one of the greatest of crimes. My task looked difficult, but an unknown agency came to my aid.

Count Fosco was a traitor to one of the world-wide Italian secret societies. The knowledge came to me by chance, but it served me in good stead. I went to his house one night and bartered my silence for the evidence of Laura's existence. Count Fosco, in a long exposition, gave the details of his own and Sir Percival's cunning. Then he left England forever. To clear up the last shred of mystery surrounding the Woman in White I sought out her childhood home. I pieced together her story from her old friends and relatives. Fate had made her the illegitimate half-sister of her counterpart and the chance possessor of Sir Percival's secret.

My labors ended, Marian Halcombe and her sister, who was now my wife, returned to the happy companionship of those days at Limmeridge House before Sir Percival's cunning had usurped the consummation of our love. On the death of Laura's uncle some months later her son and mine became the heir of the estate and fortune of the house of Limmeridge.

WUTHERING HEIGHTS

by

EMILY BRONTË

CONDENSATION BY MARGARET GILLETT

EMILY BRONTË (1818–1848), poet and novelist, was born at Thornton in Yorkshire, the fourth of five girls, three of whom became novelists. (Each of the three published a novel in the same year—1847: Charlotte, "Jane Eyre"; Anne, "Agnes Grey"; and Emily, "Wuthering Heights.") Their father, an austere Irish parson, was left a widower with six children (the girls had one brother) before Emily was four.

Although she had little formal schooling, Emily went to

Halifax in 1836 as a governess, but returned home after six months because of the drudgery of teaching. Except for brief excursions to the nearby towns with her sisters, Emily spent the rest of her life on the moors in a continuous gloomy struggle against poverty and disease. At thirty she died of consumption, having exhausted herself in an attempt to save her brother, who was addicted to opium and alcohol, and who preceded her to the grave by three months.

In the beginning of their literary efforts, the three sisters wrote under the name of Bell. Because of the prejudice of their time against women authors, they took three Christian names of indeterminable sex in order to conceal their female identities. Their first publication was a book of verse which received little notice. "Wuthering Heights," on the other hand, caused some comment, most of it bad in the beginning, as the critics were shocked by its passionate intensity. Later they acclaimed it but Emily did not live to know her fame, which indeed increased, later, until "Wuthering Heights" is now considered one of the classics of English literature.

Laid against the background of the bleak Yorkshire moors its author knew so well, it is a gripping, knotty narrative set in a brilliant design. Although intensely real, it is larger than life and has been described as an expression of the total conflict of the society of mid-nineteenth century England.

Mr. Heathcliff (my landlord) and I were a suitable pair to divide the desolation of the moors between us. He was a dark-skinned gipsy in aspect, in dress and manners a gentleman with an erect and handsome figure but, like myself, a man of great reserve.

My first call on him at Wuthering Heights could not be said to have been received cordially and yet, my curiosity being aroused by the strange manner of the place, I volunteered another visit on the morrow.

The ancient dwelling was situated on an exposed edge of the moor, and the architect, realizing the stormy weather it would have to endure, had defended it at the corners with large jutting stones that gave the effect of battlements. The interior was hardly less fortified. Above the chimney were sundry villainous old guns and a couple of horse-pistols. The stone floor, the heavy, high-backed oaken chairs, the great black table in the center, hardly relieved the impression of a garrison. Under an arch in one of the dark recesses of the room was a huge, liver-coloured bitch pointer with a swarm of squirming, squealing puppies.

My second visit was met, if anything, with less hospitality than my first. A beautiful but grim young woman, who turned out to be Mr. Heathcliff's daughter-in-law, first treated me with studied incivility, then a rough young man whom I supposed to be her husband but who turned out to be a cousin, eyed me with fierce hostility. The whole place, with all its inmates, began to take on the aspect of a madhouse, and I wondered what absurdity had prompted me to undertake this second visit.

Meanwhile, the weather, which had been threatening, had grown immeasurably worse as night fell over the countryside, and I knew I could not find my way back through the deep snow to Thrushcross Grange without a guide. There was no one to spare to show me the path, my morose host informed me, so that finally I was forced to spend the night, much against his wishes and, indeed, contrary to my own as well.

That night was a nightmare of discomfort and alarm, and I left at dawn when, by some whimsey, Mr. Heathcliff himself decided to accompany me to the entrance to Thrushcross Park. As we journeyed the difficult distance I thought many times that I could not have made the trip without a guide in that weather even in daylight.

After I recovered from this ordeal, I was more curious than ever about my incredible landlord, and I inquired further from my own housekeeper, Mrs. Dean, who had been on the premises for eighteen years and could be counted on to know the history of the neighbourhood. In such a remote, unsociable place, it was not difficult to persuade her to sit with me for a little chat when she brought my supper.

From her I learned that Heathcliff had really been a gipsy foundling, salvaged from the Liverpool streets by old Mr. Earnshaw, then master of Wuthering Heights and the present rough young man's grandfather. The old man grew to dote on the orphan child, preferring him to his own son, Hindley. Naturally, Hindley hated Heathcliff as an interloper, while Catherine, his sister, who had a passionate temperament, flew to the waif's defense. As they grew up, the girl as wild as the boy, they became inseparable companions.

Some years later, after Hindley Earnshaw had been in college three years, his father (Heathcliff's benefactor) died. When the son came home to the funeral all were surprised that he brought with him a young wife. At first she seemed contented enough as mistress of the household, but soon she became peevish with her husband's sister, Catherine, and finally took a dislike to Heathcliff, too, who was thereupon banished to the servants' quarters.

Soon after the birth of her first child, Hareton (now the uncouth young man I had met on my second visit to Wuthering Heights), Mrs. Earnshaw died, a victim of consumption and her husband, who adored her and hated the baby as the cause of her death, took to drink with abandon. He neglected Hareton and became quite unmanageable until his sister, Catherine, partly in an effort to escape his drunken fits and partly to be in a position to rescue Heathcliff from his clutches, married Edgar Linton and moved to Thrushcross. But this was a desperate choice for her, as she confessed to Mrs. Dean at the time:

"I've no more business to marry Edgar Linton than I have to be in Heaven, but it would degrade me to marry Heathcliff now; so he shall never know how I love him; and that, not because he's handsome, Nelly, but because he's more myself than I am. Whatever our souls are made of, his and mine are the same; and Linton's is as different as a moonbeam from lightning, or frost from fire."

After this, Heathcliff, unable to cope with the loss of his Catherine, disappeared. At the end of another three years, he returned, no longer a boy but a man. Although not exactly a man of grace, there was a dignity and correctness in his bearing that suggested he may have been in the army. He had evidently amassed a fortune of his own during his absence, and Hindley, who had already drunk himself into debt, tolerated Heathcliff as a lodger because he could lend him money for gaming and liquor.

By a strange quirk of fate, Isabella Linton, his beloved Catherine's sister-in-law, became infatuated with the returned gipsy whom she considered the very incarnation of all that was romantic. This attachment naturally appalled her brother, Edgar, who angrily warned Heathcliff never to come to Thrushcross again. Disregarding her brother's interdiction, Isabella ran off with Heathcliff, who married her apparently just to spite Catherine, since he really cared nothing for her himself. And to spite Catherine he did. As a result of the shock, she developed a brain fever which, for two months, threatened her life. It was not so long, however, before poor Isabella discovered her mistake and Heathcliff's duplicity, and she grew to hate him as the devil himself.

At the birth of her daughter, destined to be named after her, Catherine died. Heathcliff was inconsolable. As if reflecting the compounding of tragedy, the very weather changed, bringing rain then sleet and snow. All was dreary, chill, and dismal, and Isabella suffered unspeakable abuse from the distraught Heathcliff. Finally, unable to bear the torment any longer, she ran away, stopping only long enough at Thrushcross to change her clothes, so fearful was she of being pursued by her maddened husband. She fled to London where, a few months later, she, too, bore a child whom she named Linton. When the boy was twelve, his mother died and his father claimed him.

Less than six months after Catherine's death, her brother, Hindley, was driven to his bitter end by the indefatigable Heathcliff who had cunningly taken title to all his property through gaming debts and was at last master of Wuthering Heights. Not satisfied with his conquest of the one household, he determined to control adjacent Thrushcross Grange as well. Since young Catherine would inherit her father's estate, Heathcliff planned a marriage between her and his son, Linton, a very effeminite lad of exceedingly feeble constitution.

By devious means the plotting father forced the two young cousins to marry just in time before Edgar Linton died. The young husband did not survive him by many days but, according to the plan, he willed all of Thrushcross Grange to his father. Heathcliff's ambition was achieved. He was master of both properties and of all their residents.

Thus ended my housekeeper's story and, after hearing it to the bitter end, I decided I should not spend another winter at Thrushcross Grange. My greedy landlord could find himself another tenant at the end of my year's lease—and so I proposed to inform him. In fact, I returned to London almost immediately after only a small part of my term of occupancy had expired. However, in September, while I was still legally master of the Grange, I had occasion to pass within a few miles of it and followed a morbid impulse to pay a visit.

I found things considerably changed. Mrs. Dean, my former housekeeper, had moved to Wuthering Heights where I had to proceed to learn the reasons, since the caretakers at the Grange were too suspicious to give me any information.

As I approached the fortlike structure, it seemed to have a more amiable, less embattled look. Both doors and lattices were open, and the gate was unlocked, I marvelled to discover. But I was even more amazed when I met Mrs. Dean and heard the incredible news.

"Ah, Mr. Lockwood, then you have not known of Mr. Heathcliff's death."

"Heathcliff dead!" I exclaimed, astonished. He had seemed quite indestructible. "How long ago?" I asked.

"Three months since," she answered and went on to tell me how he had unaccountably died in his bed. The doctor was unable to ascribe any ailment to him; a bad conscience was his trouble, she conjectured.

It seems that in the last few months, Catherine, or "young Mrs. Heathcliff," as the housekeeper called her, had been teaching Hareton to read and in general civilizing the ruffian, who responded brilliantly. They had fallen in love, Mrs. Dean related, and planned to marry and live at Thrushcross Grange.

They will be the new tenants, I thought wryly and shook my head at the irony of it all. Well, perhaps, they will lift the curse from the place at last.